Name ____________________

High School Math Solution

MATHbook

ALGEBRA I • VOL. 2 STUDENT EDITION

4th Edition

AUTHORING TEAM

Sandy Bartle Finocchi | Amy Jones Lewis

Josh Fisher | Janet Sinopoli | Victoria Fisher | Sarah Galasso

501 Grant Street, Suite 1075
Pittsburgh, PA 15219
Phone: 888-851-7094
Customer Service Phone: 412-690-2444

www.carnegielearning.com

Foundation Authors (2010)

William S. Hadley
Algebra and Proportional Reasoning

Mary Lou Metz
Data Analysis and Probability

Mary Lynn Raith
Number and Operations

Janet Sinopoli
Algebra

Jaclyn Snyder
Geometry and Measurement

Acknowledgments

- The members of the Carnegie Learning Production Team—Sara Kozelnik, Sara Schmidt Boldon, Laura Norris, Mary Travis, Jaana Bykonich, Michelle Rohm, Bob Dreas, Karen Jack, and Craig Goding
- The members of Carnegie Learning Cognitive Scientist Team—John Connelly, Bob Hausmann, and Martina Pavelko—for their insight in learning science and collaboration on MATHia Software
- **Primary Design:** Abbe Eckstein
- **Design Support:** Madison Kalo, Douglas Fuchs, and Heather Greenwood
- **Production Vendors:** Paul Leveno, BizeeWorks, LLC, Lumina Datamatics, LTD, Trivium Education Services, and QBS Services

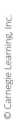

Copyright © 2022 by Carnegie Learning, Inc. All rights reserved. Carnegie Learning and MATHia are registered marks of Carnegie Learning, Inc. All other company and product names mentioned are used for identification purposes only and may be trademarks of their respective owners. Permission is granted for photocopying rights within licensed sites only. Any other usage or reproduction in any form is prohibited without the expressed consent of the publisher.

Credits: Art and Photo Credits follow the Index.

ISBN: 978-1-68459-743-7

Student Edition

Printed in the United States of America

4 5 6 7 8 9 MS 26 25 24 23

Cover Design by Anne Milliron and Moncur (thinkmoncur.com)

© Carnegie Learning, Inc.

LONG + LIVE + MATH

Mathematics is so much more than memorizing rules. It is learning to reason, to make connections, and to make sense of the world. Focus on the journey and the process.

No matter where you are starting from, your effort will lead to improvement.

We believe in Learning by Doing™ — and we believe in YOU!

Introducing Carnegie Learning's High School Math Solution

You will develop a deep understanding of key mathematical ideas by actively engaging with them in various ways — in print and online, together and individually, through concept and application.

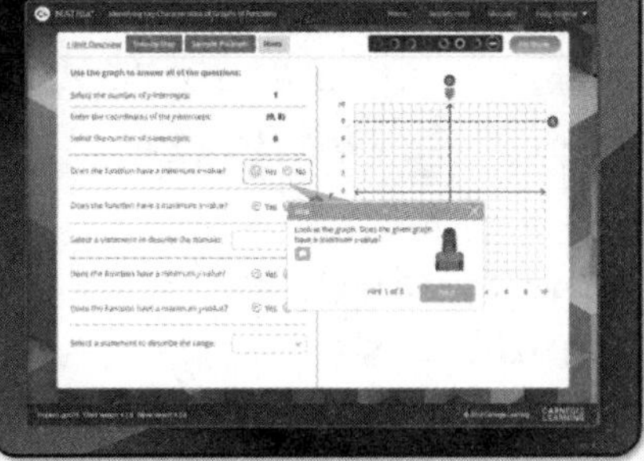

LEARN
TOGETHER WITH

MATHbook

When you work in this textbook, you'll collaborate, create, communicate, and problem-solve together with your peers.

LEARN
INDIVIDUALLY WITH

MATHia

When you work in this software, you'll work at your own pace and receive 1-to-1 coaching that adapts to your needs as you go.

EXPLORE FAMILY RESOURCES ONLINE
www.carnegielearning.com/home-connection/

Table of Contents

Download MATHia progress trackers!
www.carnegielearning.com/login

ALGEBRA I • VOL. 1

MODULE 1 Searching for Patterns

TOPIC 1 Quantities and Relationships

TOPIC 2 Sequences

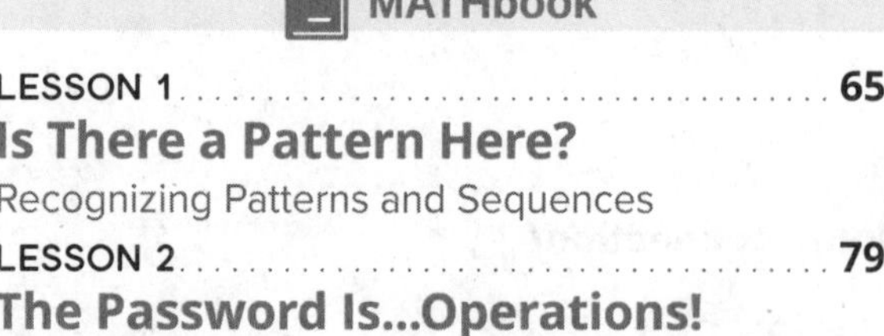

© Carnegie Learning, Inc.

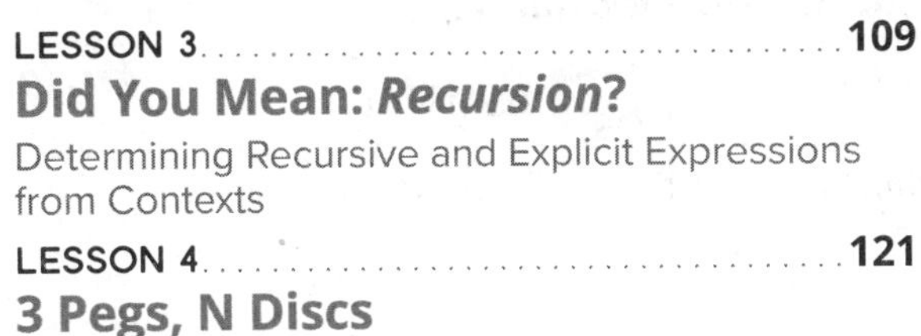

TOPIC 3 Linear Regressions

MATHbook

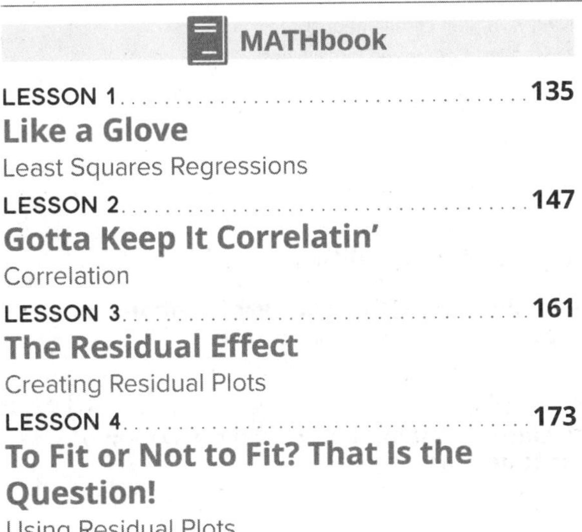

MATHia

ALGEBRA I • VOL. 1

MODULE 2 Exploring Constant Change

TOPIC 1 Linear Functions

MATHbook

MATHia

© Carnegie Learning, Inc.

TOPIC 2 Solving Linear Equations and Inequalities

MATHbook

TOPIC 3 Systems of Equations and Inequalities

MATHbook

TOPIC 4 Functions Derived from Linear Relationships

MATHbook

© Carnegie Learning, Inc.

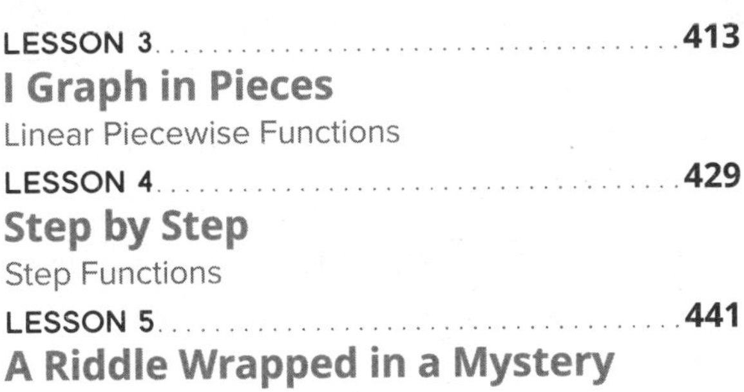

ALGEBRA I • VOL. 2

MODULE 3 Investigating Growth and Decay

TOPIC 1 Introduction to Exponential Functions

MATHbook

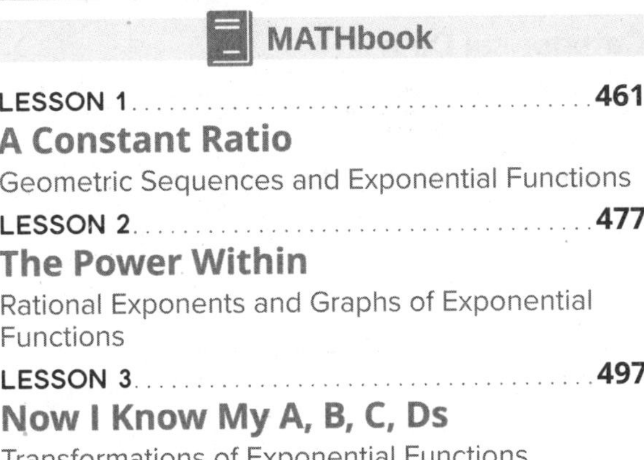

MATHia

TOPIC 2 Using Exponential Equations

MATHbook

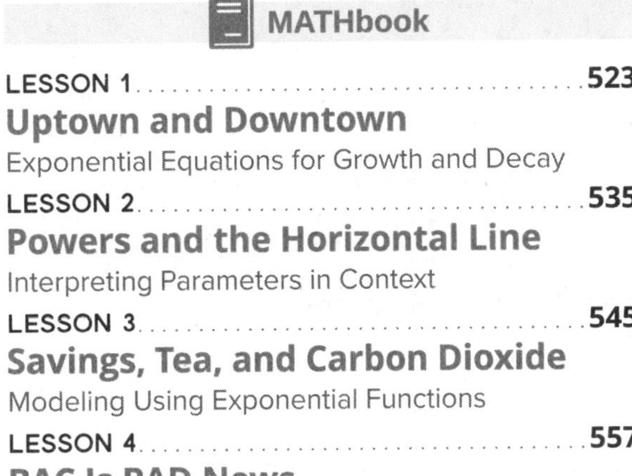

MATHia

© Carnegie Learning, Inc.

ALGEBRA I • VOL. 2

MODULE 4 Describing Distributions

TOPIC 1 One-Variable Statistics

TOPIC 2 Two-Variable Categorical Data

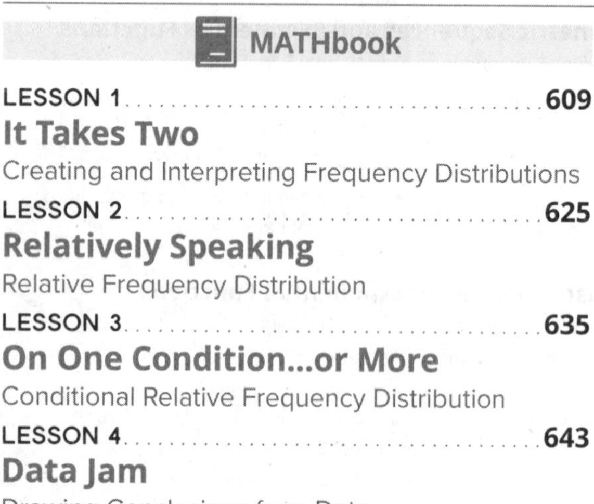

ALGEBRA I • VOL. 2

MODULE 5 Maximizing and Minimizing

TOPIC 1 Introduction to Quadratic Functions

© Carnegie Learning, Inc.

TOPIC 2 Solving Quadratic Equations

MATHbook

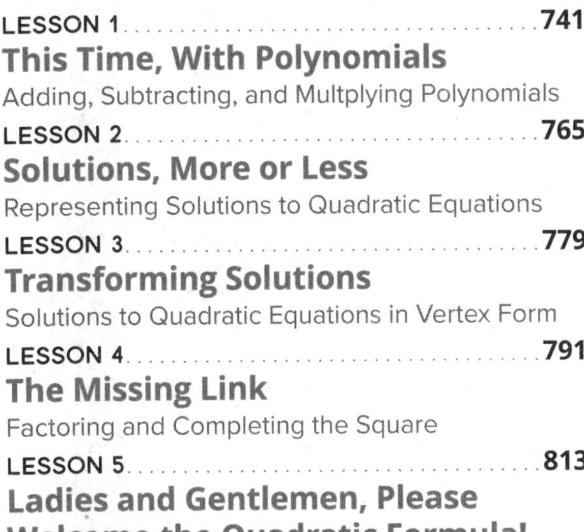

MATHia

TOPIC 3 Applications of Quadratics

MATHbook

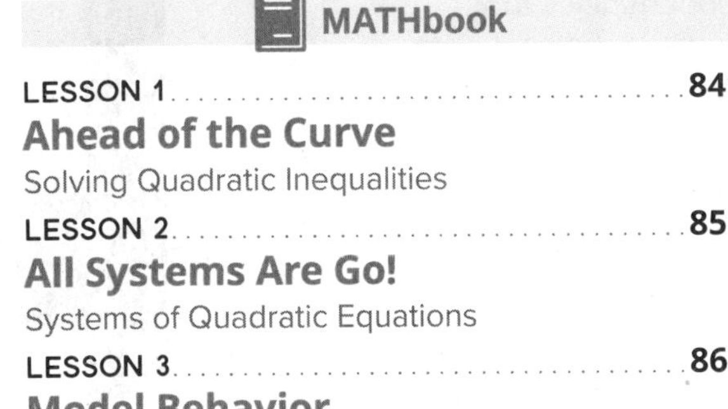

MATHia

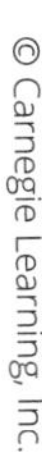

© Carnegie Learning, Inc.

Let's Get Started!

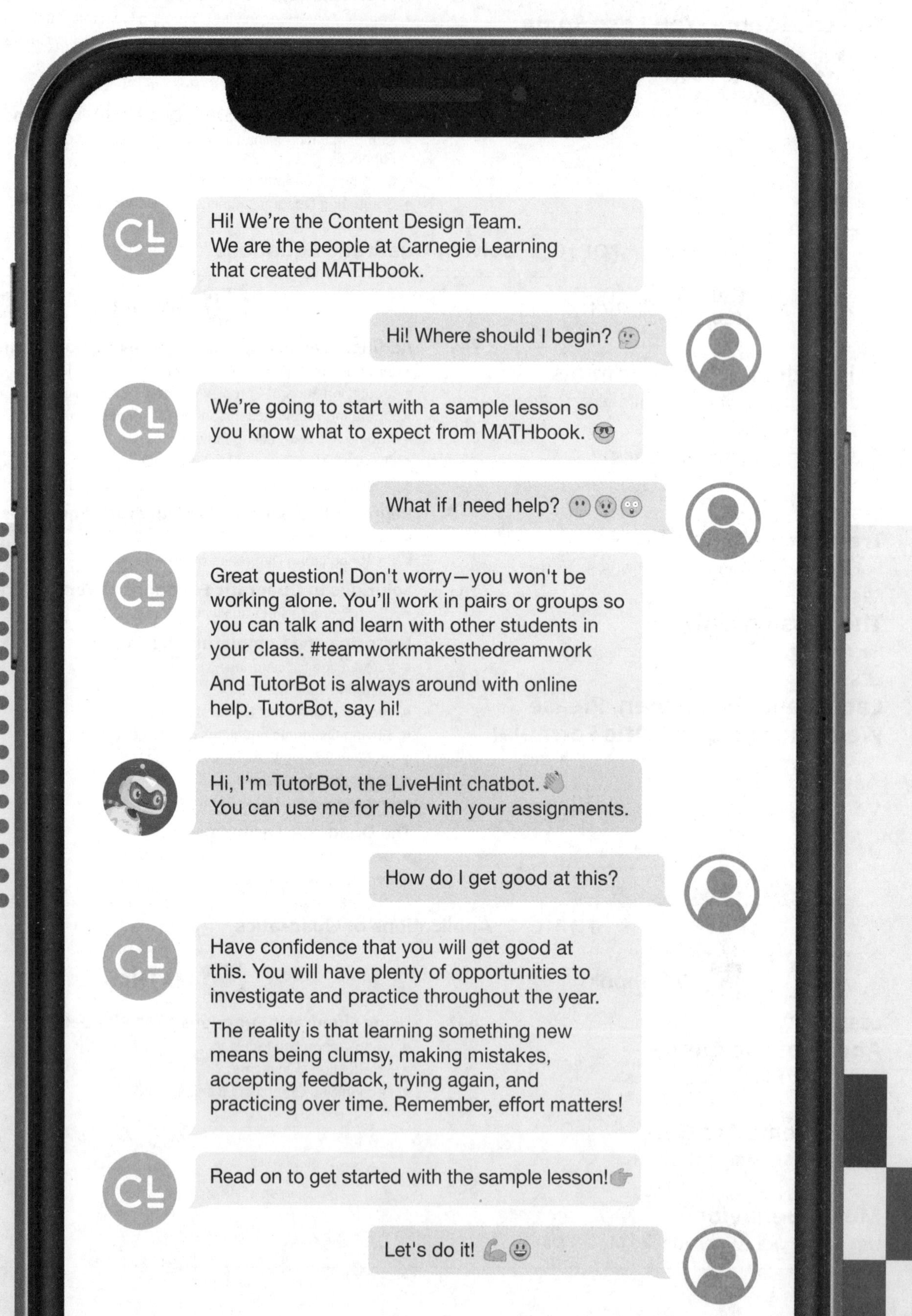

Hi! We're the Content Design Team.
We are the people at Carnegie Learning that created MATHbook.
Hi! Where should I begin?
We're going to start with a sample lesson so you know what to expect from MATHbook.
What if I need help?
Great question! Don't worry—you won't be working alone. You'll work in pairs or groups so you can talk and learn with other students in your class. #teamworkmakesthedreamwork
And TutorBot is always around with online help. TutorBot, say hi!
Hi, I'm TutorBot, the LiveHint chatbot.
You can use me for help with your assignments.
How do I get good at this?
Have confidence that you will get good at this. You will have plenty of opportunities to investigate and practice throughout the year.
The reality is that learning something new means being clumsy, making mistakes, accepting feedback, trying again, and practicing over time. Remember, effort matters!
Read on to get started with the sample lesson!
Let's do it!

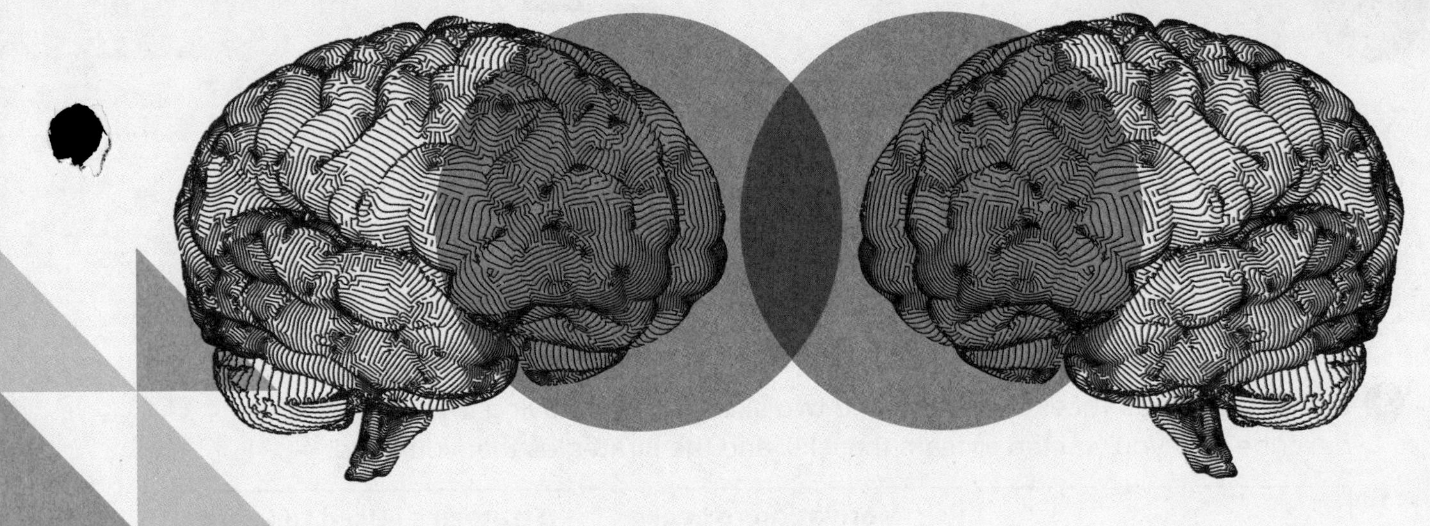

A Meeting of the Minds

An Introduction to MATHbook and Your Learning Resources

KEY TERMS

yet

Learning Goals

- Establish a community of learners.
- Preview the contents of MATHbook.
- Consider how you will interact with MATHbook to make your learning visible.
- Understand how MATHia software supports each MATHbook topic.
- Set personal goals to take ownership of your learning.

REVIEW (1–2 minutes)

The questions in this section review a skill you will need in the lesson.

> Consider each question. Be prepared to share your strategies, conclusions, and questions.

1 Why is it helpful to review what you already know before learning something new?

TAKE NOTE . . .
Each lesson opens with a statement that connects what you have learned with a question to ponder.

In previous math classes, you explored transformations, analyzed patterns and relationships, and learned about functions, operations with real numbers, probability and statistics, and geometry.

How can you use MATHbook and MATHia software to meet the goals of this course?

You Already Know a Lot

Each lesson in this book begins with a Getting Started that gives you the opportunity to use what you know about the world and what you have learned in previous math classes. You know a lot from a variety of learning experiences.

> Think about how you learn.

1 List two skills you recently learned and two skills you are striving to improve. Then, describe why you wanted to learn that skill and the strategies that you used.

Skill	Motivation to Learn or Improve the Skill	Strategies I Used to Learn or Improve This Skill

One learning strategy is to talk with your peers. In this course, you will work with your classmates to solve problems, discuss strategies, and learn together.

> Compare and discuss your list with a classmate.

2 Which strategies do you have in common? Which strategies does your classmate have that you did not think of on your own?

ASK YOURSELF . . .
How do your strategies change based on what you are learning and what you already know?

THINK ABOUT . . .
Listening well, cooperating with others, and appreciating different perspectives are essential life skills.

> Be prepared to share your list of learning strategies with the class.

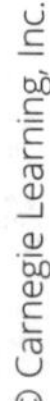
© Carnegie Learning, Inc.

ACTIVITY 1

Learning Together with MATHbook

HABIT OF MIND

- Make sense of problems and persevere in solving them.

In this course, you will learn new math concepts by exploring and investigating ideas, reading, writing, and talking to your classmates. You will even learn by making mistakes with concepts you haven't mastered *yet.*

> Flip through the first module of your MATHbook.

1. What do you find interesting? Does anything look familiar?

THINK ABOUT . . .

Using the word **yet** should remind you that the process is more important than answer-getting. So, take risks!

2. Compare the title and subtitle of several lessons. **What do you notice?**

3. Describe the icons you see within the lessons.

You will encounter different problem types as you work through activities.

Worked Example	Thumbs Up	Thumbs Down	Who's Correct
WORKED EXAMPLE			

When you see one of these problem types, take your time and read through it. Question your own understanding, think about the connections between steps, consider why the method is correct, or analyze what error was made.

> Search through the different activities in module 1 and locate a Worked Example, Thumbs Up, Thumbs Down, or Who's Correct.

4. What topic, lesson, and activity are you in? **How do you know?**

5. How do you see these problem types helping you learn?

© Carnegie Learning, Inc.

In MATHbook, you can mark up the pages in any way that is helpful to you as you take ownership of your learning.

> Analyze a page from Brody's MATHbook.

6 What strategies did Brody use to make sense of the key term and diagrams?

Brody

4 Analyze the relation represented verbally. Is the relation a function? Explain your reasoning.

It is a function because each student (input) only has one birthday (output).

tool not a reason

discrete graph

The **vertical line test** is a visual method used to determine whether a relation represented as a graph is a function. To apply the vertical line test, consider all of the vertical lines that could be drawn on the graph of a relation. If any of the vertical lines intersect the graph of the relation at more than one point, then the relation is not a function.

continuous

one input goes to two outputs

function

not a function

DID YOU KNOW?
A **discrete graph** is a graph of isolated points. A **continuous graph** is a graph of points that are connected by a line or smooth curve on the graph. Continuous graphs have no breaks.

The vertical line test applies for both *discrete* and *continuous graphs*.

7 Locate the term **discrete graph** in the glossary. What page is it on?

Through the process of writing, you clarify your understanding and improve your communication skills. The Academic Glossary on page FM-20 is your guide as you engage with the kind of thinking you do as you are learning the content.

DID YOU KNOW . . .
Colleges and employers highly value candidates with strong verbal communication skills.

8 Locate the phrase **explain your reasoning** in the Academic Glossary. Which of the Ask Yourself questions might Brody have asked himself?

It is not just about what mathematical content you are learning but how you are learning it. Did you notice the Habits of Mind beside each activity title? You can locate the full list on page FM-19.

9 What is the Habit of Mind for this **Using MATHbook** activity? **How will developing this habit help you?**

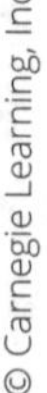
© Carnegie Learning, Inc.

10 How will Learning Together help you learn math?

ACTIVITY 2

MATHia CONNECTION

- Pre-Launch Protocol

Learning Individually with MATHia

To learn the concepts in each topic, you will work with your classmates to complete the lessons within MATHbook, and you will work individually to complete workspaces in the MATHia software.

HABITS OF MIND

- Look for and make use of structure.
- Look for and express regularity in repeated reasoning.

> Watch the animation about MATHia.

1. How are supports included to help you solve problems within MATHia?

You will notice that there are MATHia Connections at the start of some activities.

> Analyze this Worked Example.

WORKED EXAMPLE

ACTIVITY 2

MATHia CONNECTION

- Identifying Quantities

The MATHia Connection indicates the workspaces that have similar content to this activity. In the workspaces listed, you will practice the skills you are developing in a lesson.

TAKE NOTE . . .

If you are without access to MATHia, a Skills Practice workbook is available for you to practice each topic's skills and mathematical concepts.

2. How many workspaces are associated with Topic 1 *Quantities and Relationships*?

3. How will learning individually support your mathematical understanding?

© Carnegie Learning, Inc.

So, Give It a Shot!

The Talk the Talk activity is your opportunity to reflect on the main ideas of the lesson.

- Be honest with yourself.
- Ask questions to clarify anything you don't understand yet.
- Show what you know!

REMEMBER . . .
Revisit the question posed on the lesson opening page to gauge your understanding.

1. Why is it important to take time to reflect on your progress?

2. Describe the different ways you will learn math this year.

3. It is important to set personal and academic goals for the year. List three goals for this school year.

   - ________________________________
   - ________________________________
   - ________________________________

There are resources to assist you as you review the concepts in each topic. See page FM-18 for *Your Tools for Review*.

4. Where do you locate a Topic Summary? How can you use this resource to prepare for an assessment?

© Carnegie Learning, Inc.

INTRO LESSON ASSIGNMENT

> Use a separate piece of paper for your Journal entry.

JOURNAL

If how you felt about learning math this year were a meme, what would the meme be? Sketch or include your meme and explain your reasoning.

REMEMBER

In this course, you will build on your work with solving equations, systems of equations, statistics, and recognizing functions. You will apply your knowledge of transformations to explore a variety of function families. You will investigate non-linear functions such as exponential and quadratic functions.

PRACTICE

> Share the Family Guide for Topic 1 *Quantities and Relationships* with an adult.

1. Follow this QR code or URL to access the digital file.

ONLINE RESOURCES FOR FAMILIES
www.carnegielearning.com/home-connection/

2. What information does the Family Guide provide?

As you complete the Practice section of each assignment, LiveHint is your textbook assistant. LiveHint allows you to obtain real-time hints from any device on questions through the TutorBot. With LiveHint, you never have to navigate through assignments on your own.

> Go to **LiveHint.com**.

LiveHint™

3. Follow the instructions to access hints to this question.

- First hint: ______________________
- Second hint: ______________________
- Third hint: ______________________

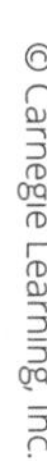
© Carnegie Learning, Inc.

STRETCH Optional

Why do you think Module 1 is titled **Searching for Patterns**?

Your Tools for Review

There are topic-level resources to assist you as you review the concepts and prepare for an assessment.

MIXED PRACTICE

At the end of each topic, a **Mixed Practice** worksheet provides practice with skills from previous topics and this topic.

Spaced Review
Fluency and problem solving from previous topics

End-of-Topic Review
Review problems from this topic

Log in to MyCL for a version with **additional space** for you to write your answers.

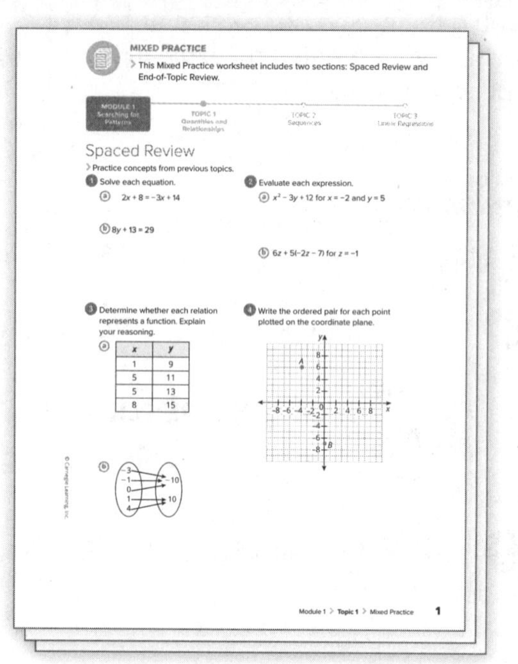

TOPIC SUMMARY

A **Topic Summary** is available online for review of the key terms and main ideas of each lesson.

ASK YOURSELF . . .

- Do I know the meaning of each key term?
- Do I remember the main concepts of each lesson?
- Do I understand the strategy used to solve the Worked Example?

Log in to MyCL to download the **Topic Summary**.

Watch a video of each **Worked Example**.

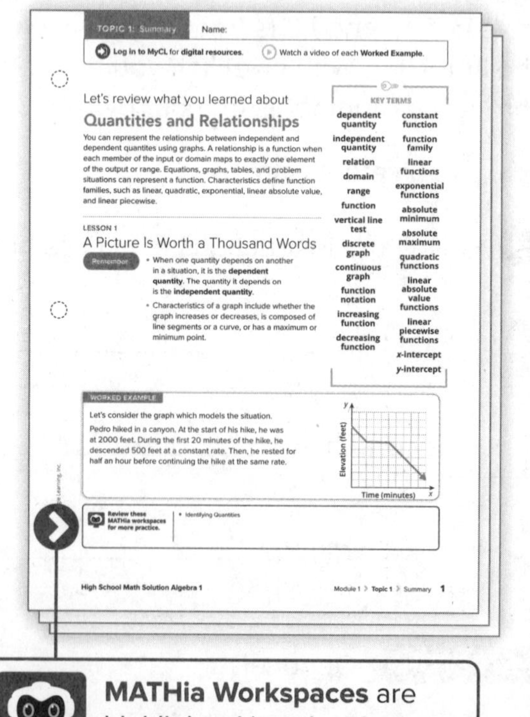

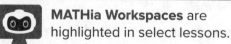

MATHia Workspaces are highlighted in select lessons.

© Carnegie Learning, Inc.

HABITS OF MIND

> Tear out this page and use it as a guide as you engage with the the kind of thinking you do as you are learning the content.

Mathematical Practices

The types of activities within this book require you to make sense of mathematics and to demonstrate your reasoning through problem solving, writing, discussing, and presenting.

FOR ALL LESSONS . . .

Make sense of problems and persevere in solving them.

ASK YOURSELF . . .

- What is this problem asking, and what is my plan for answering it?
- What tools do I need to solve this problem?
- Does my answer make sense?

TAKE NOTE . . .

To help develop these Habits of Mind, ask yourself the types of questions listed as you work.

Each activity denotes the practice or pair of practices intentionally being developed. With practice, you can develop the Habits of Mind of a productive mathematical thinker.

WHEN YOU SEE . . .	ASK YOURSELF . . .	WHAT DOES THIS MEAN FOR YOU?
HABITS OF MIND • Reason abstractly and quantitatively. • Construct viable arguments and critique the reasoning of others.	• What representation can I use to solve this problem? • How can this problem be represented with symbols and numbers? • How can I explain my thinking? • How does my strategy compare to my partner's?	
HABITS OF MIND • Model with mathematics. • Use appropriate tools strategically.	• What expression or equation could represent this situation? • What tools would help me solve this problem? • Which representations best show my thinking? • How does this answer make sense in the context of the original problem?	
HABIT OF MIND • Attend to precision.	• Is my answer accurate? • Did I use the correct units or labels? • Is there a more efficient way to solve this problem? • Is there more sophisticated vocabulary that I could use in my explanation?	
HABITS OF MIND • Look for and make use of structure. • Look for and express regularity in repeated reasoning.	• What characteristics of this expression or equation are made clear through this representation? • How can I use what I know to explain why this works? • Can I develop a more efficient method? • How could this problem help me to solve another problem?	

© Carnegie Learning, Inc.

ACADEMIC GLOSSARY

There are important terms you will encounter throughout this book.

Knowing what is meant by these terms and using these terms will help you think, reason, and communicate your ideas. You will often see these phrases in highlighted questions throughout each activity.

TERM	DEFINITION	ASK YOURSELF	RELATED PHRASES
Analyze	To analyze means to study or look closely for patterns. Analyzing can involve examining or breaking a concept down into smaller parts to gain a better understanding of it.	• Do I see any patterns? • Have I seen something like this before? • What happens if the shape, representation, or numbers change?	**Examine** **Evaluate** **Determine** **Observe** **Consider** **Investigate** **What do you notice?** **What do you think?** **Sort and match**
Explain Your Reasoning	To explain your reasoning means to give details or describe how to determine an answer or solution. Explaining your reasoning helps justify conclusions.	• How should I organize my thoughts? • Is my explanation logical? • Does my reasoning make sense? • How can I justify my answer to others?	**Show your work** **Explain your calculation** **Justify** **Why or why not?**
Represent	To represent means to display information in various ways. Representing mathematics can be done using words, tables, graphs, or symbols.	• How should I organize my thoughts? • How do I use this model to show a concept or idea? • What does this representation tell me? • Is my representation accurate?	**Show** **Sketch** **Draw** **Create** **Plot** **Graph** **Write an equation** **Complete the table**
Estimate	To estimate means to make an educated guess based on the analysis of given data. Estimating first helps inform reasoning.	• Does my reasoning make sense? • Is my solution close to my estimation?	**Predict** **Approximate** **Expect** **About how much?**
Describe	To describe means to represent or give an account of in words. Describing communicates mathematical ideas to others.	• How should I organize my thoughts? • Is my explanation logical? • Did I consider the context of the situation? • Does my reasoning make sense?	**Demonstrate** **Label** **Display** **Compare** **Determine** **Define** **What are the advantages?** **What are the disadvantages?** **What is similar?** **What is different?**

© Carnegie Learning, Inc.

Investigating Growth and Decay

TOPIC 1
Introduction to Exponential Functions

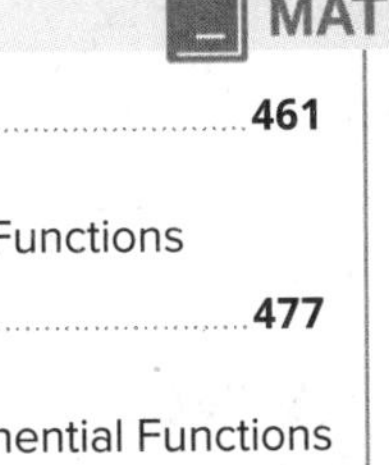

MATHbook

MATHia

Geometric Sequences and Exponential Functions
- Writing Sequences as Exponential Functions

Rational Exponents
- Using the Properties of Exponents
- Properties of Rational Exponents
- Rewriting Expressions with Radical and Rational Exponents
- Solving Contextual Exponential Relations Using Common Bases

Transformations of Exponential Functions
- Introduction to Transforming Exponential Functions
- Vertically Translating Exponential Functions
- Horizontally Translating Exponential Functions
- Reflecting and Dilating Exponential Functions Using Graphs
- Transforming Exponential Functions Using Tables
- Multiple Transformations of Exponential Functions

TOPIC 2
Using Exponential Equations

MATHbook

MATHia

Exponential Equations for Growth and Decay
- Recognizing Linear and Exponential Models
- Calculating and Interpreting Average Rate of Change
- Recognizing Growth and Decay
- Comparing Exponential Functions in Different Forms

Solving Exponential Equations
- Modeling Equations with a Starting Point of 1
- Modeling Equations with a Starting Point Other Than 1
- Solving Exponential Equations Using a Graph
- Transforming Exponential Expressions

Modeling Using Exponential Functions
- Relating the Domain to Exponential Functions
- Exploring Exponential Regressions

© Carnegie Learning, Inc.

Getting Ready for Module 3

Investigating Growth and Decay

You will extend your work with geometric sequences and common ratios to develop exponential functions. You will investigate the relationship between rational exponents and radicals. You will transform exponential functions. You will distinguish between exponential growth and decay and solve real-world problems modeled by exponential functions.

The lessons in this module build on your prior experiences with exponents, prime factorization, and the Properties of Powers.

Review these key terms and Properties of Powers to get ready to investigate growth and decay.

KEY TERMS

exponent

The exponent of the power is the number of times the base is used as a factor.

$2^3 = 2 \times 2 \times 2$

↑ exponent

$8^4 = 8 \times 8 \times 8 \times 8$

↑ exponent

prime factorization

Prime factorization is the process of writing numbers as the product of prime factors. You can use a factor tree to determine prime factors.

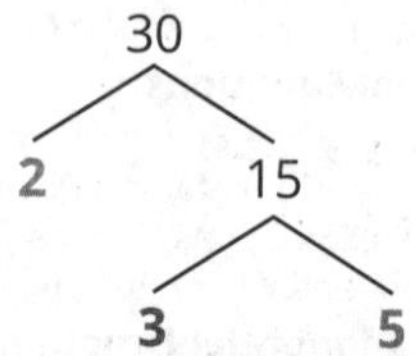

$30 = 2 \cdot 3 \cdot 5$

Brush up on your skills.
If you need more practice with these skills, ask your teacher for access to corresponding workspaces in MATHia.

SKILLS YOU WILL NEED

Product Rule of Powers

$a^m \cdot a^n = a^{m+n}$

$3^4 \cdot 3^3 = 3^7$

Power to a Power Rule

$(a^m)^n = a^{mn}$

$(3^4)^3 = 3^{12}$

Using Properties of Powers

You can use the Properties of Powers to rewrite expressions.

Consider the expression $x^5 \cdot (x^2)^3$.

$x^5 \cdot (x^2)^3$	
$x^5 \cdot x^6$	Power to a Power Rule
x^{11}	Product Rule of Powers

So, $x^5 \cdot (x^2)^3$ is equivalent to x^{11}.

You can also use the Properties of Powers to rewrite an expression like k^8 as $k^3 \cdot k^5$ or $(k^4)^2$.

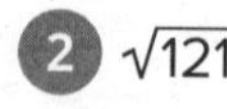

> Evaluate each expression.

1. $\sqrt{49}$
2. $\sqrt{121}$
3. $\sqrt[3]{27}$
4. $\sqrt[3]{125}$

See Appendix on page 879 for answers.

© Carnegie Learning, Inc.

LESSON 1

A Constant Ratio

Geometric Sequences and Exponential Functions

Learning Goals

- Write a geometric sequence as an exponential function in the form $f(x) = a \cdot b^x$.
- Identify the constant ratio and y-intercept in different representations of exponential functions.
- Recognize when a relationship is exponential.
- Use algebra to show that for an exponential function in the form $f(x) = a \cdot b^x$, the ratio $\frac{f(x+1)}{f(x)}$ is constant and equal to b, and the y-intercept is represented by the ordered pair $(0, a)$.

REVIEW (1–2 minutes)

> Use the explicit formula to generate the first four terms of each geometric sequence.

1. $g_n = 2 \cdot 3^{x-1}$

2. $g_n = 8240 \cdot 1.05^{x-1}$

3. $g_n = 100 \cdot \left(\frac{1}{2}\right)^{x-1}$

4. $g_n = (-2) \cdot 4^{x-1}$

© Carnegie Learning, Inc.

You have learned about geometric sequences and have briefly explored exponential functions.

How can you use geometric sequences to define exponential functions?

Compare and Contrast

Recall that a geometric sequence is a sequence of values in which consecutive terms are separated by a common ratio, or constant ratio. For example, this sequence is a geometric sequence with a constant ratio of 2.

$$1, \quad 2, \quad 4, \quad 8, \quad 16, \ldots$$

(×2 from 4 to 8; ÷2 from 8 to 4)

> Consider the graphs of the six different geometric sequences.

Graph A

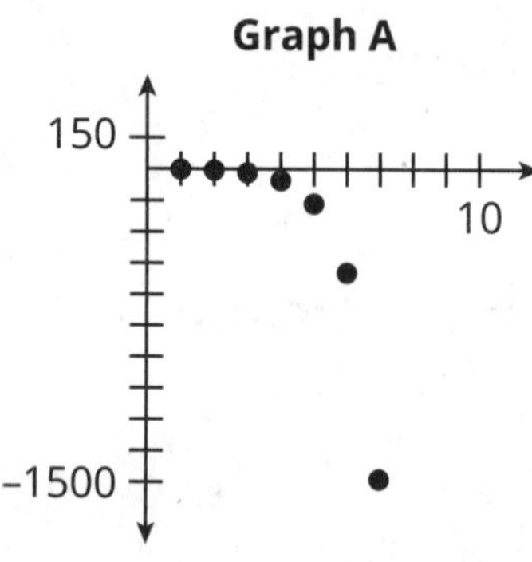

Graph B

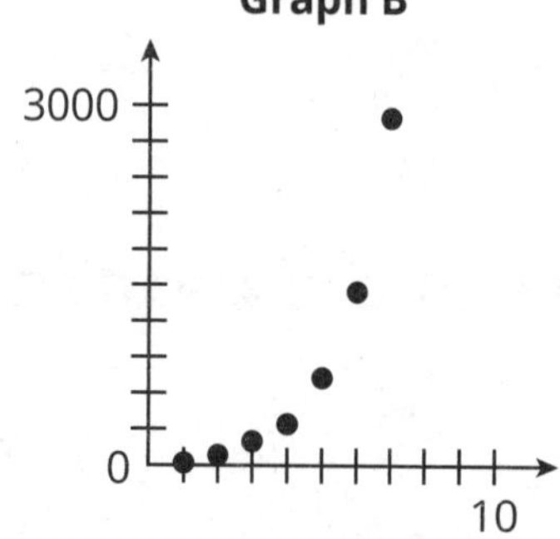

Graph C

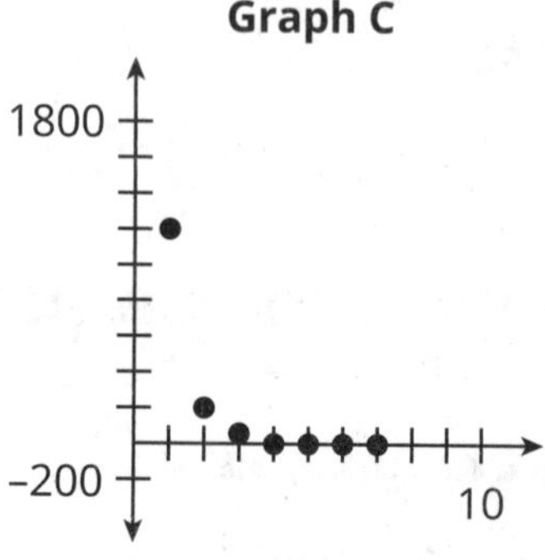

Graph D

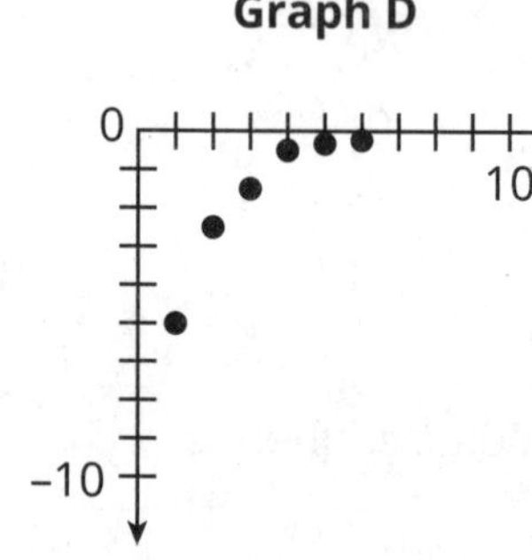

Graph E

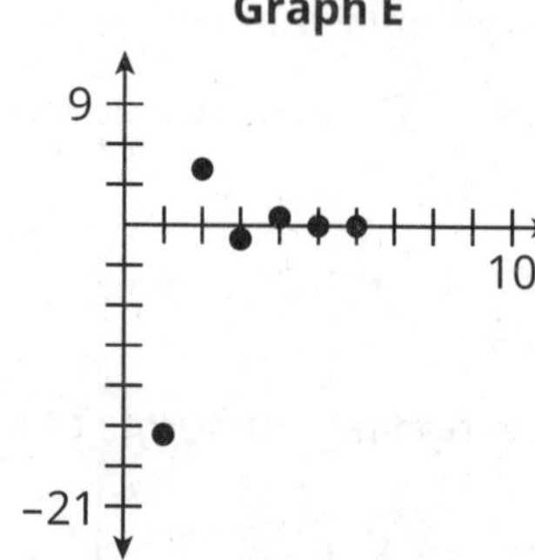

Graph F

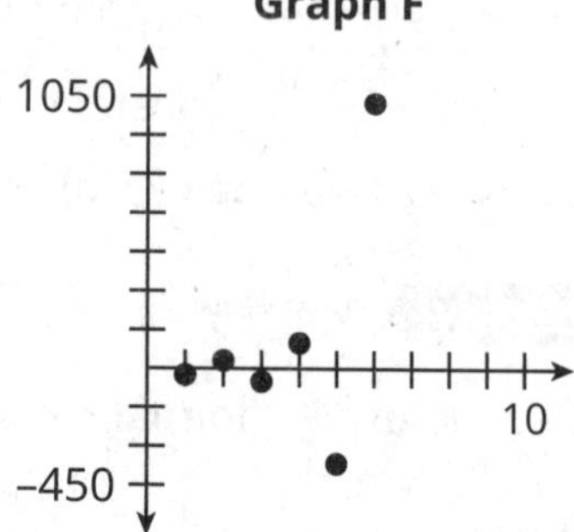

© Carnegie Learning, Inc.

1. Identify similarities and differences among the graphs. **What do you notice?**

Identifying the Constant Ratio in Geometric Sequences

HABITS OF MIND
- Look for and make use of structure.
- Look for and express regularity in repeated reasoning.

Recall that the explicit formula for a geometric sequence is $g_n = g_1 \cdot r^{n-1}$.

> Consider the table of values, graph, and explicit formula given for the six geometric sequences in the Getting Started.

1. Identify the constant ratio in each representation.

(a) Sequence A

x	y
1	−2
2	−6
3	−18

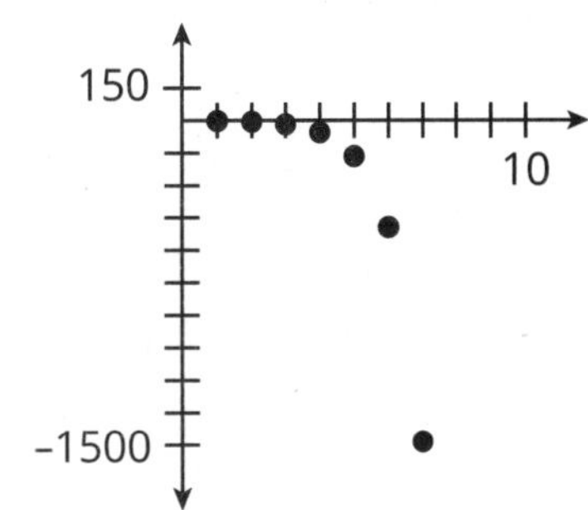

$y = -2 \cdot 3^{x-1}$

(b) Sequence B

x	y
1	45
2	90
3	180

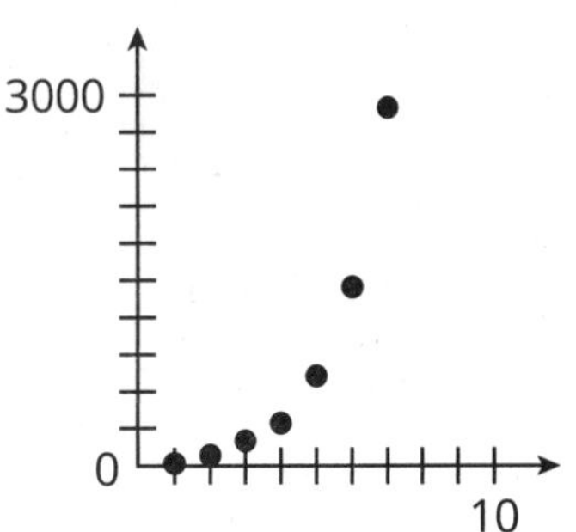

$y = 45 \cdot 2^{x-1}$

(c) Sequence C

x	y
1	1234
2	123.4
3	12.34

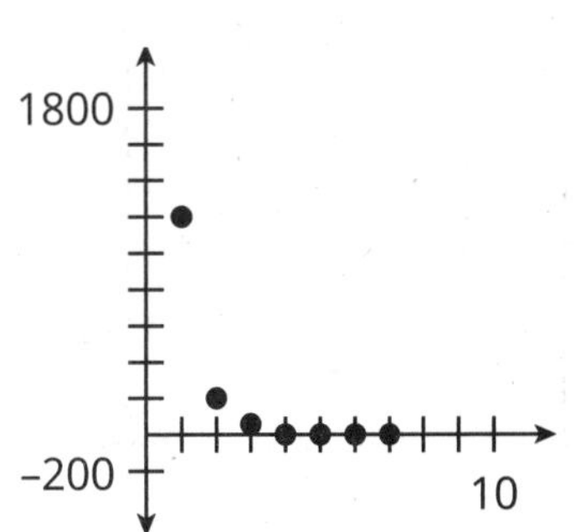

$y = 1234 \cdot 0.1^{x-1}$

© Carnegie Learning, Inc.

(d) Sequence D

x	y
1	−5
2	−2.5
3	−1.25

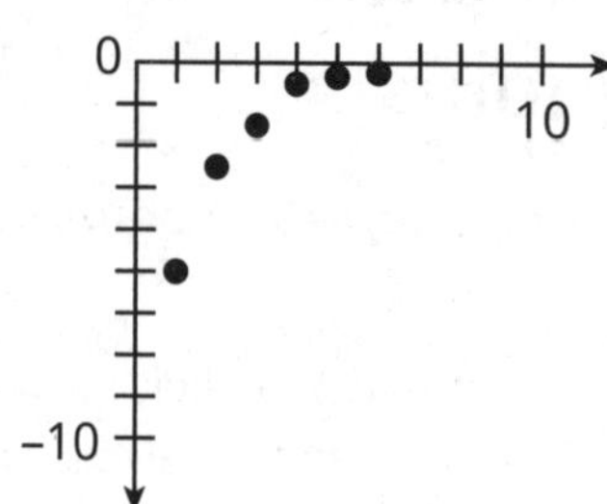

$y = -5 \cdot \left(\frac{1}{2}\right)^{x-1}$

(e) Sequence E

x	y
1	−16
2	4
3	−1

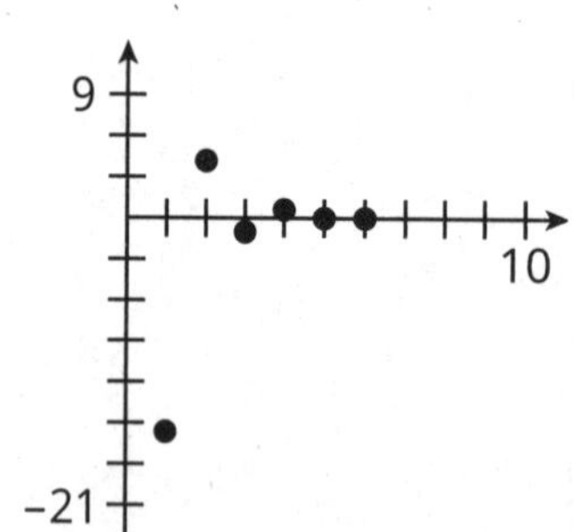

$y = -16 \cdot \left(-\frac{1}{4}\right)^{x-1}$

(f) Sequence F

x	y
1	−4
2	12
3	−36

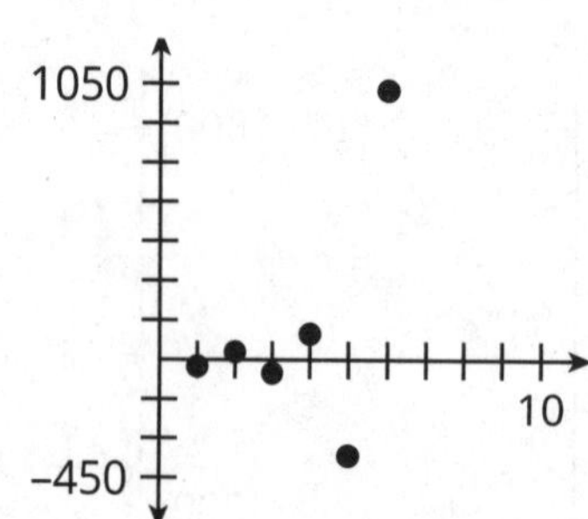

$y = -4 \cdot (-3)^{x-1}$

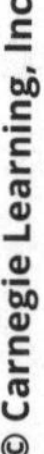
© Carnegie Learning, Inc.

2 What strategies did you use to identify the constant ratio for each sequence?

3 Analyze the graphs of the geometric sequences. Do any of the graphs appear to belong to a specific function family? If so, identify the function family. **Explain your reasoning.**

REMEMBER . . .
You can represent all arithmetic sequences as linear functions. Is there a function family that can represent geometric sequences?

© Carnegie Learning, Inc.

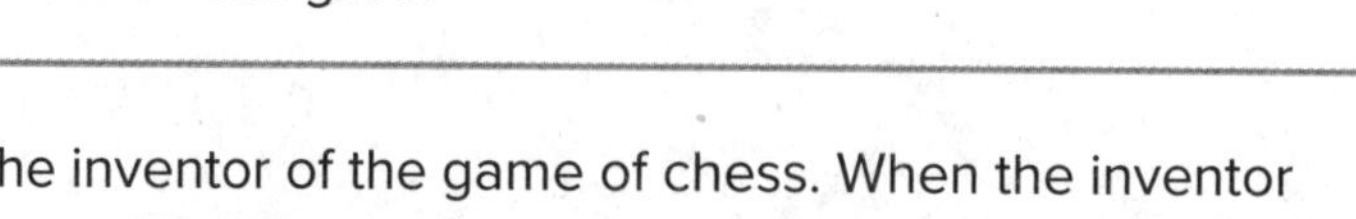

Exponential Growth

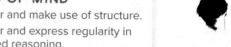

HABITS OF MIND

- Look for and make use of structure.
- Look for and express regularity in repeated reasoning.

You have identified the constant ratio in different kinds of geometric sequences. Let's now look at how geometric sequences—or certain exponential functions—can grow.

A famous legend tells the story of the inventor of the game of chess. When the inventor showed the new game to the emperor of India, the emperor was so astonished, he said to the inventor, "Name your reward!"

The wise inventor asked the emperor for 1 grain of rice for the first square of the chessboard, 2 grains for the second square, 4 grains for the third square, 8 grains for the fourth square, and so on.

1. Determine the number of rice grains on the next four squares and include them in the table. Complete the third column by writing each number of rice grains as a power with the same base.

Square Number	Number of Rice Grains	Power
1	1	
2	2	
3	4	
4	8	
5		
6		
7		
8		

2. **What pattern do you notice in the table?**

3. Graph the points from your table. The first few points have been plotted. Describe the meaning of the plotted points and then identify the function family represented.

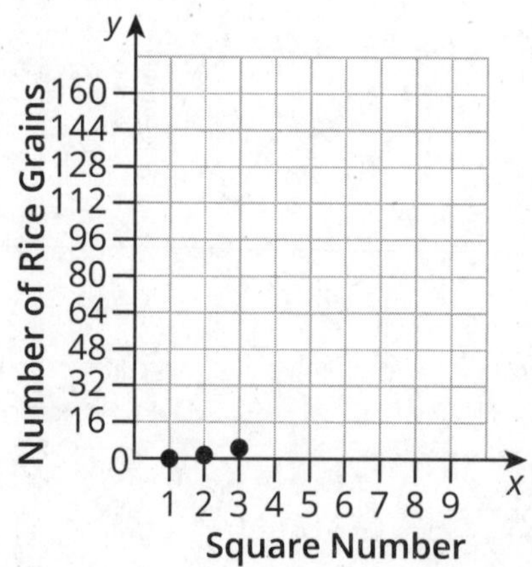

© Carnegie Learning, Inc.

4 Identify the constant ratio in the graph, in the table, and in the situation.

Pat and George each used different methods to write an exponential function to represent the number of rice grains for any square number on the chessboard.

Pat

I compared the exponents of the power to the square number in the table. Each exponent is 1 less than the square number.

$f(s) = 2^{s-1}$

I know the constant ratio is 2. If I extend the pattern back, I get the y-intercept of $\left(0, \frac{1}{2}\right)$, so I can rewrite the function as $f(s) = \frac{1}{2}(2)^s$.

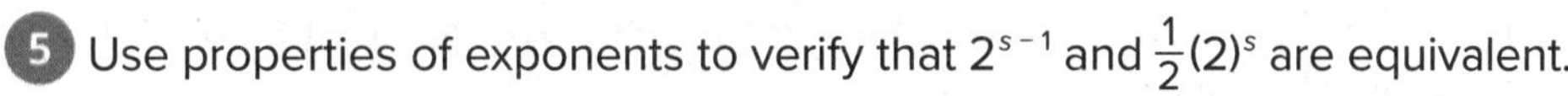

5 Use properties of exponents to verify that 2^{s-1} and $\frac{1}{2}(2)^s$ are equivalent.

© Carnegie Learning, Inc.

The function that George wrote is in exponential form. Recall that a function in the exponential function family has the form $f(x) = a \cdot b^x + c$, where a, b, and c are real numbers and b is greater than 0 but is not equal to 1.

Let's consider exponential functions where $c = 0$, such as George's function. These functions are in the form $f(x) = a \cdot b^x$.

6 What do the a-value and b-value represent in terms of the equation and graph?

7 Use the exponential function and technology to determine the number of rice grains on the very last square of the chessboard. A chessboard has 64 squares.

You can write the explicit formula for geometric sequences in function notation.

WORKED EXAMPLE

Represent $g_n = 45 \cdot 2^{n-1}$ as a function in the form $f(x) = a \cdot b^x$.

$g_n = 45 \cdot 2^{n-1}$

$f(n) = 45 \cdot 2^{n-1}$

Next, rewrite the expression $45 \cdot 2^{n-1}$.

$f(n) = 45 \cdot 2^n \cdot 2^{-1}$ Product Rule of Powers

$f(n) = 45 \cdot 2^{-1} \cdot 2^n$ Commutative Property

$f(n) = 45 \cdot \frac{1}{2} \cdot 2^n$ Definition of negative exponent

$f(n) = \frac{45}{2} \cdot 2^n$ Multiply.

So, $g_n = 45 \cdot 2^{n-1}$ written in function notation is $f(n) = \left(\frac{45}{2}\right) \cdot 2^n$, or $f(n) = (22.5) \cdot 2^n$

THINK ABOUT . . .

The Product Rule of Exponents allows you to rewrite the product of two powers with the same base.

$2^n \cdot 2^{(-1)} = 2^{n-1}$

$6^x \cdot 6^y = 6^{x+y}$

In the previous activity, you identified some of the geometric sequences as exponential functions and some that were not exponential functions.

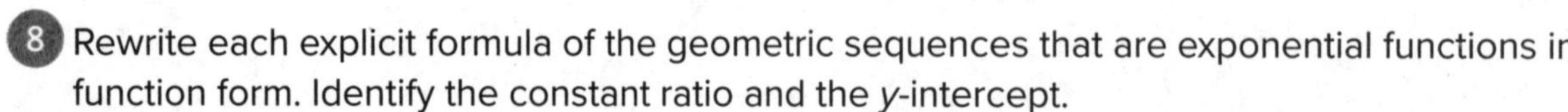

8 Rewrite each explicit formula of the geometric sequences that are exponential functions in function form. Identify the constant ratio and the *y*-intercept.

Sequence	Explicit Formula	Exponential Function	Constant Ratio	*y*-Intercept
A	$-2 \cdot 3^{x-1}$			
B	$45 \cdot 2^{x-1}$			
C	$1234 \cdot 0.1^{x-1}$			
D	$-5 \cdot \left(\frac{1}{2}\right)^{x-1}$			

© Carnegie Learning, Inc.

Based on the graphs of Sequences E and F, you can tell they do not represent exponential functions.

9. Rewrite each explicit formula in function form and explain why these geometric sequences are not exponential functions.

   a) Sequence E: $y = -4 \cdot (-3)^{x-1}$

   b) Sequence F: $y = -16 \cdot \left(-\frac{1}{4}\right)^{x-1}$

10. You know that all arithmetic sequences are linear functions. What can you say about the relationship between geometric sequences and exponential functions?

11. Complete the table by writing each part of the exponential function that corresponds to each part of the geometric sequence.

Geometric Sequence $g_n = g_1 \cdot r^{n-1}$	**Exponential Function** $f(x) = a \cdot b^x$	**Mathematical Meaning**
g_n		
$\frac{g_1}{r}$		
r		
n		

© Carnegie Learning, Inc.

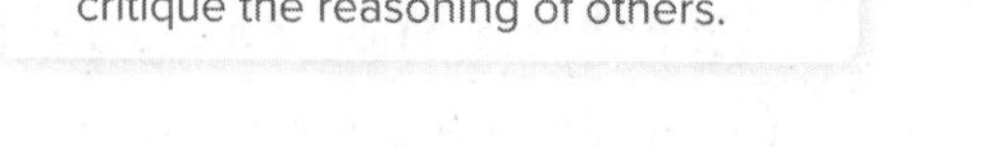

Identifying Exponential Functions

Let's identify exponential functions in a real-world situation.

HABITS OF MIND
- Reason abstractly and quantitatively.
- Construct viable arguments and critique the reasoning of others.

As part of a project in health class, Aliyah, Kim, and Reese are raising awareness and challenging others to eat a healthy breakfast each morning.

- Today, they each sent selfies of themselves eating a healthy breakfast to 4 friends and challenged them to do the same the next day.
- This next day, when others send selfies of themselves eating a healthy breakfast, it will be considered Day 1 of their results.
- The following day, only those contacted the previous day will send selfies to 4 friends, and the challenge will continue to spread.

Assume everyone contacted completes the challenge and new participants are contacted each day.

1. Write an exponential function, $f(x)$, to represent the number of new participants of the challenge as a function of the day number, x.

REMEMBER . . .
The constant ratio of an exponential function must be greater than 0 and not equal to 1.

> Analyze the table summarizing the first four days of the challenge.

Time (Day)	Number of New Participants
1	12
2	48
3	192
4	768

© Carnegie Learning, Inc.

2 The relationship between time and number of participants is exponential.

ⓐ Verify the relationship is exponential by identifying the constant ratio.

ⓑ What is the number of new participants for Day 0? **Explain your answer.**

ⓒ If $f(x) = a \cdot b^x$ represents the number of new participants for Day 0, then $f(x + 1) = a \cdot b^{(x+1)}$ can represent the number of new participants for Day 1. Complete the table to show the number of new participants as a function of the day in terms of x and $f(x)$.

Time (Day)	Number of New Participants		Function Form
x	$f(x)$		$f(x) = a \cdot b^x$
0	$f(x)$		$f(x) = a \cdot b^x$
1	$f(x + 1)$	12	$f(x + 1) = a \cdot b^{(x+1)}$
2		48	
3		192	
4		768	

ⓓ Use the expressions from the Function Form column of the table and algebra to prove that the table shows a constant ratio between consecutive output values of the function.

REMEMBER . . .

The Quotient Rule of Powers states that when dividing powers with the same base, you can subtract their exponents.

$$\frac{b^{x+2}}{b^{x+1}} = b^{(x+2)-(x+1)}$$

© Carnegie Learning, Inc.

Writing Exponential Functions

You have identified an exponential function in a situation. Now, let's write an exponential function to represent a situation.

HABITS OF MIND
- Model with mathematics.
- Use appropriate tools strategically.

The Amazing Aloysius is practicing one of his tricks. As part of the trick, he cuts a rope into many pieces and then magically puts the pieces of rope back together.

- He begins the trick with a 10-foot rope and then cuts it in half.
- He takes one of the halves and cuts that piece in half.
- He keeps cutting the pieces in half until he is left with a piece so small that he can't cut it anymore.

1. Complete the table to show the length of rope after each of Aloysius's cuts. Write each length as a whole number, a mixed number, or a fraction. Then, graph the points from the table.

Number of Cuts	Length of Rope (feet)
0	
1	
2	
3	
4	
5	

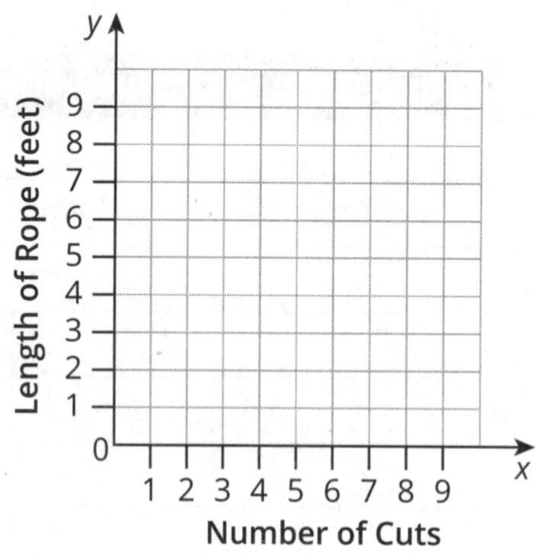

2. Write the function, $L(c)$, to represent the length of the rope as a function of the cut number, c.

3. Use your function to determine the length of the rope after the 7th cut.

© Carnegie Learning, Inc.

4 Write an exponential function of the form $f(x) = a \cdot b^x$ for each table and graph.

Ⓐ

x	y
0	4
1	2
2	1
3	$\frac{1}{2}$

Ⓑ

x	y
−2	$-\frac{1}{2}$
−1	−2
0	−8
1	−32

Ⓒ

x	y
0	1
1	4
2	16
3	64

Ⓓ

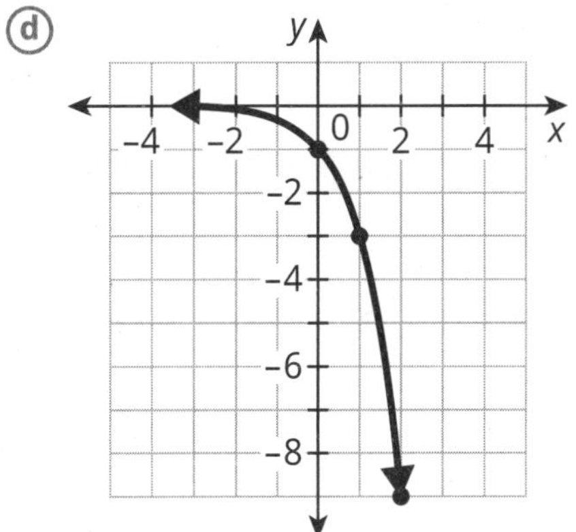

© Carnegie Learning, Inc.

Did We Mention Constant Ratio?

> Consider the functions from this lesson.

1. For an exponential function of the form $f(x) = a \cdot b^x$, what is the relationship between the base of the power, the expression $\frac{f(x+1)}{f(x)}$, and the common ratio of the corresponding geometric sequence?

2. How can you decide whether a geometric sequence of the form $g_n = g_1 \cdot b^{n-1}$ represents an exponential function?

© Carnegie Learning, Inc.

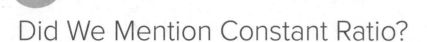

LESSON 1 ASSIGNMENT

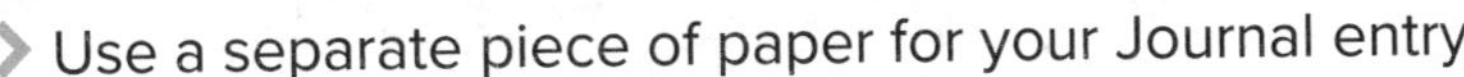

> Use a separate piece of paper for your Journal entry.

JOURNAL

Describe the differences between a linear function and an exponential function, using your own words.

REMEMBER

All sequences are functions, and some geometric sequences are exponential functions.

The form of an exponential function is $f(x) = a \cdot b^x$, where a and b are real numbers and $b > 0$, but $b \neq 1$. The a-value represents the y-intercept and the b-value represents the constant ratio, or constant multiplier.

PRACTICE

1. Each table shows the population of a city over a three-year period. Write an exponential function to represent each population as a function of time.

ⓐ

Blueville	
1	7098
2	7197
3	7298

ⓑ

Youngstown	
1	12,144
2	12,290
3	12,437

ⓒ

Greenville	
1	7860
2	7722
3	7587

2. Consider each situation. If possible, identify a constant ratio and write an exponential function to represent the relationship. Be sure to define your variables.

ⓐ Manuel works in a lab. The table shows the number of bacteria over time in a petri dish he is studying.

Bacteria	
Time (hours)	**Number of Bacteria**
0	605
1	2420
2	9680
3	38,720

© Carnegie Learning, Inc.

Go to LiveHint.com for help on the PRACTICE questions.

ⓑ Jessica has been studying the honey bee population. The table shows the number of honey bees she documents over time.

Honey Bee Population	
Time (years)	Number of Honey Bees
1	52,910
2	43,069
3	35,058
4	28,537

ⓒ Jackson started depositing money into a savings account. The table shows the amount of money over time in the account.

Savings Account	
Time (years)	Value ($)
5	875
10	1200
15	1525
20	1850

STRETCH Optional

1 Which of the functions does not fit with the others? Explain your answer.

Function A

The exponential function that goes through (0, −3) and (5, −96)

Function B

$f(x) = -1 \cdot 6^x$

Function C

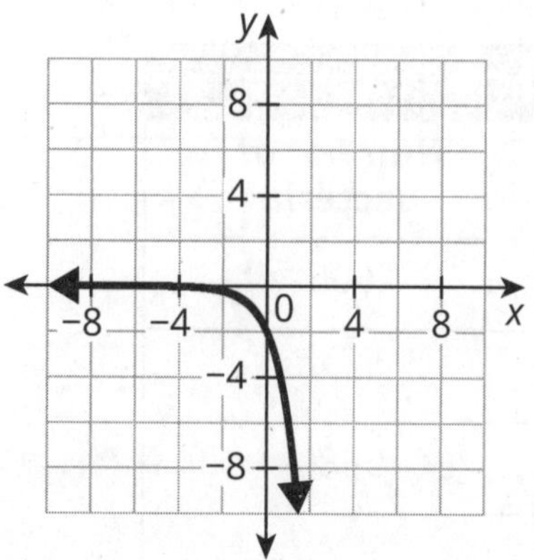

Function D

x	y
1	$\frac{2}{3}$
2	$\frac{2}{9}$
3	$\frac{2}{27}$

© Carnegie Learning, Inc.

LESSON 2

The Power Within

KEY TERMS

extracting square roots

horizontal asymptote

Rational Exponents and Graphs of Exponential Functions

Learning Goals

- Rewrite powers with rational exponents as radical expressions.
- Rewrite radical expressions as powers with rational exponents.
- Use the properties of exponents to interpret output values for non-integer input values in exponential functions.
- Construct exponential functions and identify a common ratio between output values in a graph, a table, and the equation.
- Solve simple exponential equations using common bases.

REVIEW (1–2 minutes)

> Use the Properties of Powers to rewrite each expression.

1. $\frac{b^3}{b^0}$

2. $\frac{a \cdot x^5}{a \cdot x^4}$

3. $a \cdot b^2 \cdot a^2 \cdot b^3$

4. $b^{-2} \cdot b^2 \cdot a^0$

© Carnegie Learning, Inc.

You have determined the constant ratio of exponential functions with integer inputs.

How can you use a constant ratio to determine output values with non-integer inputs?

Squares and Cubes

> Write an expression to represent the side length, s, of each square given its area. Then, approximate the value of s. **Show your work.**

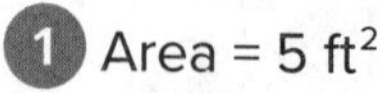
1 Area = 5 ft^2

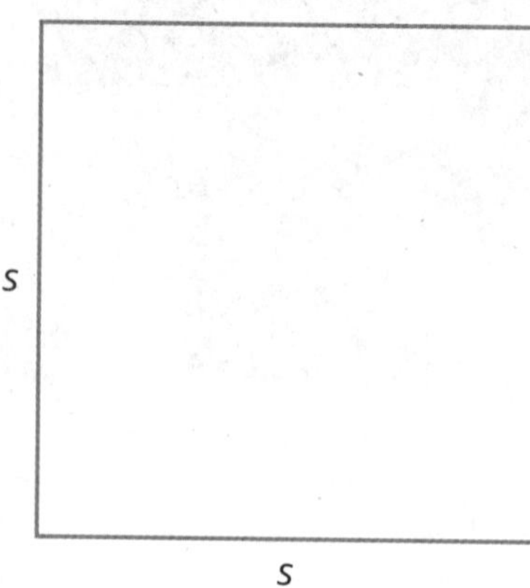

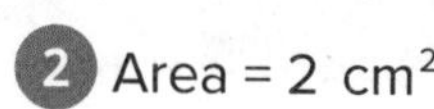
2 Area = 2 cm^2

3 Area = 81 in.^{2}

> Write an expression to represent the side length, s, of each cube given its volume. Then, approximate the value of s. **Show your work.**

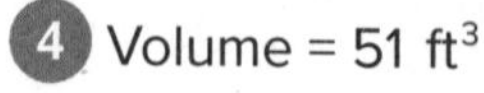
4 Volume = 51 ft^3

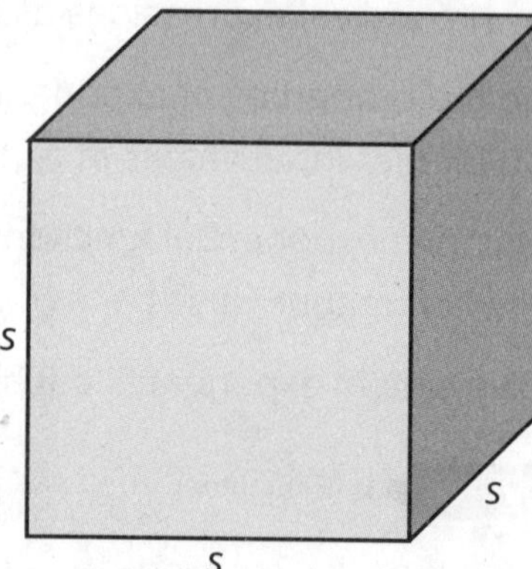

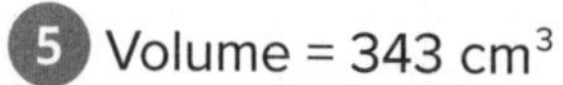
5 Volume = 343 cm^3

6 Volume = 2 in.^{3}

© Carnegie Learning, Inc.

ACTIVITY 1

MATHia CONNECTION

- Using the Properties of Exponents

Characteristics of Exponential Growth

HABITS OF MIND

- Model with mathematics.
- Use appropriate tools strategically.

How are different characteristics of exponential functions revealed in situations?

In a laboratory experiment, a certain bacteria doubles each hour.

1 Suppose a bacteria population starts with just 1 bacterium.

(a) Complete the table to show the population of bacteria, $f(x)$, over time, x.

x	1	2	3	4
$f(x)$				

(b) Determine the constant ratio and y-intercept. Then, write the exponential function that represents the growth of the bacteria population over time. **Show your work.**

(c) How is the constant multiplier evident in the problem situation?

REMEMBER . . .
The constant ratio is a multiplier. To determine the next term of a geometric sequence, you multiply by this value.

2 Tear out the coordinate plane located on page 493. Graph the exponential function to show bacteria growth over time.

© Carnegie Learning, Inc.

The Square Root Constant Ratio of an Exponential Function

What effect, if any, is there on the constant multiplier of an exponential function if the input interval is different?

HABITS OF MIND
- Look for and make use of structure.
- Look for and express regularity in repeated reasoning.

This table represents the function $f(x) = 2^x$, which models the laboratory experiment that a certain population of bacteria can double each hour.

x	0	1	2	3
$f(x)$	2^0	2^1	2^2	2^3
	1	2	4	8

REMEMBER . . .
An exponential function is continuous, meaning that there is a value $f(x)$ for every real number value x.

In the table, the interval between the input values is 1, and the constant multiplier is 2 at the point when the interval changes.

1 Consider the ratio $\frac{f(2)}{f(0)}$.

(a) Describe the interval of input values. Then, determine the multiplier.

(b) Write two additional ratios that have the same multiplier. **Explain your reasoning.**

(c) Write a new pair of ratios that have the same multiplier but span a different input interval than the intervals you have already analyzed. **Justify your answer.**

© Carnegie Learning, Inc.

Vicky, Nate, and Taylor are interested in the population of bacteria at each $\frac{1}{2}$-hour interval. They have values for the exponential function, $f(x)$, when x is an integer. They need the values of the exponential function when x is a rational number between integers.

2 The three students used the idea of the constant multiplier to estimate the value of $f\left(\frac{1}{2}\right)$ for the function $f(x) = 2^x$.

Vicky

I know the constant multiplier for an interval of 1 is 2. I want to split each interval of 1 into two equal parts, which means I need two equal multipliers.

multiply by 2

x	0	$\frac{1}{2}$	1
$f(x)$	2^0	$2^{\frac{1}{2}}$	2^1
	1		2

$1 \cdot r \cdot r = 2$

So, $r^2 = 2$.

Nate

If r is a constant multiplier for the function as it grows by consecutive integers, I can split it into two equal multipliers of $\sqrt{r}$ because I can split r into two equal factors of $\sqrt{r}$.

$(\sqrt{r})^2 = r$

Taylor

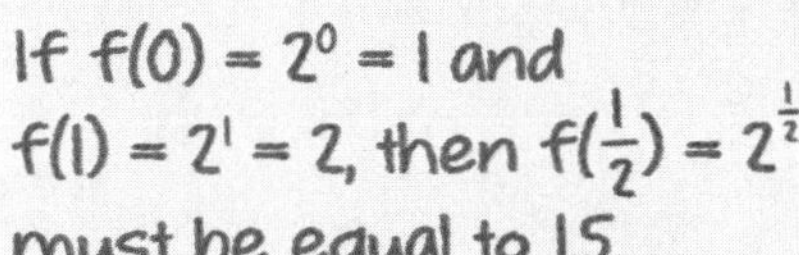

If $f(0) = 2^0 = 1$ and $f(1) = 2^1 = 2$, then $f\left(\frac{1}{2}\right) = 2^{\frac{1}{2}}$ must be equal to 1.5.

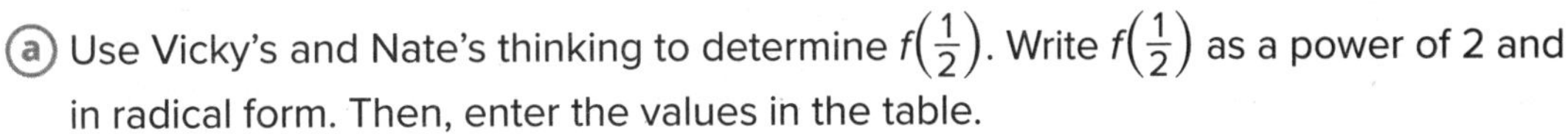

(a) Use Vicky's and Nate's thinking to determine $f\left(\frac{1}{2}\right)$. Write $f\left(\frac{1}{2}\right)$ as a power of 2 and in radical form. Then, enter the values in the table.

x	0	$\frac{1}{2}$	1	2	3
$f(x)$	2^0		2^1	2^2	2^3
	1		2	4	8

(b) Use the graph you created in the previous activity to approximate $f\left(\frac{1}{2}\right)$ as a decimal.

(c) **Explain why Taylor's thinking is incorrect.**

© Carnegie Learning, Inc.

The expression $\sqrt{2} = 2^{\frac{1}{2}}$. You can interpret the square root symbol ($\sqrt{\ }$) as the rational exponent $\frac{1}{2}$. All the properties with integer exponents you previously earned continue to apply even when the exponent is a rational number.

REMEMBER . . .
The number $\sqrt{2}$ is an irrational number because you cannot represent it as the ratio of two integers.

> Consider these tables, which represent two different equivalent representations of the constant multiplier, $2^{\frac{1}{2}}$ or $\sqrt{2}$, for the function $f(x) = 2^x$.

	Rational Exponent Representation	
$f(0)$	2^0	$2^0 \cdot 2^{\frac{1}{2}}$
$f(\frac{1}{2})$	$2^{\frac{1}{2}}$	$2^{\frac{1}{2}} \cdot 2^{\frac{1}{2}}$
$f(1)$	2^1	$2^1 \cdot 2^{\frac{1}{2}}$
$f(\frac{3}{2})$	$2^{\frac{3}{2}}$	

	Radical Form Representation	
$f(0)$	1	$1 \cdot \sqrt{2}$
$f(\frac{1}{2})$	$\sqrt{2}$	$\sqrt{2} \cdot \sqrt{2}$
$f(1)$	2	$2 \cdot \sqrt{2}$
$f(\frac{3}{2})$	$2\sqrt{2}$	

3 Use the properties of exponents to justify that $2^1 \cdot 2^{\frac{1}{2}} = 2^{\frac{3}{2}}$. Then, use the graph to estimate $2^{\frac{3}{2}}$ as a decimal.

You can rewrite a rational exponent in radical form using the definition $a^{\frac{1}{n}} = \sqrt[n]{a}$. When the index is 2, it is usually implied rather than written.

Let's consider the properties of exponents to rewrite expressions in equivalent forms.

TAKE NOTE . . .
In the expression $\sqrt[n]{a}$, the *n* is the index.

WORKED EXAMPLE

Consider the expression $2^{\frac{3}{2}}$.

Using the Power to a Power Rule: $2^{\frac{3}{2}} = \left(2^{\frac{1}{2}}\right)^3$ or $(2^3)^{\frac{1}{2}}$.

You can use the definition of rational exponents to rewrite each expression in radical form.

$$\begin{aligned}\left(2^{\frac{1}{2}}\right)^3 &= (\sqrt{2})^3 \\ &= \sqrt{2} \cdot \sqrt{2} \cdot \sqrt{2} \\ &= (\sqrt{2} \cdot \sqrt{2}) \cdot \sqrt{2} \\ &= 2\sqrt{2}\end{aligned}$$

$$\begin{aligned}(2^3)^{\frac{1}{2}} &= \sqrt{2^3} \\ &= \sqrt{2 \cdot 2 \cdot 2} \\ &= \sqrt{2^2 \cdot 2} \\ &= 2\sqrt{2}\end{aligned}$$

TAKE NOTE . . .
The process of removing perfect square numbers from under a radical symbol is **extracting square roots**.

© Carnegie Learning, Inc.

Now, let's consider how to use the Product Rule of Powers to rewrite the expression with rational exponents in radical form.

WORKED EXAMPLE

Consider the expression $2^{\frac{3}{2}}$.

Using the Product Rule of Powers:

$2^{\frac{3}{2}} = 2^{\frac{1}{2}+\frac{1}{2}+\frac{1}{2}}$

$= (2^{\frac{1}{2}})(2^{\frac{1}{2}})(2^{\frac{1}{2}})$

$= \sqrt{2} \cdot \sqrt{2} \cdot \sqrt{2}$

$= \sqrt{2 \cdot 2 \cdot 2}$

You can use the definition of rational exponents to rewrite each expression in radical form.

REMEMBER . . .
The Product Property of Radicals states that $\sqrt{a} \cdot \sqrt{b} = \sqrt{a \cdot b}$ when a and b are greater than 0.

4 Analyze the Worked Examples.

(a) Explain why $\sqrt{2} \cdot \sqrt{2} = 2$.

(b) Explain why $\sqrt{2^2} = 2$.

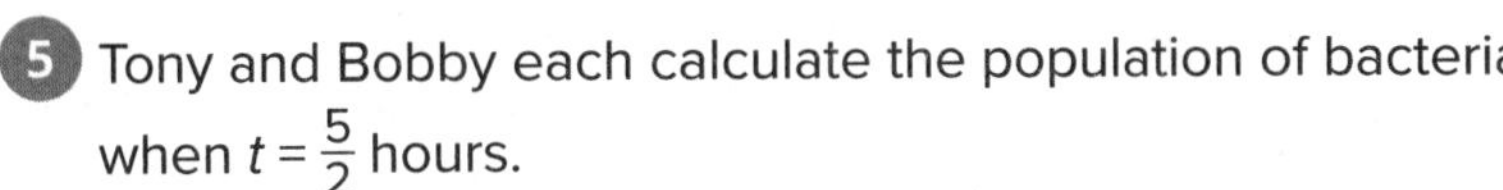

5 Tony and Bobby each calculate the population of bacteria when $t = \frac{5}{2}$ hours.

Tony says that when $t = \frac{5}{2}$ hours, $f\left(\frac{5}{2}\right) = (\sqrt{2})^5$ bacteria. Bobby says that $f\left(\frac{5}{2}\right) = 4\sqrt{2}$ bacteria. Who's correct? **Use definitions and rules to justify your reasoning.** Then, use the graph you created in Activity 1 to estimate the value of $f\left(\frac{5}{2}\right)$ as a decimal.

TAKE NOTE . . .
You will learn and practice more with rational exponents later in this lesson.

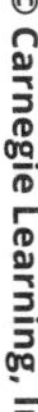

© Carnegie Learning, Inc.

The Cube Root Constant Ratio of an Exponential Function

HABITS OF MIND
- Look for and make use of structure.
- Look for and express regularity in repeated reasoning.

In the previous activity, you looked at the exponential function $f(x) = 2^x$. When the input interval is 1, the constant ratio is 2^1, and when the input interval is $\frac{1}{2}$, the constant multiplier is $2^{\frac{1}{2}}$.

Now, let's think about the constant multiplier when the input interval is $\frac{1}{3}$.

×2

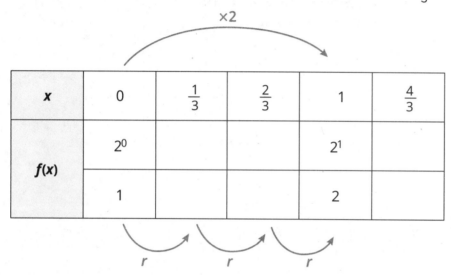

x	0	$\frac{1}{3}$	$\frac{2}{3}$	1	$\frac{4}{3}$
f(*x*)	2^0			2^1	
	1			2	

r *r* *r*

THINK ABOUT . . .
What is the constant multiplier you can use to build this relationship over intervals of $\frac{1}{3}$?

1 Complete the table of values for the exponential function $f(x) = 2^x$. Represent $f(x)$ as a rational exponent and in radical form. **Show your work.**

THINK ABOUT . . .
In the expression $\sqrt[n]{a}$, only $n = 2$ is implied rather than written. You must write all other index values.

2 Write the points represented in the table as ordered pairs. Use the graph you created in Activity 1 to estimate each output value as a decimal.

© Carnegie Learning, Inc.

Negative Exponents and Asymptotes

HABITS OF MIND
- Look for and make use of structure.
- Look for and express regularity in repeated reasoning.

You have explored output values with integer and rational exponents for the exponential function $f(x) = 2^x$. What happens when x is a negative value?

1 Use what you know about negative exponents to complete the table for the function $f(x) = 2^x$.

x	−4	−3	−2	−1	0
f(x)					

REMEMBER . . .
The Negative Power Rule states that $a^{-1} = \frac{1}{a}$, $a^{-2} = \frac{1}{a^2}$, and so on.

2 Consider the table of values you just completed. How does $f(x)$ change as x approaches negative infinity?

An exponential function has a *horizontal asymptote*. A **horizontal asymptote** is a horizontal line that a function gets closer and closer to. The graph of an exponential function will never intersect its horizontal asymptote.

3 Label the function $f(x) = 2^x$ on this coordinate plane. Identify the horizontal asymptote.

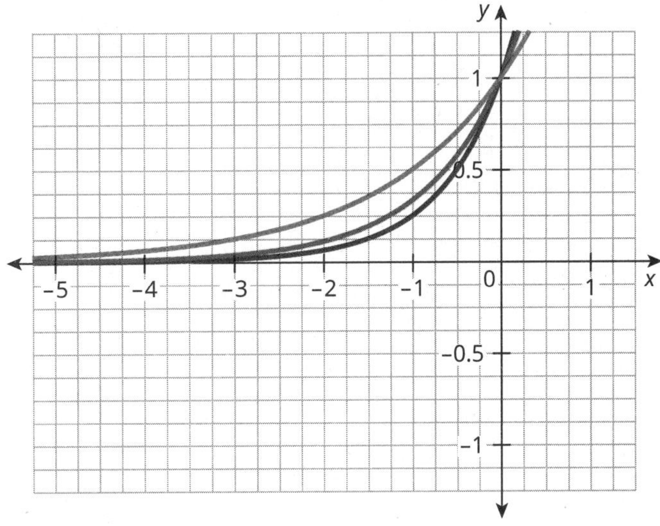

© Carnegie Learning, Inc.

4 The functions $g(x) = 3^x$ and $h(x) = 4^x$ are also graphed on the coordinate plane.

(a) Identify each function. **Explain your reasoning.**

(b) Determine the horizontal asymptotes for the functions. **Compare these with the horizontal asymptote of $f(x) = 2^x$.**

5 Compare how each of the three functions approaches its horizontal asymptote. **What is the same and what is different?**

© Carnegie Learning, Inc.

MATHia CONNECTION
- Properties of Rational Exponents
- Rewriting Expressions with Radical and Rational Exponents
- Solving Contextual Exponential Relations Using Common Bases

Rational Exponents and Common Bases

HABIT OF MIND
- Attend to precision.

In this lesson, you have been writing powers with rational exponents. You have shown that you can rewrite a rational exponent in radical form, $a^{\frac{1}{n}} = \sqrt[n]{a}$.

REMEMBER . . .
In the expression $\sqrt[n]{a}$, the n is the index.

1. Rewrite each expression as a power.

   a. $\sqrt[3]{7}$ b. $\sqrt[5]{x}$ c. $\sqrt{y}$

2. Rewrite each expression in radical form.

   a. $8^{\frac{1}{4}}$ b. $z^{\frac{1}{5}}$ c. $m^{\frac{1}{3}}$

3. Use the properties of exponents to rewrite $a^{\frac{m}{n}}$ in radical form.

4. Rewrite each expression in radical form.

   a. $4^{\frac{3}{2}}$ b. $5^{\frac{3}{4}}$ c. $x^{\frac{4}{5}}$ d. $y^{\frac{2}{3}}$

5. Rewrite each expression as a power with a rational exponent.

   a. $\left(\sqrt[4]{2}\right)^3$ b. $(\sqrt{5})^4$ c. $\left(\sqrt[5]{x}\right)^8$ d. $\left(\sqrt[5]{y}\right)^{10}$

© Carnegie Learning, Inc.

Let's analyze the product of radicals.

WORKED EXAMPLE

You can rewrite the numeric expression $(\sqrt[3]{2})^2(\sqrt{2})$ in radical form using the rules of exponents.

$(2^{\frac{1}{3}})^2(2)^{\frac{1}{2}}$	Definition of rational exponents
$(2^{\frac{2}{3}})(2^{\frac{1}{2}})$	Power to a Power Rule
$2^{\frac{2}{3}+\frac{1}{2}}$	Product Rule of Powers
$2^{\frac{7}{6}}$	Add fractions.
$\sqrt[6]{2^7}$	Definition of rational exponents

6 Tonya rewrote the expression $\sqrt[6]{2^7}$ in a different way. Is she correct? **Justify your reasoning.**

Tonya

$2^{\frac{7}{6}} = 2^{\frac{6}{6}} \cdot 2^{\frac{1}{6}} = 2\sqrt[6]{2}$

Let's revisit the Product Property of Radicals and the process of extracting roots.

Suppose you have the product $\sqrt{15} \cdot \sqrt{5}$. You can use properties of exponents to rewrite this radical expression.

WORKED EXAMPLE

$$\begin{aligned}\sqrt{15} \cdot \sqrt{5} &= 15^{\frac{1}{2}} \cdot 5^{\frac{1}{2}} \\ &= (15 \cdot 5)^{\frac{1}{2}} \\ &= (3 \cdot 5 \cdot 5)^{\frac{1}{2}} \\ &= (3 \cdot 5^2)^{\frac{1}{2}} \\ &= 3^{\frac{1}{2}} \cdot 5 \\ &= 5\sqrt{3}\end{aligned}$$

$$\begin{aligned}\sqrt{15} \cdot \sqrt{5} &= \sqrt{15 \cdot 5} \\ &= \sqrt{3 \cdot 5 \cdot 5} \\ &= \sqrt{3 \cdot 5^2} \\ &= 5\sqrt{3}\end{aligned}$$

© Carnegie Learning, Inc.

7 Rewrite each radical expression by extracting perfect squares.

(a) $\sqrt{50}$

(b) $\sqrt{24}$

(c) $3\sqrt{20}$

(d) $\sqrt{3} \cdot \sqrt{6}$

(e) $\sqrt{3} \cdot \sqrt{12}$

(f) $\sqrt{8} \cdot \sqrt{12}$

8 Explain how the properties of rational exponents extend from the properties of integer exponents.

9 Consider the calculations you made throughout this lesson and the definition of a rational number to answer each question.

(a) Is the product of a nonzero rational number and an irrational number always, sometimes, or never a rational number? **Explain your reasoning.**

(b) Is the product of an irrational number and an irrational number always, sometimes, or never a rational number? **Explain your reasoning.**

© Carnegie Learning, Inc.

WORKED EXAMPLE

You can rewrite the numeric expression $\frac{\sqrt[3]{x}\sqrt{x}}{\sqrt[6]{x}}$ in radical form using rules of exponents.

$\frac{x^{\frac{1}{3}}x^{\frac{1}{2}}}{x^{\frac{1}{6}}}$	Rewrite using rational exponents.
$\frac{x^{\frac{1}{3}+\frac{1}{2}}}{x^{\frac{1}{6}}}$	Apply the Product Rule of Powers.
$\frac{x^{\frac{5}{6}}}{x^{\frac{1}{6}}}$	Add fractions.
$x^{\frac{4}{6}}$	Apply the Quotient Rule of Powers.
$x^{\frac{2}{3}}$	Rewrite the fraction.
$\sqrt[3]{x^2}$	Rewrite in radical form.

10 Rewrite each expression using the rules of exponents. Write responses in radical form.

ⓐ $\left(3^{\frac{3}{2}}\right)^3$

ⓑ $\frac{\left(2^{-\frac{1}{2}}\right)^3}{\left(2^{\frac{1}{2}}\right)^{-1}}$

ⓒ $\left(2x^{\frac{1}{2}}y^{\frac{1}{3}}\right)\left(3x^{\frac{1}{2}}y\right)$

ⓓ $\left(\frac{24m^{\frac{3}{4}}n^{\frac{5}{2}}}{36m^{\frac{2}{7}}n^{\frac{2}{5}}}\right)^0$

Suppose a population of rabbits triples every year. The table shows their numbers.

11 Write a function, *f*, to represent the rabbit population over time, *x*.

Time (years)	Rabbit Population
0	2
1	6
2	18
3	54

12 Use your equation to evaluate the population of rabbits for each number of years.

ⓐ $f(10)$

ⓑ $f(20)$

ⓒ $f(30)$

© Carnegie Learning, Inc.

How long did it take for the population of rabbits to reach a population of 4374? To answer this question, you must solve the equation $4374 = 2(3)^x$. This is equivalent to the equation $2187 = 3^x$.

REMEMBER . . .
A number is divisible by 3 when the sum of the digits is divisible by 3.

WORKED EXAMPLE

To solve the exponential equation $2187 = 3^x$, first determine the power of 3 that gives the result of 2187:

$$(3)(3)(3)(3)(3)(3)(3) = 2187$$

$$3^7 = 2187$$

Then, rewrite the equation to show common bases:

$$3^7 = 3^x$$

Because the expressions on both sides of the equals sign have the same base, you can set up and solve an equation using the exponents.

$$7 = x$$

So, it will take 7 years for the rabbits to reach a population of 4374.

13 Use the method from the Worked Example to determine approximately how long it will take the rabbit population to reach 1 million. **Explain your reasoning.**

14 Solve each equation for x.

a) $3^x = 81$

b) $2^{4x} = 1$

c) $4^{8-x} = \frac{1}{64}$

d) $5^{9x} = 1$

e) $\frac{1}{3^{x+5}} = 243$

f) $2^{-x} = \frac{1}{2}$

© Carnegie Learning, Inc.

May the Fourths Be with You

> Consider the exponential function $f(x) = 2^x$.

1 Complete the table. Then, compare the table of fourths to the tables you completed for halves and thirds. **What patterns do you notice in the multiplier?**

x	0	$\frac{1}{4}$	$\frac{2}{4}$	$\frac{3}{4}$	1
$f(x)$	2^0				2^1
	1				2

2 Match each expression with a rational exponent to the appropriate radical expression.

Expression with a Rational Exponent	Rational Expression
$2^{\frac{5}{10}}$	$\sqrt[5]{10^2}$
$10^{\frac{5}{2}}$	$\sqrt[5]{2^{10}}$
$10^{\frac{2}{5}}$	$\sqrt[10]{2^5}$
$5^{\frac{10}{2}}$	$\sqrt[2]{10^5}$
$2^{\frac{10}{5}}$	$\sqrt[2]{5^{10}}$
$5^{\frac{2}{10}}$	$\sqrt[10]{5^2}$

3 Solve for x and explain each step.

$4^x = \left(\frac{1}{2}\right)^{x-15}$

© Carnegie Learning, Inc.

Graph of $f(x) = 2^x$

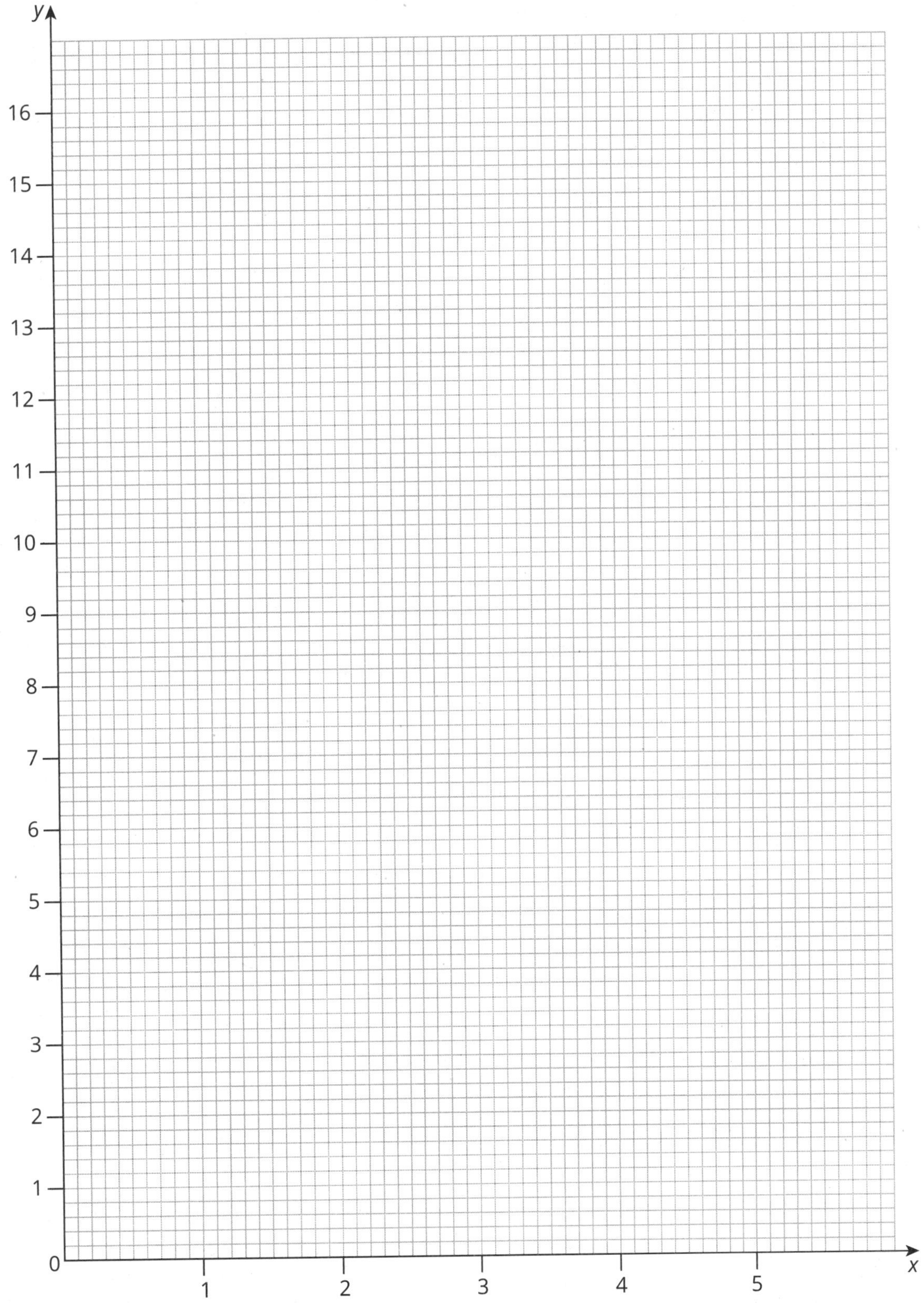

y

16
15
14
13
12
11
10
9
8
7
6
5
4
3
2
1
0

1 2 3 4 5

x

© Carnegie Learning, Inc.

Why is this page blank?

So you can tear out the coordinate plane on the other side

© Carnegie Learning, Inc.

LESSON 2 ASSIGNMENT

> Use a separate piece of paper for your Journal entry.

JOURNAL

Describe the relationship between the components of radical form and rational exponent form of an equivalent expression.

REMEMBER

When the difference in the input values is the same, an exponential function shows a constant multiplier between output values, no matter how large or how small the gap between input values.

When n is an integer greater than 1, then $\sqrt[n]{a} = a^{\frac{1}{n}}$.

PRACTICE

1. Rewrite each radical using a rational exponent.

   a. $\sqrt[4]{88}$

   b. $\sqrt[10]{46}$

   c. $\sqrt[6]{x}$

   d. $\sqrt{z}$

2. Rewrite each power in radical form.

   a. $9^{\frac{1}{3}}$

   b. $5^{\frac{1}{2}}$

   c. $20^{\frac{1}{5}}$

   d. $41^{\frac{1}{8}}$

3. Rewrite each power in radical form. Extract roots, if possible.

   a. $16^{\frac{3}{2}}$

   b. $5^{\frac{7}{4}}$

   c. $12^{\frac{2}{5}}$

   d. $8^{\frac{4}{3}}$

   e. $2^{\frac{5}{6}}$

   f. $15^{\frac{6}{7}}$

© Carnegie Learning, Inc.

Go to LiveHint.com for help on the PRACTICE questions.

4 Rewrite each expression using a rational exponent in lowest terms.

(a) $(\sqrt[5]{10})^4$

(b) $(\sqrt[4]{t})^4$

(c) $(\sqrt{w})^6$

(d) $(\sqrt[9]{h})^3$

5 Rewrite each radical expression by extracting perfect squares.

(a) $\sqrt{12}$

(b) $\sqrt{30}$

(c) $\sqrt{27}$

(d) $3\sqrt{75}$

(e) $\sqrt{15} \cdot \sqrt{6}$

(f) $\sqrt{14} \cdot \sqrt{2}$

(g) $\sqrt{8} \cdot \sqrt{7}$

(h) $\sqrt{10} \cdot \sqrt{15}$

6 Solve each exponential equation for *x*.

(a) $4^x = 256$

(b) $6^{3x} = 36$

(c) $2^{5-x} = \frac{1}{16}$

(d) $3^{-2x} = \frac{1}{81}$

(e) $4^{x+3} = 4$

(f) $\frac{1}{5^{x+4}} = 625$

© Carnegie Learning, Inc.

STRETCH Optional

1 How do rational exponents help you to multiply or divide two radicals with different indices ($\sqrt[m]{a} \cdot \sqrt[n]{a}$ or $\frac{\sqrt[m]{a}}{\sqrt[n]{a}}$, when $m \neq n$)? Include two examples to support your answer.

TOPIC 1
Introduction to Exponential Functions

1 | A Constant Ratio

2 | The Power Within

3 | Now I Know My A, B, C, Ds

TOPIC 2
Using Exponential Equations

LESSON 3

Now I Know My A, B, C, Ds

Transformations of Exponential Functions

Learning Goals

- Graph exponential functions and transformations of exponential functions.
- Graph and analyze vertical translations and horizontal translations of exponential functions.
- Graph and analyze horizontal and vertical reflections of exponential functions.
- Graph and analyze horizontal dilations of exponential functions.
- Write equations of transformed functions from a graph and from a description.
- Rewrite exponential functions in different forms.

REVIEW (1–2 minutes)

© Carnegie Learning, Inc.

1. Describe the effect of changing the A-value of the function $A \cdot f(x)$ given the basic function $f(x) = x$.

2. Describe the effect of changing the D-value of the function $f(x) + D$ given the basic function $f(x) = x$.

You know how to transform linear and absolute value functions.

Do transformations of exponential functions behave in the same way?

H, I, J, ...

> Consider the function graphed.

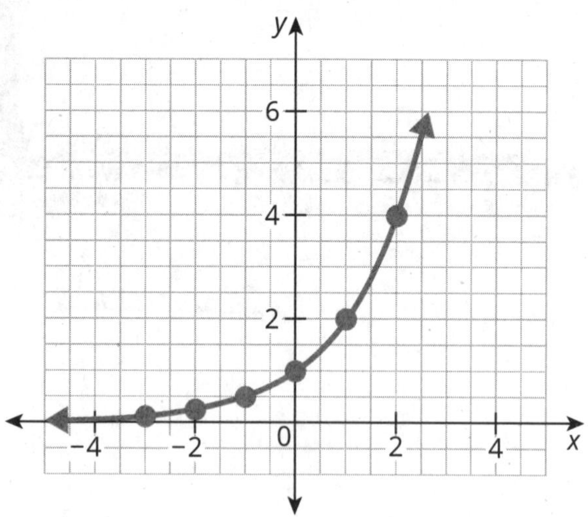

1 Identify each part of the graphed function.

(a) Domain

(b) Range

(c) Horizontal asymptote

Recall that you can write the transformation form of a function $y = f(x)$, as shown.

outside the function

$$g(x) = A \cdot f(x - C) + D$$

inside the function

2 How do the A-, C-, and D-values affect the graph of $f(x)$?

© Carnegie Learning, Inc.

MATHia CONNECTION
- Introduction to Transforming Exponential Functions
- Vertically Translating Exponential Functions

Vertical Translations of Exponential Functions

HABITS OF MIND
- Model with mathematics.
- Use appropriate tools strategically.

Let's look at vertical translations of exponential functions.

> Consider the three exponential functions: h, r, and t.

$h(x) = 2^x$ $\qquad r(x) = 2^x + 3$ $\qquad t(x) = 2^x - 3$

In this case, $h(x) = 2^x$ is the basic function because it is the simplest exponential function with a base of 2. It is in the form $f(x) = a \cdot b^x$, where $a = 1$ and $b = 2$.

1. Write the functions $r(x)$ and $t(x)$ in terms of the basic function $h(x)$. Then, describe the operation performed on the basic function $h(x)$ to result in each of the equations for $r(x)$ and $t(x)$.

   $r(x) =$ ______________

   ____

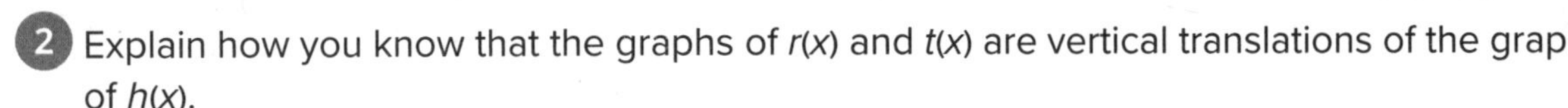

2. Explain how you know that the graphs of $r(x)$ and $t(x)$ are vertical translations of the graph of $h(x)$.

3. Sketch and label the graphs of each function. **Identify key points.**

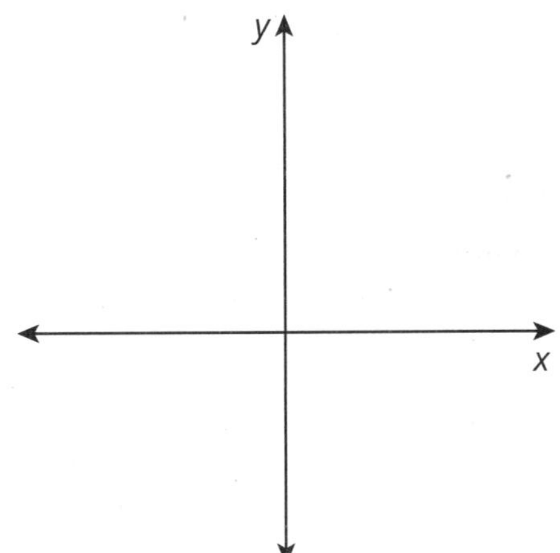

THINK ABOUT . . .
When graphing an exponential function, consider the points when $x = -1$, 0, and 1.

TOPIC 1

© Carnegie Learning, Inc.

4 Compare the y-intercepts of the graphs of $r(x)$ and $t(x)$ to the y-intercept of the graph of the basic function $h(x)$. **What do you notice?**

5 Compare the horizontal asymptotes of the graphs of $r(x)$ and $t(x)$ to the horizontal asymptote of the graph of the basic function $h(x)$. **What do you notice?**

6 Write the y-value of each of the corresponding reference points on $r(x)$ and $t(x)$.

$h(x) = 2^x$	$r(x) = 2^x + 3$	$t(x) = 2x - 3$
$\left(-2, \frac{1}{4}\right)$		
$\left(-1, \frac{1}{2}\right)$		
(0, 1)		
(1, 2)		
(2, 4)		

7 Use the table to compare the ordered pairs of the graphs of $r(x)$ and $t(x)$ to the ordered pairs of the graph of the basic function $h(x)$. **What do you notice?**

© Carnegie Learning, Inc.

TOPIC 1

8 Complete each sentence with the coordinate notation to represent the vertical translation of each function.

(a) $r(x) = h(x) + 3$

Each point (x, y) on the graph of $h(x)$ becomes the point ______________ on $r(x)$.

(b) $t(x) = h(x) - 3$

Each point (x, y) on the graph of $h(x)$ becomes the point ______________ on $t(x)$.

Recall that for the basic function, the D-value of the transformed function $y = f(x) + D$ affects the output values of the function.

- For $D > 0$, the graph vertically shifts up.
- For $D < 0$, the graph vertically shifts down.
- The magnitude of the vertical shift is given by $|D|$.

9 What generalization can you make about the effects of vertical translations on the domain, range, and asymptotes of exponential functions?

© Carnegie Learning, Inc.

MATHia CONNECTION

- Horizontally Translating Exponential Functions

Horizontal Translations of Exponential Functions

HABITS OF MIND

- Model with mathematics.
- Use appropriate tools strategically.

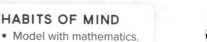

Now, let's consider horizontal translations of exponential functions.

> Consider these three exponential functions, where $h(x) = 2^x$ is the basic function.

- $h(x) = 2^x$
- $v(x) = 2^{(x + 3)}$
- $w(x) = 2^{(x - 3)}$

The operations are performed on x, which is the argument of the function.

You can write the given functions $v(x)$ and $w(x)$ in terms of the basic function $h(x)$.

WORKED EXAMPLE

To write $v(x)$ in terms of $h(x)$, you just substitute $x + 3$ into the argument for $h(x)$, as shown.

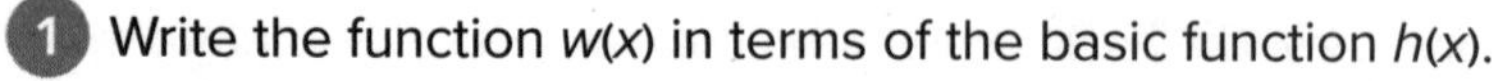

$$h(x) = 2^x$$

$$v(x) = h(x + 3) = 2^{(x + 3)}$$

So, $x + 3$ replaces the variable x in the function $h(x) = 2^x$.

REMEMBER . . .

Recall that the argument of a function is the variable on which the function operates.

1 Write the function $w(x)$ in terms of the basic function $h(x)$.

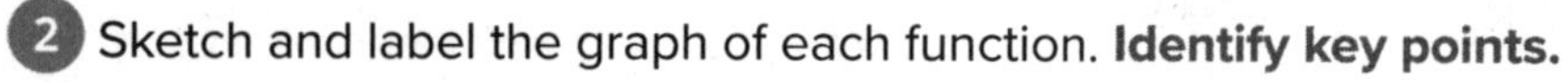

2 Sketch and label the graph of each function. **Identify key points.**

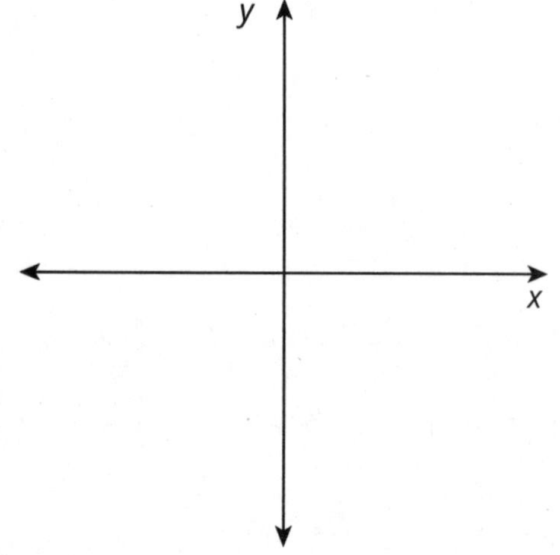

THINK ABOUT . . .

Sketch the graphs one at a time to help you see which is which.

© Carnegie Learning, Inc.

3 Compare the graphs of $v(x)$ and $w(x)$ to the graph of the basic function. **What do you notice?**

4 Write the x-value of each of the corresponding reference points on $v(x)$ and $w(x)$.

$h(x) = 2^x$	$v(x) = 2^{(x+3)}$	$w(x) = 2^{(x-3)}$
$\left(-2, \frac{1}{4}\right)$		
$\left(-1, \frac{1}{2}\right)$		
(0, 1)		
(1, 2)		
(2, 4)		

5 Use the table to compare the ordered pairs of the graphs of $v(x)$ and $w(x)$ to the ordered pairs of the graph of the basic function $h(x)$. **What do you notice?**

THINK ABOUT . . .
Notice there are no negative y-values in this table. Are negative values included in the range of h, v, or w?

© Carnegie Learning, Inc.

6 Complete each sentence with the coordinate notation to represent the horizontal translation of each function.

(a) $v(x) = h(x + 3)$

Each point (x, y) on the graph of $h(x)$ becomes the point

_______________ on $v(x)$.

(b) $w(x) = h(x - 3)$

Each point (x, y) on the graph of $h(x)$ becomes the point

_______________ on $w(x)$.

THINK ABOUT . . .

When a constant is added or subtracted outside a function, like $g(x) + 3$ or $g(x) - 3$, then only the y-values change, resulting in a vertical translation. And, when a constant is added or subtracted inside a function, like $g(x + 3)$ or $g(x - 3)$, then only the x-values change, resulting in a horizontal translation.

7 Describe each graph in relation to the basic function $h(x) = 2^x$.

(a) Compare $f(x) = h(x - C)$ to the basic function for $C > 0$.

(b) Compare $f(x) = h(x - C)$ to the basic function for $C < 0$.

Recall that for the basic function, the C-value of the transformed function $y = f(x - C)$ affects the input values of the function.

- For $C > 0$, the graph is translated to the right.
- For $C < 0$, the graph is translated to the left.
- The magnitude of the horizontal shift is given by $|C|$.

8 What generalization can you make about the effects of horizontal translations on the domain, range, and asymptotes of exponential functions?

© Carnegie Learning, Inc.

MATHia CONNECTION
- Reflecting and Dilating Exponential Functions Using Graphs
- Transforming Exponential Functions Using Tables

Reflections and Dilations of Exponential Functions

HABITS OF MIND
- Model with mathematics.
- Use appropriate tools strategically.

Consider these three exponential functions, where $h(x) = 2^x$ is the basic function.

- $h(x) = 2^x$
- $m(x) = -(2^x)$
- $n(x) = 2^{(-x)}$

1 Write the functions $m(x)$ and $n(x)$ in terms of the basic function $h(x)$.

$m(x) =$ ____________

$n(x) =$ ____________

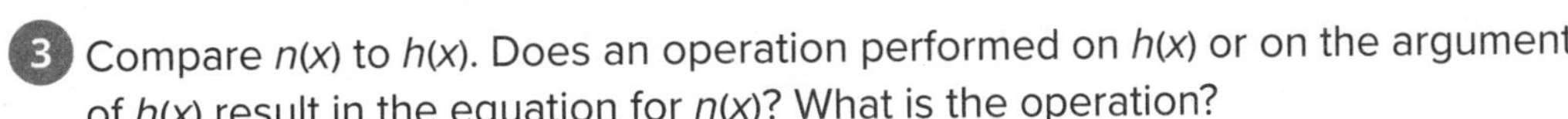

2 Compare $m(x)$ to $h(x)$. Does an operation performed on $h(x)$ or on the argument of $h(x)$ result in the equation for $m(x)$? What is the operation?

3 Compare $n(x)$ to $h(x)$. Does an operation performed on $h(x)$ or on the argument of $h(x)$ result in the equation for $n(x)$? What is the operation?

4 Use technology to sketch and label each function.

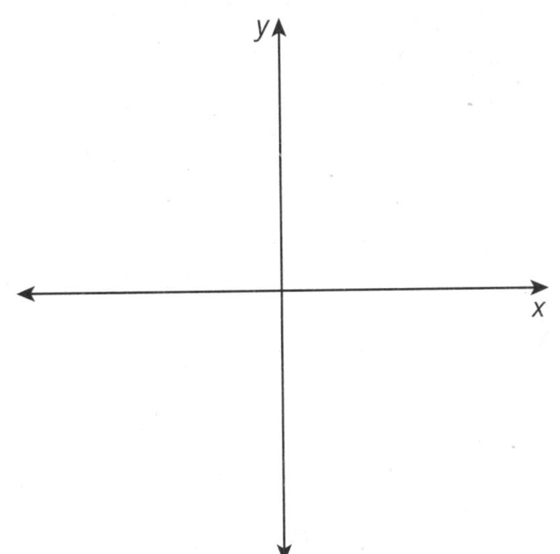

© Carnegie Learning, Inc.

5 Compare the graphs of $m(x)$ and $n(x)$ to the graph of the basic function $h(x)$.
What do you notice?

6 Write the y-value of each of the corresponding reference points on $m(x)$ and $n(x)$.

$h(x) = 2^x$	$m(x) = -(2^x)$	$n(x) = 2^{(-x)}$
$\left(-2, \frac{1}{4}\right)$		
$\left(-1, \frac{1}{2}\right)$		
(0, 1)		
(1, 2)		
(2, 4)		

7 Use the table to compare the ordered pairs of the graphs of $m(x)$ and $n(x)$ to the ordered pairs of the graph of the basic function $h(x)$.
What do you notice?

THINK ABOUT . . .

When the negative is on the outside of the function, like $-g(x)$, all the y-values become the opposite of the y-values of $g(x)$. The x-values remain unchanged.

When the negative is on the inside of the function, like $g(-x)$, all the x-values become the opposite of the x-values of $g(x)$. The y-values remain unchanged.

Remember, a reflection of a graph is a mirror image of the graph about a line of reflection. A line of reflection is the line that the graph is reflected across. A horizontal line of reflection affects the y-coordinates, and a vertical line of reflection affects the x-coordinates.

8 Consider the graphs of $m(x)$ and $n(x)$.

(a) Which function represents a reflection of $h(x)$ across a horizontal line? Name the line of reflection.

(b) Which function represents a reflection of $h(x)$ across a vertical line? Name the line of reflection.

© Carnegie Learning, Inc.

9 Complete each sentence with the coordinate notation to represent the reflection of each function.

(a) $m(x) = -h(x)$

Each point (x, y) on the graph of $h(x)$ becomes the point _______________ on $m(x)$.

(b) $n(x) = h(-x)$

Each point (x, y) on the graph of $h(x)$ becomes the point _______________ on $n(x)$.

Recall that for the basic function, the A-value of the transformed function $y = A \cdot f(x)$ affects the output values of the function.

- For $|A| > 1$, the graph vertically stretches.
- For $0 < |A| < 1$, the graph vertically compresses.
- For $A = -1$, the graph reflects across the line $y = 0$, or the x-axis.

For the basic function, the B-value of the transformed function $y = f(Bx)$ affects the input values of the function. For $B = -1$, the graph reflects across the line $x = 0$, or the y-axis.

Let's consider different B-values and their effect on a basic function.

> Consider the exponential functions, where $h(x) = 2^x$ is the basic function.

- $w(x) = 2^{\frac{1}{2}x}$
- $z(x) = 2^{2x}$

10 Write the function $w(x)$ and $z(x)$ in terms of $h(x)$.

11 Use technology to sketch and label the graph of each function.

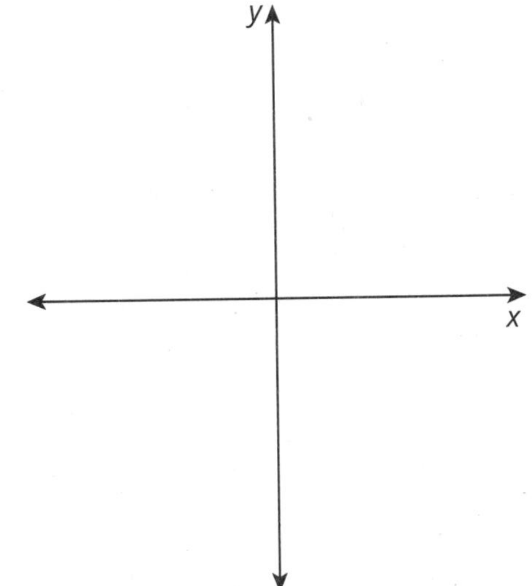

© Carnegie Learning, Inc.

12 Compare the graphs of $w(x)$ and $z(x)$ to the graph of the basic function $h(x)$. **What do you notice?**

13 Write the x-value of each of the corresponding reference points on $w(x)$ and $z(x)$.

$h(x) = 2^x$	$w(x) = 2^{\left(\frac{1}{2}x\right)}$	$z(x) = 2^{(2x)}$
$\left(-2, \frac{1}{4}\right)$		
$\left(-1, \frac{1}{2}\right)$		
(0, 1)		
(1, 2)		
(2, 4)		

14 Use the table to compare the ordered pairs of the graphs of $w(x)$ and $z(x)$ to the ordered pairs of the graph of the basic function $h(x)$. **What do you notice?**

15 Given that the point (x, y) is on the graph of the function $y = f(x)$, which ordered pair describes a point on the graph of $g(x) = f(Bx)$?

© Carnegie Learning, Inc.

Interpreting and Graphing Exponential Functions

There are different ways to interpret equations of exponential functions and transformations of exponential functions.

HABITS OF MIND

- Reason abstractly and quantitatively.
- Construct viable arguments and critique the reasoning of others.

Jacob and Kate compare the graphs of two exponential functions.

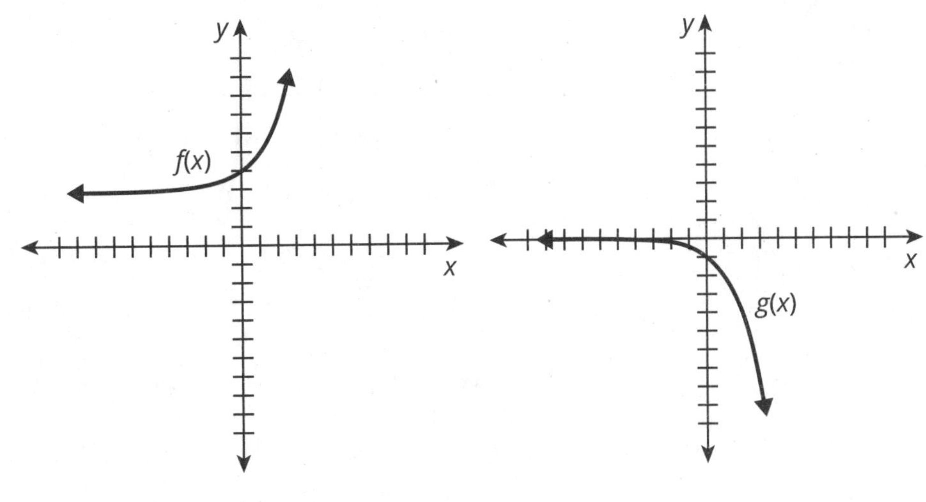

1 Jacob says that to get the graph of $g(x)$, first translate $f(x)$ down 3 units and then reflect across the line $y = 0$. Kate says that to get the graph of $f(x)$, first reflect $g(x)$ across the line $y = 0$ and then translate up 3 units. Who is correct? **Explain your reasoning.**

© Carnegie Learning, Inc.

2 Consider the function $f(x) = -2^{(x-3)} + 4$.

ⓐ Mike and Amy used the basic function in different ways to graph $f(x)$. Provide the step-by-step reasoning used by each student.

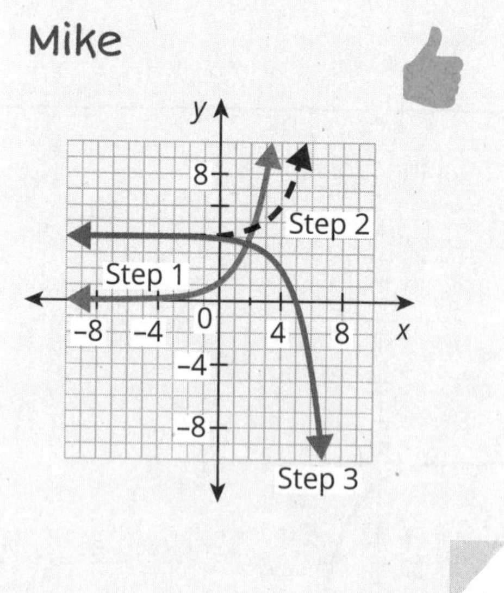

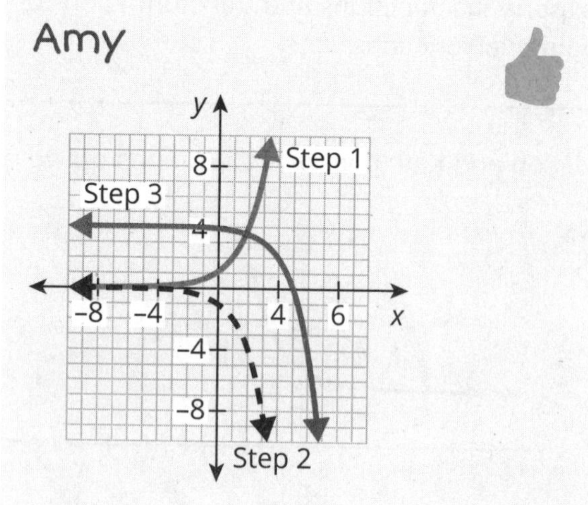

ⓑ Explain how changing the order of the transformations affects the line of reflection.

© Carnegie Learning, Inc.

One way to indicate the transformation of a function is by using the prime symbol. The function $f'(x)$ is a transformation of $f(x)$.

3 Use the given characteristics to write an equation and then graph $f'(x)$, given the basic function $f(x) = 2^x$. **Label key points.**

(a) $f'(x) = f(x) + 5$

Equation: $f'(x) =$ ________________

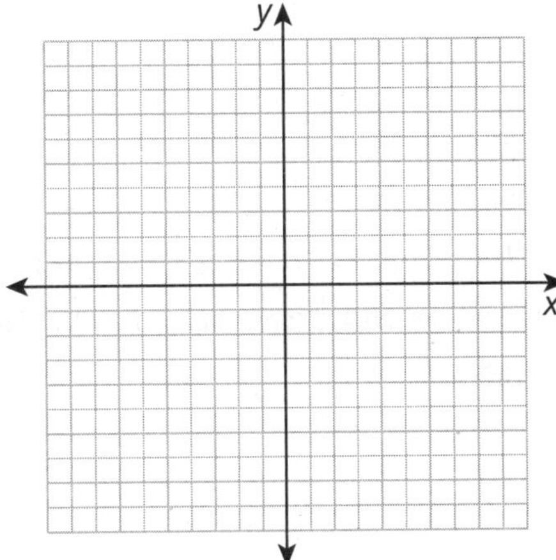

(b) $f'(x) = -f(x) + 5$

Equation: $f'(x) =$ ________________

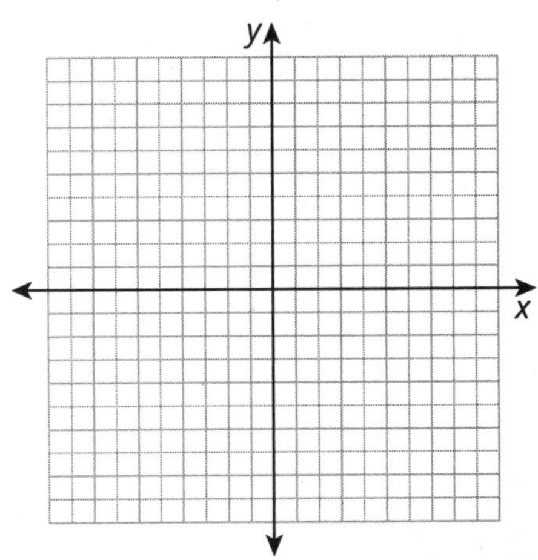

(c) $f'(x) = f(-x) + 5$

Equation: $f'(x) =$ ________________

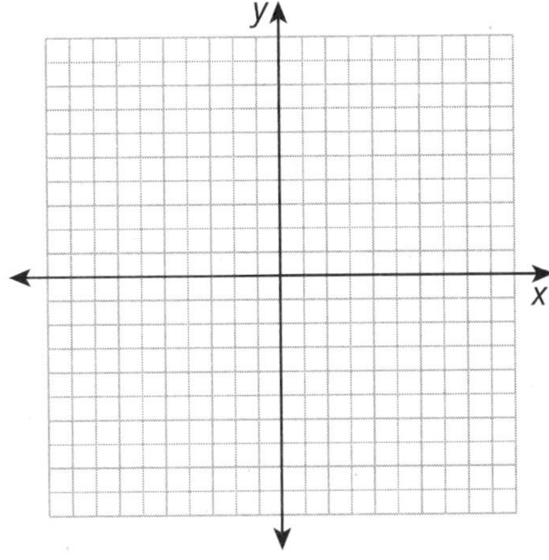

(d) $f'(x) = -f(x) - 5$

Equation: $f'(x) =$ ________________

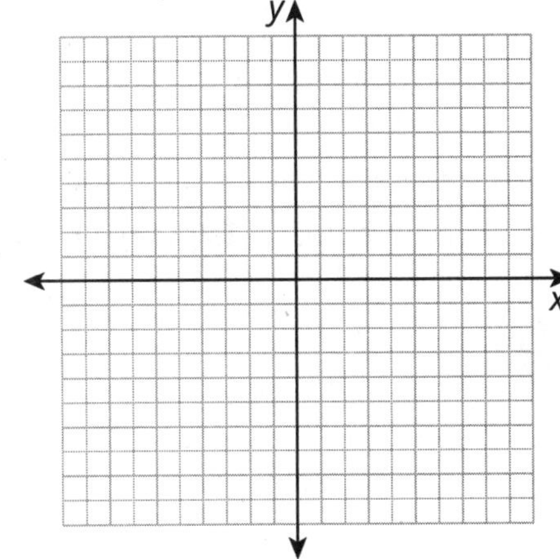

© Carnegie Learning, Inc.

You have analyzed different ways to graph transformations of the basic function $h(x) = 2^x$. Now, let's consider different ways to interpret the equations of function transformations.

4 Andres and Tomas each described the effects of transforming the graph of $f(x) = 3^x$ such that $p(x) = 3f(x)$. Who's correct? **Explain your reasoning.**

Andres

$p(x) = 3f(x)$

The A-value is 3, so the graph vertically stretches by a scale factor of 3.

Tomas

$p(x) = 3f(x)$

$p(x) = 3 \cdot 3^x$

$p(x) = 3^{(1 + x)}$

$p(x) = f(x + 1)$

The C-value is -1, so the graph horizontally translates 1 unit to the left.

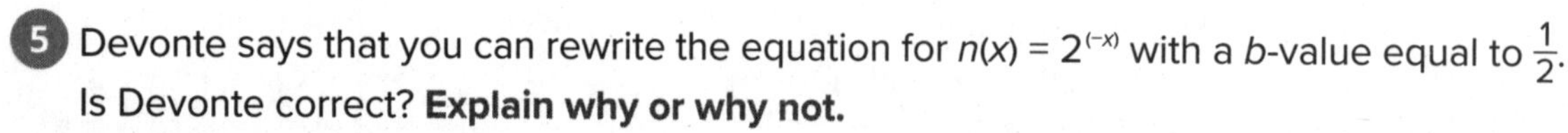

5 Devonte says that you can rewrite the equation for $n(x) = 2^{(-x)}$ with a b-value equal to $\frac{1}{2}$. Is Devonte correct? **Explain why or why not.**

© Carnegie Learning, Inc.

You can rewrite an exponential function to show an expression with no *C*- or *B*-value transformations.

WORKED EXAMPLE

Given the function $h(x) = 2^x$, consider the functions $v(x) = h(x + 3)$ and $t(x) = h(3x)$.

$v(x) = h(x + 3)$ $\qquad$ $t(x) = h(3x)$

$v(x) = 2^{x+3}$ $\qquad$ $t(x) = 2^{3x}$

You can rewrite *v*(*x*) with no *C*-value and *t*(*x*) with no *B*-value.

$$v(x) = 2^{x+3} = 2^x \cdot 2^3 = 8 \cdot 2^x$$

$$t(x) = 2^{3x} = (2^3)^x = 8^x$$

6 Explain the steps to rewrite a function with no *C*-value and with no *B*-value. **What effect does rewriting have on the *b*-value of the original function?**

7 Given the function $f(x) = 2^x$:

(a) Rewrite $c(x) = f(x - 2)$ as an exponential function with no *C*-value transformation.

(b) Rewrite $b(x) = f(-2x)$ as an exponential function with no *B*-value transformation.

© Carnegie Learning, Inc.

Writing Exponential Functions Given Graphs and Descriptions

HABITS OF MIND

- Reason abstractly and quantitatively.
- Construct viable arguments and critique the reasoning of others.

1 Consider the function, $f(x) = 2^x$. Write the function in transformation function form in terms of the transformations described, then write the equivalent equation.

Transformation	Transformation Function Form	Equation
Reflection across the *y*-axis		
Reflection across the *x*-axis		
Horizontal translation of 2 units to the left and a vertical translation of 3 units up		
Vertical stretch of 2 units and a reflection across the line $y = 0$		
Reflection across the line $y = 3$		
Horizontal translation of 3 units to the right, a vertical translation down 2 units, and a vertical dilation of $\frac{1}{2}$		
Horizontal compression by a factor of 3		
Horizontal stretch by a factor of 3		
Vertical compression by a factor of 4		
Vertical stretch by a factor of 4		

© Carnegie Learning, Inc.

2 Analyze the graphs of $f(x)$ and $g(x)$. Describe the transformations performed on $f(x)$ to create $g(x)$. Then, write an equation for $g(x)$ in terms of $f(x)$. For each set of points shown on $f(x)$, the corresponding points are shown on $g(x)$.

ⓐ $g(x) =$ ______________

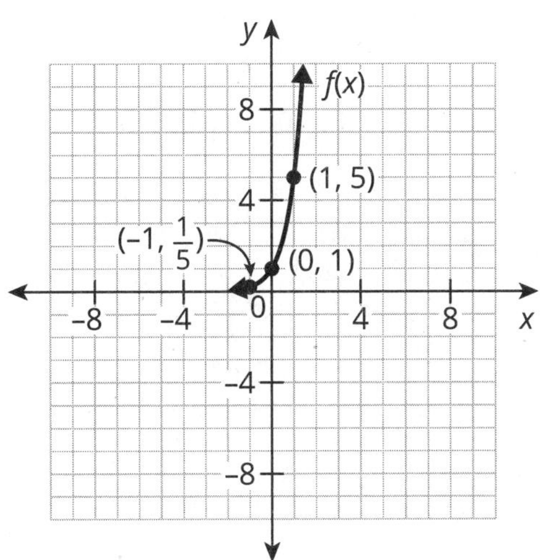

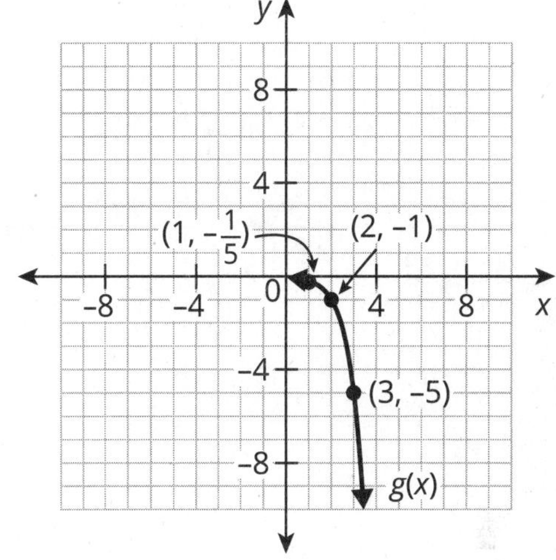

ⓑ $g(x) =$ ______________

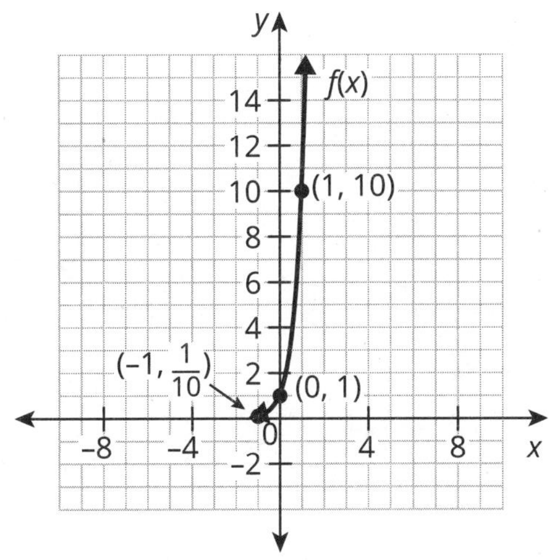

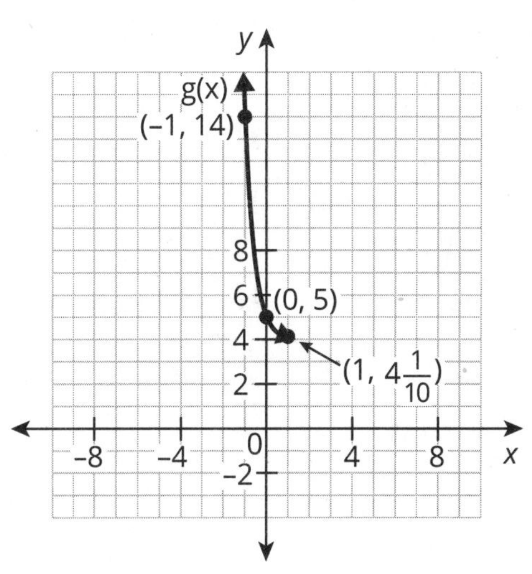

© Carnegie Learning, Inc.

ⓒ $g(x) =$ ______________

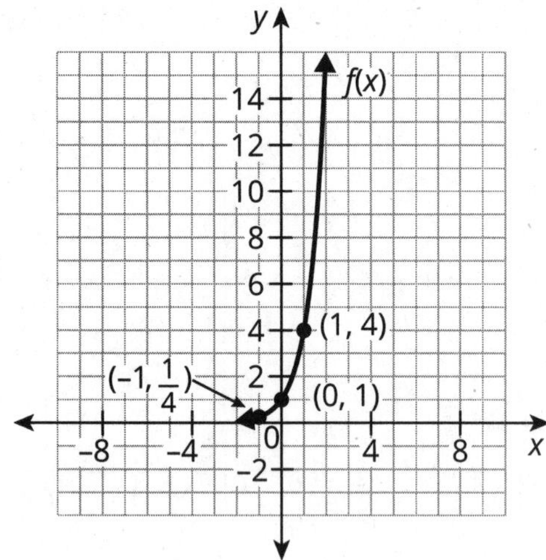

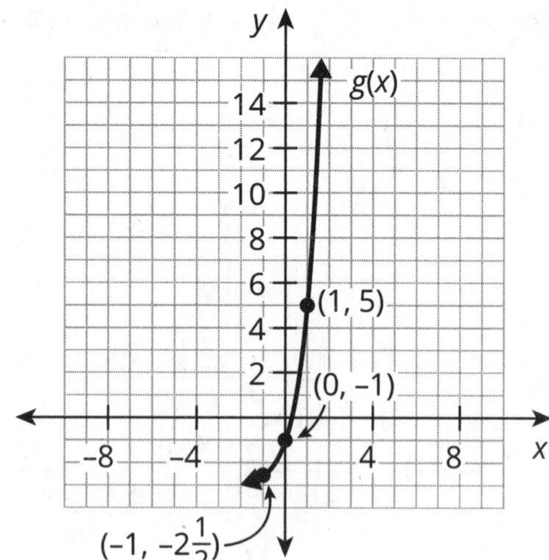

© Carnegie Learning, Inc.

Next Time, Won't You Sing with Me?

1 Determine whether each statement is true or false. If the statement is false, rewrite the statement as true.

(a) Key characteristics of basic exponential functions include a domain of non-negative numbers, a range of real numbers, and a vertical asymptote at $y = 0$.

(b) The domain of exponential functions is not affected by translations or dilations.

(c) Vertical translations do not affect the range and the horizontal asymptote of exponential functions.

(d) Horizontal translations do not affect the range and the horizontal asymptote of exponential functions.

(e) Vertical dilations do not affect the range and the horizontal asymptote of exponential functions.

(f) Horizontal dilations do not affect the range and the horizontal asymptote of exponential functions.

© Carnegie Learning, Inc.

2 You can write the basic exponential function as $A \cdot 2^{B(x - C)} + D$. When $A = 1$, $B = 1$, $C = 0$, and $D = 0$, the function is equivalent to $f(x) = 2^x$. Complete the graphic organizer on page 518 to summarize the transformations of an exponential function.

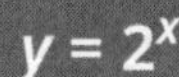

$y = 2^x$

A-Value

$y = A \cdot 2^x$

B-Value

$y = 2^{Bx}$

C-Value

$y = 2^{x - C}$

D-Value

$y = 2^x + D$

© Carnegie Learning, Inc.

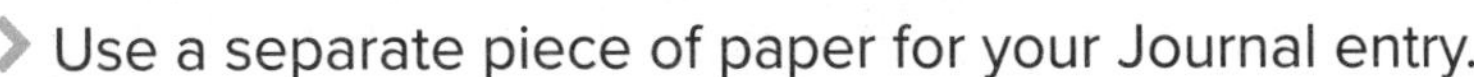

LESSON 3 ASSIGNMENT

> Use a separate piece of paper for your Journal entry.

JOURNAL

Given a basic function and the equation for a reflection of a basic function, explain how to determine whether the line of reflection will be the x-axis or the y-axis.

REMEMBER

You can describe transformations performed on any function $f(x)$ with the transformation function $g(x) = Af(B(x - C)) + D$, where the D-value translates the function $f(x)$ vertically, the C-value translates $f(x)$ horizontally, the A-value vertically stretches or compresses $f(x)$, and the B-value horizontally stretches or compresses $f(x)$.

PRACTICE

1. Complete the table to determine the corresponding points on $c(x)$ given reference points on $f(x)$. Then, graph $c(x)$ on the same coordinate plane as $f(x)$ and state the domain, range, and asymptotes of $c(x)$.

   a. $f(x) = 2^x$

   $c(x) = f(x - 1)$

Reference Points on $f(x)$	Corresponding Points on $c(x)$
$\left(-1, \frac{1}{2}\right)$	
(0, 1)	
(1, 2)	

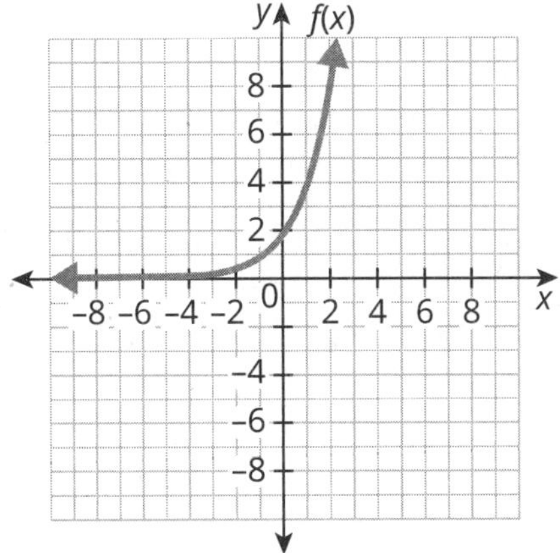

   b. $f(x) = 4^x$

   $c(x) = -f(x) - 2$

Reference Points on $f(x)$	Corresponding Points on $c(x)$
$\left(-1, \frac{1}{4}\right)$	
(0, 1)	
(1, 2)	

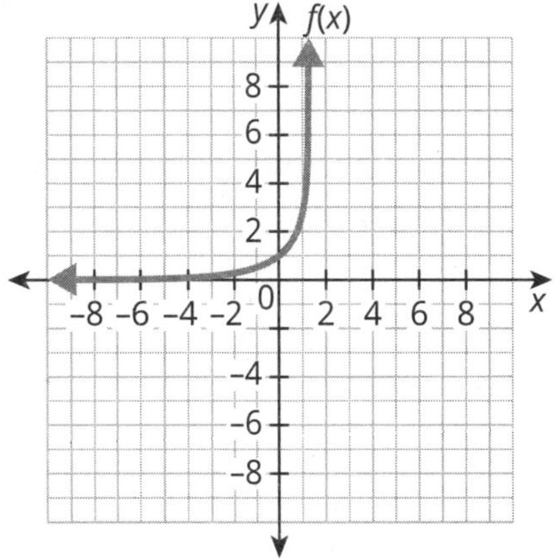

© Carnegie Learning, Inc.

Go to LiveHint.com for help on the PRACTICE questions.

(c) $f(x) = 2^x$

$c(x) = 4f(x)$

Reference Points on $f(x)$	Corresponding Points on $c(x)$
$\left(-1, \frac{1}{2}\right)$	
(0, 1)	
(1, 2)	

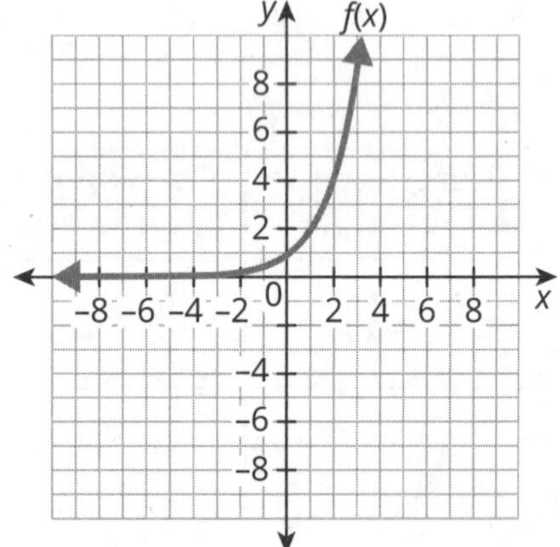

(d) $f(x) = 4^x$

$c(x) = f(-x)$

Reference Points on $f(x)$	Corresponding Points on $c(x)$
$\left(-1, \frac{1}{4}\right)$	
(0, 1)	
(1, 4)	

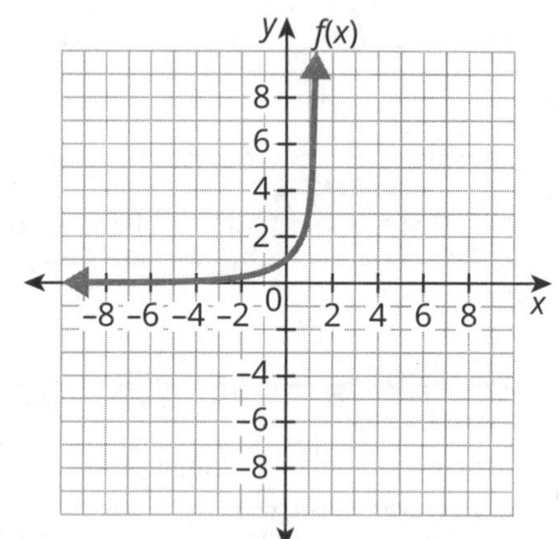

2 Describe the transformations performed on $m(x)$ that produced $t(x)$. Then, write an exponential equation for $t(x)$.

(a) $m(x) = 3^x$

$t(x) = -m(x + 1)$

(b) $m(x) = 5^x$

$t(x) = 3m(x) - 2$

© Carnegie Learning, Inc.

STRETCH Optional

1 Research real-world examples for which exponential functions provide good models. Write a short paragraph explaining why an exponential model works well for at least one of the examples.

MIXED PRACTICE

> This Mixed Practice worksheet includes two sections: Spaced Review and End-of-Topic Review. **Use a separate piece of paper to show your work.**

Spaced Review

> Practice concepts from previous topics.

1. Lucia and Danna both recently purchased fitness watches. The watches count the number of steps that they walk in a day. At lunchtime, Lucia has 5445 steps and Danna has 4995 steps. Lucia averages 800 steps per hour, and Danna averages 900 steps per hour.

   (a) Write and solve a system of linear equations that represents the total number of steps each person takes.

   (b) Interpret the meaning of the solution in terms of the problem situation.

2. Brown's Tree Farm Company is going to plant pine trees and birch trees this planting season. On Farm A, the land type allows for them to plant 25 pine trees per acre and 75 birch trees per acre. On Farm B, the land type allows for them to plant 50 pine trees per acre and 75 birch trees per acre. There are a total of 200 pine trees and 450 birch trees available for planting.
   Write and solve a system of equations to determine how many of each tree the company will plant on each farm.

3. Calculate the average rate of change for the function $f(x) = 2x - 2$ from $x_1 = 5$ to $x_2 = 11$.

4. Solve for b in the equation $\frac{a - b}{12} = 11 - 6a$.

5. The members of a youth football program are required to sell tickets to chicken dinners for the program's fundraiser. They can sell adult tickets for \$10 and child tickets for \$5. Each athlete must bring in at least \$350 from the ticket sales.

   (a) Write an expression to represent the total amount of money an athlete makes from ticket sales. Let x represent the number of adult tickets sold and let y represent the number of child tickets sold.

   (b) Write an inequality in two variables to represent the amount an athlete must make.

   (c) Graph the inequality from part (b).

   (d) Use the graph to determine whether an athlete will bring in at least \$350 when they sell 10 adult tickets and 30 child tickets. Explain your reasoning.

© Carnegie Learning, Inc.

End-of-Topic Review

AVAILABLE ONLINE

1. A **Topic Summary** reviews the main concepts for the topic.
2. A video of the **Worked Example** is provided.

> Practice concepts you learned in *Introduction to Exponential Functions.*

6 Rewrite each expression using Properties of Powers. Write your expression in radical form.

ⓐ $(\sqrt{2})^3 \cdot (\sqrt[3]{2})$

ⓑ $\dfrac{(\sqrt[3]{3})^2}{\sqrt[4]{3}}$

7 Roberto and Maeko open a pet store and start with 5 hamsters for sale. Hamster populations usually triple every cycle. One cycle is equal to 4 months. Write an equation in function notation to represent the change in the number of hamsters as a function of the cycle number, c. Explain how you determined your equation.

8 Write an exponential function to model this table of values.

x	$f(x)$
1	0.6
2	0.06
3	0.006
4	0.0006

9 Complete the table.

Explicit Formula	Exponential Function	Constant Ratio	y-intercept
$840 \cdot 3^{x-1}$	$280 \cdot 3^x$		
	$-15 \cdot \left(\frac{1}{5}\right)^x$		

10 Rewrite each expression in rational exponent form.

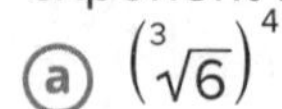

ⓐ $(\sqrt[3]{6})^4$

ⓑ $(\sqrt[8]{8})^{12}$

ⓒ $(\sqrt[7]{x})^3$

ⓓ $(\sqrt[10]{y})^5$

11 Given $f(x) = 2^x$, graph $g(x) = -f(x - 1) + 2$.

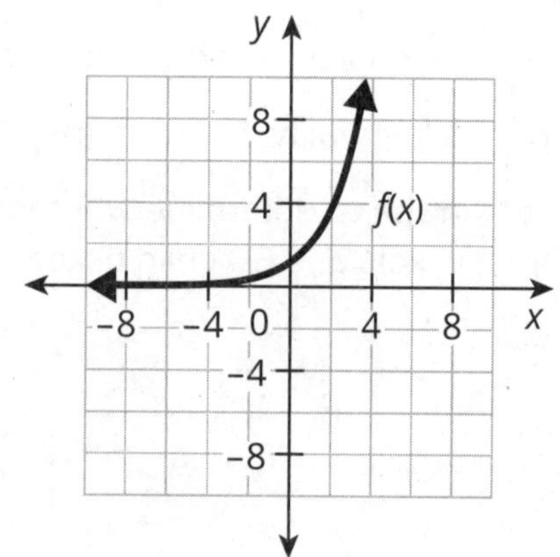

12 Write a function, $g(x)$, and sketch a graph that is translated 3 units up from and 4 units to the right of $f(x) = \left(\frac{1}{2}\right)^x$.

© Carnegie Learning, Inc.

LESSON 1

Uptown and Downtown

Exponential Equations for Growth and Decay

KEY TERMS

simple interest

compound interest

exponential growth function

exponential decay function

Learning Goals

- Classify exponential functions as increasing or decreasing.
- Compare formulas for simple interest and compound interest situations.
- Compare the average rate of change between common intervals of a linear and an exponential relationship.
- Write an exponential function that includes a percent increase or decrease with a *b*-value that is a decimal number.
- Solve exponential equations, using graphs.

REVIEW (1–2 minutes)

> Determine the constant ratio for each geometric sequence.

1. 10, 10.5, 11.025, 11.57625, 12.1550625, ...

2. $27, 9, 3, 1, \frac{1}{3}, \ldots$

3. $1, \frac{3}{4}, \frac{9}{16}, \frac{27}{64}, \ldots$

You have analyzed linear and exponential functions and their graphs.

How can you compare linear and exponential functions as increasing and decreasing functions?

© Carnegie Learning, Inc.

Up or Down?

> Consider each of these functions.

$f(x) = -2x + 5$	$g(x) = 2^x - 1$	$h(x) = 0.95^x$
$p(x) = 6 \cdot \left(\frac{5}{8}\right)^x + 2$	$q(x) = 3(x - 4) - 1$	$r(x) = 2 \cdot (1 - 0.5)^x$
$v(x) = 4 \cdot 1.10^{(x+5)}$	$w(x) = -5 \cdot 3^x + 1$	$z(x) = -x + 10$

ASK YOURSELF . . .
What does the structure of each function equation tell you?

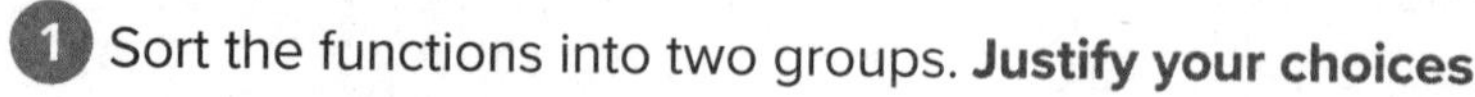

1. Sort the functions into two groups. **Justify your choices.**

Increasing Functions | **Decreasing Functions**

© Carnegie Learning, Inc.

MATHia CONNECTION
- Recognizing Linear and Exponential Models
- Calculating and Interpreting Average Rate of Change

Simple and Compound Interest

In this activity, you will compare functions you can use to calculate *simple interest* and *compound interest*.

HABITS OF MIND
- Model with mathematics.
- Use appropriate tools strategically.

Suppose that your family deposited $10,000 in an interest-bearing account for your college fund that earns simple interest each year. A friend's family deposited $10,000 in an interest-bearing account for their child's college fund that earns compound interest each year.

Time (years)	Simple Interest Balance (dollars)	Compound Interest Balance (dollars)
0	10,000	10,000
1	10,400	10,400
2	10,800	10,816
3	11,200	11,248.64
10	14,000	14,802.44

TAKE NOTE . . .

In a **simple interest** account, a percent of the starting balance is added to the account at each interval. The formula for simple interest is $I = Prt$, where P represents the starting amount, or principal, r represents the interest rate, t represents time, and I represents the interest earned.

In a **compound interest** account, the balance is multiplied by the same amount at each interval.

1. Study the table of values.

   a) Sketch a graph of each account balance in dollars as a function of the time in years.

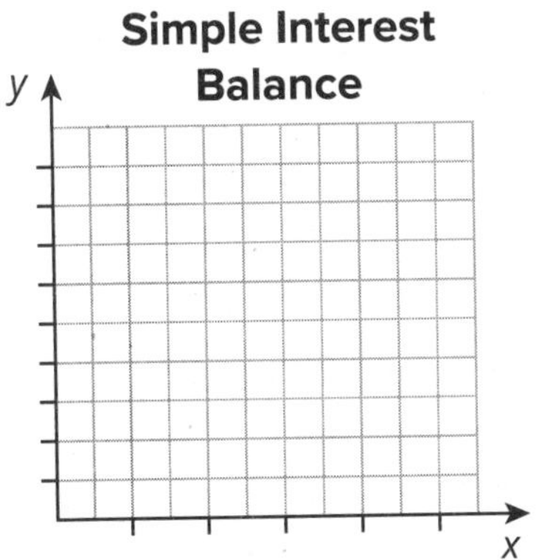

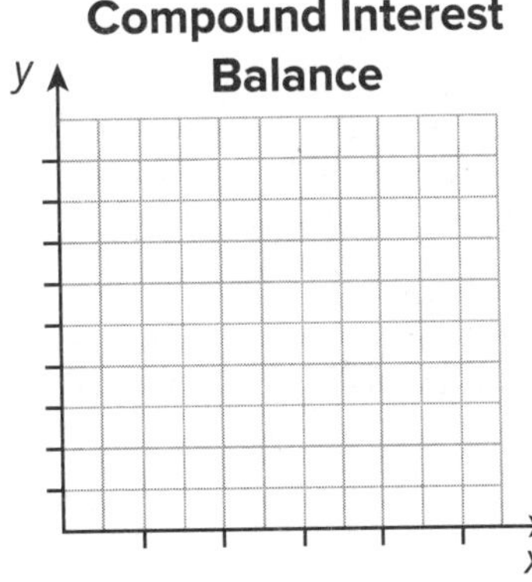

   b) Write a function, $s(x)$, to represent the simple interest account and a function, $c(x)$, to represent the compound interest account.

© Carnegie Learning, Inc.

2 Use the functions $s(x)$ and $c(x)$ to determine each value.

ⓐ $s(5)$

ⓑ $c(5)$

ⓒ $c(4)$

ⓓ $s(4)$

3 Determine the average rate of change between each pair of values given for each relationship.

Time Intervals (years)	Simple Interest Function (dollars)	Compound Interest Function (dollars)
Between $t = 0$ and $t = 1$		
Between $t = 1$ and $t = 2$		
Between $t = 2$ and $t = 5$		
Between $t = 5$ and $t = 10$		

4 Compare the average rates of change for the simple and compound interest accounts.

ⓐ **What do you notice?**

ⓑ What does this tell you about the graphs of linear and exponential functions?

© Carnegie Learning, Inc.

5 Use technology to determine when each account will reach the given dollar amount.

(a) When does the simple interest account reach $15,600?

(b) Approximately when does the compound interest account reach one million dollars?

6 Chloe says that given any increasing linear function and any exponential growth function, the output of the exponential function will eventually be greater than the output of the linear function. Is Chloe correct? **Use examples to justify your thinking.**

© Carnegie Learning, Inc.

Identifying Exponential Growth and Decay

HABITS OF MIND
- Model with mathematics.
- Use appropriate tools strategically.

You can analyze the structure of an exponential function to determine whether the function increases or decreases.

At this moment, the population of Downtown is 20,000, and the population of Uptown is 6000. But over many years, people have been moving away from Downtown at a rate of 1.5% every year. At the same time, Uptown's population has been growing at a rate of 1.8% each year.

1. What are the independent and dependent quantities in each situation?

2. Which city's population can you represent as an increasing function, and which can you represent as a decreasing function?

Let's examine the properties of the graphs of the functions for Downtown and Uptown.

3. Sketch a graph of each function. **Label key points.**

   a. Downtown: $D(t) = 20{,}000(1 - 0.015)^t$

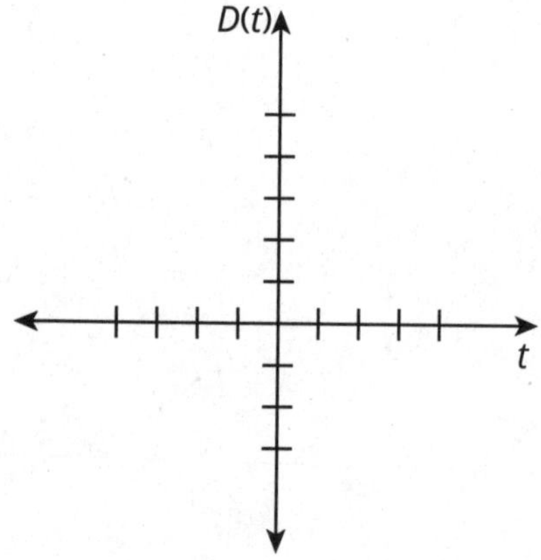

   b. Uptown: $U(t) = 6000(1 + 0.018)^t$

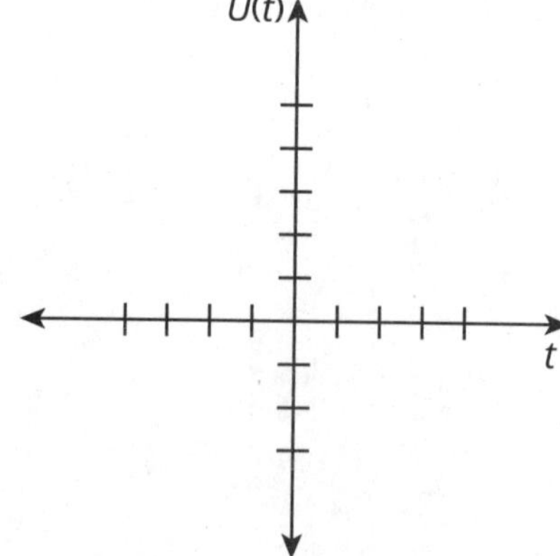

© Carnegie Learning, Inc.

4 You can write each of the functions $D(t)$ and $U(t)$ as an exponential function of the form $f(x) = a \cdot b^x$.

(a) What is the *a*-value for each function? **What does each *a*-value mean in terms of this problem situation?**

(b) What is the *b*-value for each function? **What does each *b*-value mean in terms of this problem situation?**

(c) Compare and explain the meanings of the expressions $(1 - 0.015)^t$ and $(1 + 0.018)^t$ in terms of this problem situation.

© Carnegie Learning, Inc.

5 Analyze the *y*-intercepts of each function.

ⓐ Identify the *y*-intercepts.

ⓑ Interpret the meaning of each *y*-intercept in terms of the problem situation.

ⓒ Describe how you can determine the *y*-intercept of each function, using only the formula for population increase or decrease.

An **exponential growth function** has a *b*-value greater than 1 and is of the form $y = a \cdot (1 + r)^x$, where *r* is the rate of growth. The *b*-value is $1 + r$.

An **exponential decay function** has a *b*-value greater than 0 and less than 1 and is of the form $y = a \cdot (1 - r)^x$, where *r* is the rate of decay. The *b*-value is $1 - r$.

THINK ABOUT . . .

A decreasing exponential function has a decimal or fractional *b*-value between 0 and 1, not a negative *b*-value.

© Carnegie Learning, Inc.

Comparing Exponential Functions

HABITS OF MIND
- Model with mathematics.
- Use appropriate tools strategically.

> Consider the six different population scenarios.

1. For each situation, choose the appropriate function from the bank that represents it. **Explain your reasoning.**

FUNCTION BANK

$f(x) = 7000 \cdot 0.969^x$	$f(x) = 7000 \cdot (1 + 0.028)^x$	$f(x) = 7000 \cdot 1.012^x$
$f(x) = 7000 \cdot (1 - 0.0175)^x$	$f(x) = 7000 \cdot 1.014^x$	$f(x) = 7000 \cdot 0.9875^x$

Blueville has a population of 7000. Its population increases at a rate of 1.4%.

Youngstown has a population of 7000. Its population increases at a rate of 1.2%.

West Lake has a population of 7000. Its population increases at a rate of 2.8%.

Greenville has a population of 7000. Its population decreases at a rate of 1.75%.

North Park has a population of 7000. Its population decreases at a rate of 3.1%.

Springfield has a population of 7000. Its population decreases at a rate of 1.25%.

© Carnegie Learning, Inc.

And More, Much More Than This . . .

A scientist is researching certain bacteria that have been found recently in the large animal cages at a local zoo. He starts with 200 bacteria that he intends to grow and study. He determines that every hour, the number of bacteria increases by 25%.

1. Write a function and sketch a graph to represent this problem situation. Then, estimate the number of hours the scientist should let the bacteria grow to have no more than 2000 bacteria.

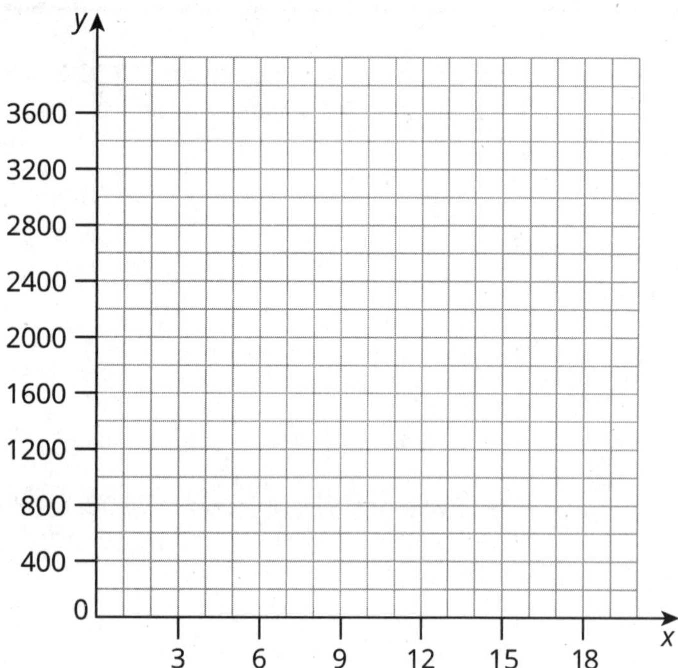

© Carnegie Learning, Inc.

LESSON 1 ASSIGNMENT

> Use a separate piece of paper for your Journal entry.

JOURNAL

Explain the difference between simple interest and compound interest.

REMEMBER

An exponential growth function has a *b*-value greater than 1 and is of the form $y = a \cdot (1 + r)^x$, where *r* is the rate of growth.
An exponential decay function has a *b*-value greater than 0 and less than 1 and is of the form $y = a \cdot (1 - r)^x$, where *r* is the rate of decay.

PRACTICE

1. Chanise just received a $2500 bonus check from her employer. She is going to put it into an account that will earn interest. The Basic savings account at her bank earns 6% simple interest. The Gold savings account earns 4.5% compound interest.

   (a) Write a function for each account that you can use to determine the balance in the account based on the year, *t*. Describe each function.

   (b) Use your answers to part (a) to create a table of values for each function. Then, use technology to sketch the graph of each function.

Time (years)	Basic Account Balance ($)	Gold Account Balance ($)

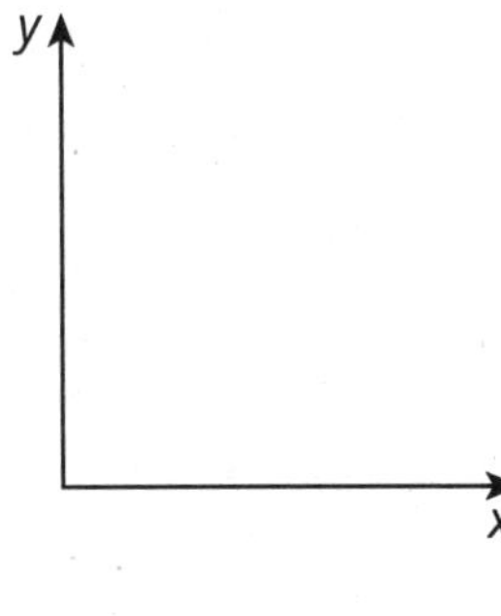

© Carnegie Learning, Inc.

Go to LiveHint.com for help on the PRACTICE questions.

(c) Into which account would you recommend that Chanise deposit her money? Explain your reasoning.

(d) After reading the pamphlet about the different accounts a little more closely, Chanise realizes that there is a one-time fee of $300 for depositing her money in the Gold account. Does this change the recommendation you made in part (c)? Why or why not?

(e) Compare the rates of change for the Basic and Gold savings accounts. Explain what the rates of change tell you about the accounts.

2 Ainsley works for the owners of a bookstore. Her starting salary is $24,500, and she gets a 3% raise each year.

(a) Write an equation in function notation to represent Ainsley's salary as a function of the number of years she has been working at the bookstore.

(b) What will Ainsley's salary be when she begins her fourth year working at the bookstore? Show your work.

© Carnegie Learning, Inc.

STRETCH Optional

> Consider a piece of paper that is 0.1 mm thick.

1 Determine how many times you must fold the paper so that it reaches the top of the Eiffel Tower. Assume the paper is as large as needed and it is possible to fold it as many times as required.

LESSON 2

Powers and the Horizontal Line

Interpreting Parameters in Context

Learning Goals

- Analyze equations and graphs of exponential functions.
- Match equations and graphs of exponential functions using the horizontal asymptote.
- Write and interpret exponential growth and decay functions.
- Use the properties of exponents to rewrite exponential functions.

REVIEW (1–2 minutes)

> Rewrite each expression using the Order of Operations.

1. $3 - (4 \cdot 5) + 6^{-1}$
2. $8 + (9^{\frac{1}{2}} - 2) \div 2$
3. $1 - \frac{5^{\frac{1}{2}}}{2} + \sqrt{5}$

© Carnegie Learning, Inc.

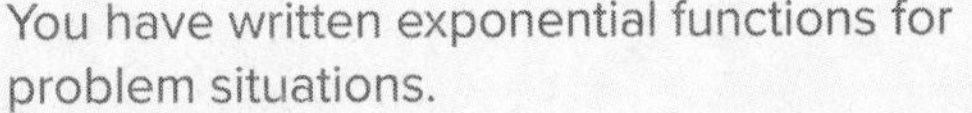
You have written exponential functions for problem situations.

What strategies can you use to write and solve exponential equations?

Match Game

> Consider these four graphs.

Graph 1

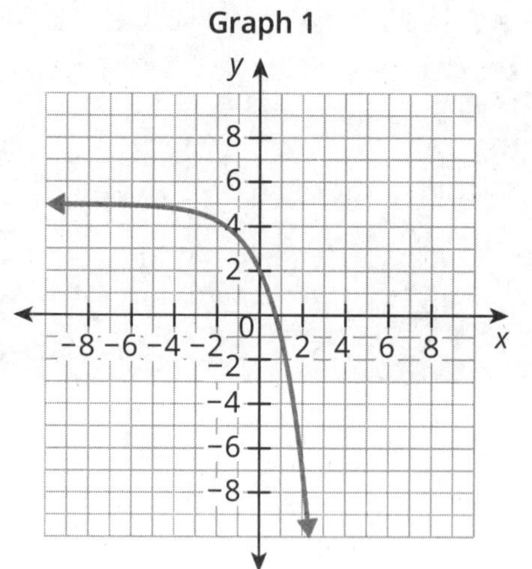

Graph 2

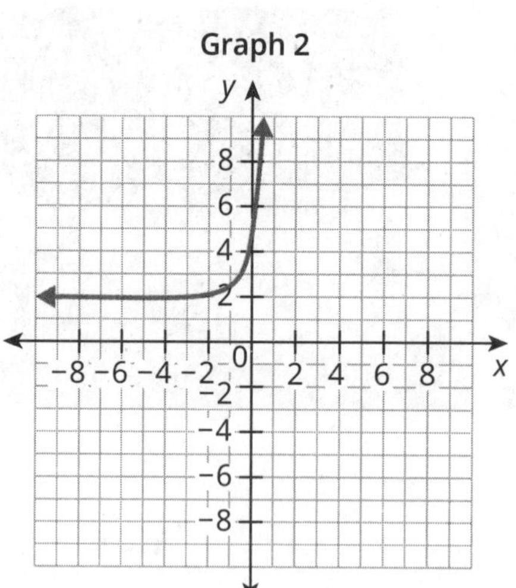

FUNCTION BANK

$f(x) = 3(5)^x + 2$

$f(x) = 5(2)^{-x}$

$f(x) = -3(2)^x + 5$

$f(x) = -2(5)^{-x} - 3$

Graph 3 **Graph 4**

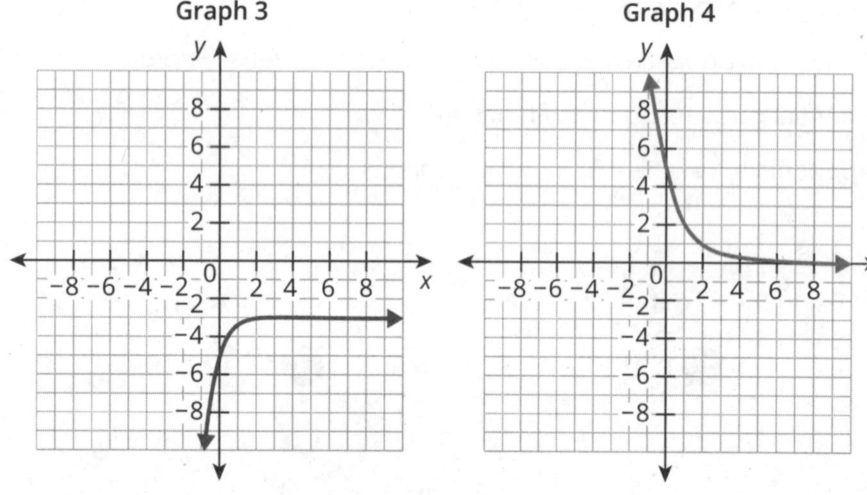

ASK YOURSELF . . .
What does the form of the equation tell you about the graph?

1. Match each graph with the correct equation from the bank.

2. **Describe the strategies you used.**

© Carnegie Learning, Inc.

3 Lucy and Michael disagree about the equation for Graph 2.

Lucy

The equation for Graph 2 is $f(x) = 5(2)^x$.

The graph intersects the y-axis at 5.

In the form $f(x) = ab^x$, a is the y-intercept.

$f(x) = 5(2)^x$ is the only equation with $a = 5$.

Michael

The equation for Graph 2 is $f(x) = 3(5)^x + 2$.
I know this because the graph has an asymptote of $y = 2$, and 2 is the D-value in the equation.

(a) What is the error in Lucy's thinking? Does Lucy's method sometimes work? **Explain your reasoning.**

(b) Which characteristic does Michael use? Will his method always work?

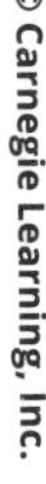

© Carnegie Learning, Inc.

MATHia CONNECTION

- Modeling Equations with a Starting Point of 1
- Modeling Equations with a Starting Point Other Than 1
- Solving Exponential Equations Using a Graph

Solving Exponential Equations by Graphing

HABIT OF MIND

- Attend to precision.

Depreciation is a decline in the value of something. Vehicles usually depreciate over time, meaning their value decreases over time. You can often represent this decrease with an exponential decay function.

A construction company bought a new bulldozer for $125,000. The bulldozer depreciates exponentially, and after 2 years, the value of the bulldozer is $80,000.

1. Write a function to represent the value of the bulldozer as a function of the number of years it is owned. Then, complete the table and graph.

Number of Years Owned	Cost of Bulldozer
0	
2.5	
5	
7	
8.5	
10	
12.5	

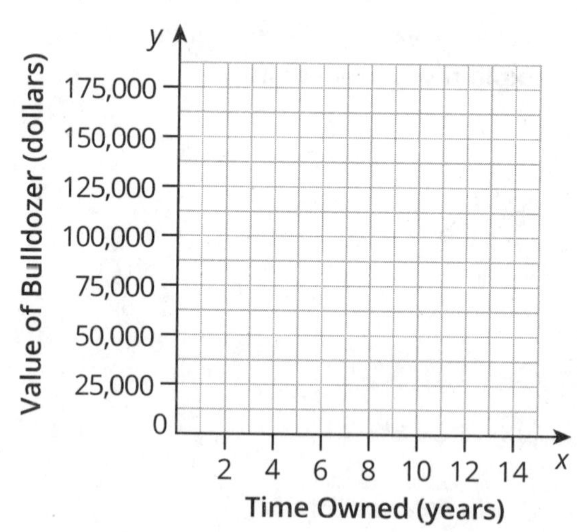

2. The company wants to sell the bulldozer and get at least $25,000 from the sale. Use the graph to estimate the amount of time the company has to achieve this goal.

3. Estimate when the bulldozer is worth each amount.

   (a) $50,000

   (b) $10,000

ASK YOURSELF . . .
What does each point on the graph represent?

4. When is the bulldozer worth $0?

© Carnegie Learning, Inc.

Interpreting the *B*-value

You can use the properties of exponents to rewrite exponential functions.

HABITS OF MIND
- Reason abstractly and quantitatively.
- Construct viable arguments and critique the reasoning of others.

Simone has invested $500 in a mutual fund that has shown an annual increase of about 10%.

1. Write a function, $f(t)$, that represents Simone's investment in terms of t, time in years.

Suppose Simone is interested in determining the monthly rate of increase. What is the approximate equivalent monthly rate of increase for her mutual fund?

> Consider the responses from two of Simone's friends.

Chitra

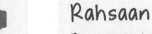

Because we are dividing up the annual rate of increase over 12 months, divide the constant ratio by 12.

$\frac{1.10}{12}$

Rahsaan

Because the annual rate of increase is represented as a multiplier, take the 12th root of the constant ratio.

$1.10^{\frac{1}{12}}$

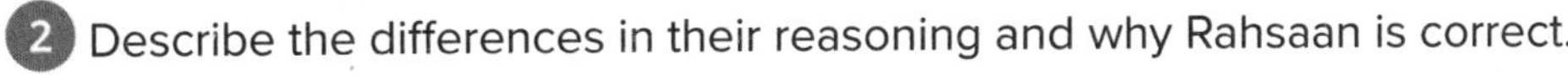

2. Describe the differences in their reasoning and why Rahsaan is correct.

© Carnegie Learning, Inc.

Kirk wants to write a function that is equivalent to the annual rate of increase but reveals the monthly rate of increase.

3 Explain why Kirk's reasoning is not correct.

Kirk

Since Simone's monthly rate of increase is the 12th root of the annual rate of increase, I can use the function $f(x) = 500 \cdot (1.10^{\frac{1}{12}})^t$.

To rewrite the function representing Simone's annual increase as an equivalent function that reflects the monthly rate of increase, you must change the B-value. You can write the B-value of an exponential function as the coefficient of x.

$$f(x) = a \cdot (b)^{Bx}$$

WORKED EXAMPLE

You can use what you know about common bases to rewrite the expression in an equivalent form.

$\left(1.10^{\frac{1}{12}}\right)^{Bx} = (1.10)^x$

$(1.10)^{\frac{Bx}{12}} = (1.10)^x$ Apply the Power to a Power Rule.

$\frac{Bx}{12} = x$ The bases are the same, so the exponents are equivalent expressions.

$Bx = 12x$ Multiply both sides by 12.

$B = 12$

So, the function $f(x) = 500 \cdot \left(1.10^{\frac{1}{12}}\right)^{12x}$ is equivalent to the function $f(x) = 500 \cdot (1.10)^x$.

© Carnegie Learning, Inc.

4 Suppose Simone wants to determine how much her mutual fund increases each quarter. Rewrite the original function in an equivalent form that reveals the approximate equivalent quarterly rate of increase.

5 What is Simone's monthly increase as a percent?

© Carnegie Learning, Inc.

Is This Uptown or Downtown?

In 2015, the population of a city was 42,500. By 2020, the population had grown to approximately 51,708 people.

1 Identify any equations that are appropriate exponential models for the population of the city. **Explain why. Then, explain why the equations you did not choose are not appropriate models for the situation.**

$f(t) = 51{,}708(1.01)^t$

$f(t) = 51{,}708(0.96)^t$

$f(t) = 42{,}500(1.04)^{5t}$

$f(t) = 51{,}708(1.04)^{\frac{1}{5}t}$

$f(t) = 42{,}500(1.04)^t$

$f(t) = 42{,}500(0.96)^t$

2 Create a presentation to explain the differences between the *b*-value and the *B*-value of an exponential function. **Use at least one example in your presentation that is not in this lesson.**

© Carnegie Learning, Inc.

LESSON 2 ASSIGNMENT

> Use a separate piece of paper for your Journal entry.

JOURNAL

Explain how you can identify an asymptote from an exponential equation and its graph.

REMEMBER

You can estimate the solution to an exponential equation graphically. First, graph both the exponential function and the constant function for the given y-value. Next, determine the point of intersection of the graph of the exponential function and the horizontal line. Lastly, identify the x-value of the coordinate pair as the solution.

PRACTICE

1. Ryan bought a brand new car for $18,000. Its value depreciated at a rate of 1.2%.

   (a) Write a function to represent the value of the car as a function of time.

   (b) Use technology to estimate the number of years it will take for the value to reach each given amount.

   - $17,000
   - $15,000
   - Half of the starting value
   - One-third the starting value
   - $0
   - $10,000

2. In 2012, the population of a city was 63,000. By 2017, the population was reduced to approximately 54,100. Identify any equations that are appropriate models for the population of the city and explain why the others are not.

   (a) $f(x) = 63{,}000(1.03)^t$

   (b) $f(x) = 54{,}100(1.03)^t$

   (c) $f(x) = 63{,}000(0.97)^t$

   (d) $f(x) = 52{,}477(0.97)^t$

© Carnegie Learning, Inc.

Go to LiveHint.com for help on the PRACTICE questions.

3 Oscar wants to own a bee colony so that he can extract honey from the hive. He starts a colony with 5000 bees. The number of bees grows exponentially with a growth factor of 12% each month.

(a) Write a function, $f(x)$, for the bee population that you can use to determine the number of bees in the colony, based on the month, x.

(b) Use technology to graph the function, $f(x)$.

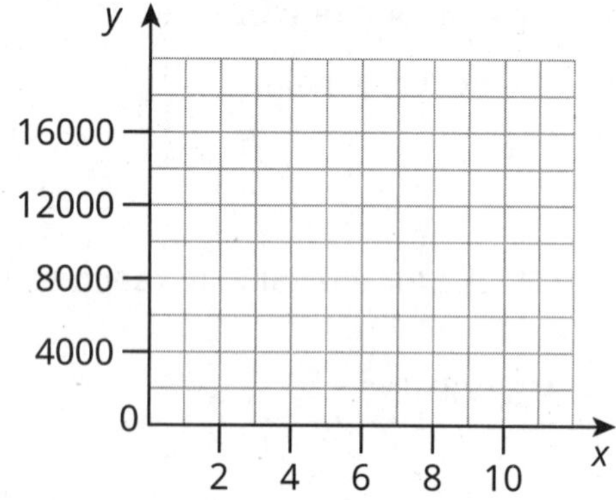

(c) Oscar feels that in order to get a decent amount of honey, there should be at least 15,000 bees in the colony. Estimate how many months it will take until he has 15,000 bees.

STRETCH Optional

Julissa and Megan developed a new art app for smartphones. The table shows the number of customers who downloaded the app by month.

1 Julissa thinks that the equation that represents the data in the table is $y = 4(2)^x$. Determine whether Julissa is correct. Explain your reasoning.

2 Determine a different exponential equation that represents the data in the table. Use the equation $y = a \cdot b^{f(x)}$, where $f(x)$ is a function of x and $a = 2$.

Month	Number of Downloads
0	4
1	8
2	16
3	32
4	64
5	128

© Carnegie Learning, Inc.

LESSON 3

Savings, Tea, and Carbon Dioxide

Modeling Using Exponential Functions

Learning Goals

- Write an exponential function to model a table of values and a graph.
- Add an exponential function and a constant function.
- Write an exponential function to model a data set.
- Use exponential models to solve problems.

REVIEW (1–2 minutes)

While driving to their vacation spot, the Mitchell family kept a record of their gas purchases. Their information is recorded in the table.

Amount of Gas (gallons)	9	16.6	11.8	10	13.2
Total Cost (dollars)	21.33	40.00	26.08	24.70	28.91

1. Use technology to write the linear regression equation.

2. What is the correlation coefficient, r? What does this value imply?

© Carnegie Learning, Inc.

You can interpret exponential scenarios, equations, tables, and graphs.

How can you use an exponential function to model real-world data?

The Elephants in the Room

The table and graph display data for two elephant populations over time, each within a different small area in Africa.

Population A

Time (years)	Elephant Population
3	3218
5	3628
7	3721
9	3871

Population B

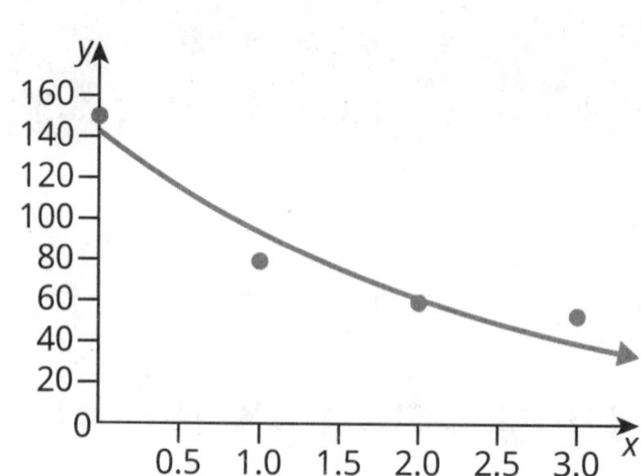

1 Estimate an exponential function for each population change over time. **Explain how you determined your functions.**

2 Use your functions and the features of each situation to describe the change in the populations over time.

© Carnegie Learning, Inc.

Adding Functions

> Analyze the different methods Autumn has of saving her money using functions.

HABITS OF MIND
- Model with mathematics.
- Use appropriate tools strategically.

1 Autumn received a graduation gift of $1000 from her wealthy aunt. She placed this money in a savings account with a 4% interest rate, compounded annually.

(a) Write a function $f(x)$ to model this situation. **Define the variables.**

(b) What will be the balance in Autumn's account after 5 years? 10 years? 15 years?

(c) Estimate when Autumn will have $1600 in her account.

2 Autumn also saved $500 that she keeps in a safe at home. She never touches it nor adds to it.

(a) Write a function $g(x)$ to model this situation. **Define the variables.**

(b) How much money will Autumn have in the safe after 5 years? 10 years? 15 years?

(c) When will Autumn have $1600 in the safe?

3 You can represent Autumn's total savings as $h(x) = f(x) + g(x)$. Write a function $h(x)$ to represent this sum and predict what the graph of $h(x)$ will look like.

© Carnegie Learning, Inc.

4 Graph $f(x)$, $g(x)$, and $h(x)$ on the coordinate plane. Label each function.

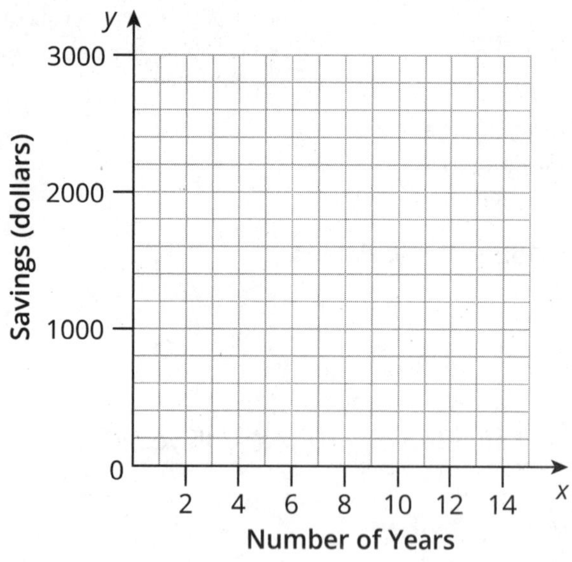

5 Did the graph of $h(x)$ appear as you predicted? How does it relate to what you learned about transformations?

6 How does the graph of $h(x)$ relate to the graphs of $f(x)$ and $g(x)$?

7 You can write the exponential function $h(x)$ in the form $h(x) = Ab^{B(x-C)} + D$. Identify three places where the value of D is evident in the graphs of the three functions.

© Carnegie Learning, Inc.

Modeling a Decreasing Exponential Function

HABITS OF MIND
- Model with mathematics.
- Use appropriate tools strategically.

You can model data with an exponential regression equation.

Caroline loves drinking green tea. One morning, after making herself a cup of hot tea, she sat in her kitchen to enjoy it.

The table shows the temperature of a cup of Caroline's tea over time.

Time (minutes)	Temperature (degrees Fahrenheit)
0	180
5	169
11	149
15	142
18	135
25	124
30	116
34	113
42	106
45	102
50	101

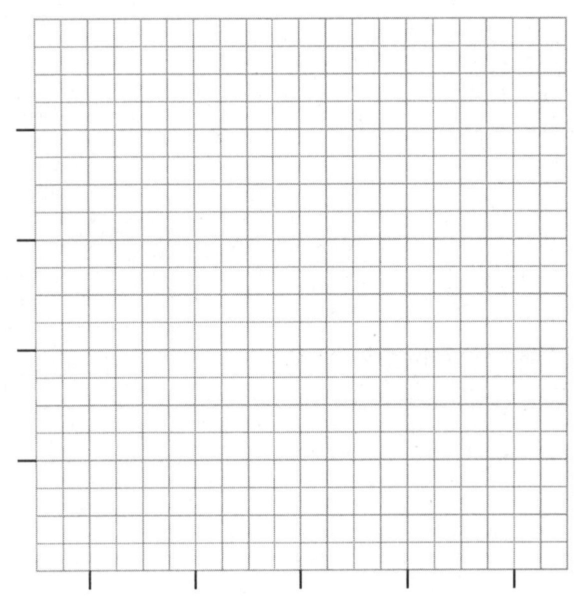

1. Model this situation.

   (a) Create a scatter plot. **Label your axes.**

   (b) Use technology to write the exponential regression equation. **Define the variables.** Identify the correlation coefficient.

   (c) Sketch the function on the same graph as your scatter plot.

© Carnegie Learning, Inc.

2 State the domain and range of the function you sketched. How do they compare to the domain and range of this problem situation?

3 Use the equation to predict the temperature of Caroline's tea after an hour.

4 Use the equation to predict the temperature of Caroline's tea after 4 hours.

5 Does your prediction make sense in terms of this problem situation? **Explain your reasoning.**

© Carnegie Learning, Inc.

Determining the Best Fit to Model Data

HABITS OF MIND
- Model with mathematics.
- Use appropriate tools strategically.

One measure of climate change is the amount of carbon dioxide in Earth's atmosphere.

The table shows the carbon dioxide concentration in Earth's atmosphere in parts per million from 1860 to 2020.

Year	Carbon Dioxide Concentration (parts per million)
1860	286
1880	291
1900	296
1920	303
1940	311
1960	317
1980	339
2000	370
2020	417

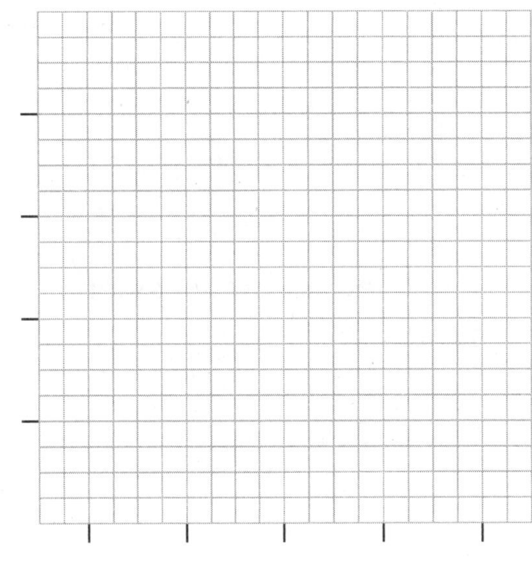

1. Model this situation.

   a. Create a scatter plot using 1860 as Year 0. **Label your axes.**

   b. Use technology to choose the correct function to model this data. Write your regression equation. **Define the variables.** Identify the correlation coefficient.

   c. Sketch the function on the same graph as your scatter plot.

© Carnegie Learning, Inc.

2 Naasira used an exponential function to model the situation. Brendan used a linear function to model the situation. Who is correct? **Explain your reasoning.**

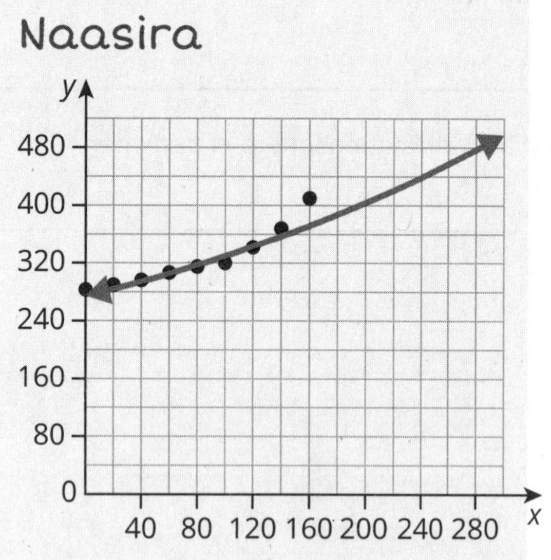

Exponential Regression Equation

$f(x) = 272.764(1.0021)^x$

$r = 0.9286$

$r^2 = 0.8622$

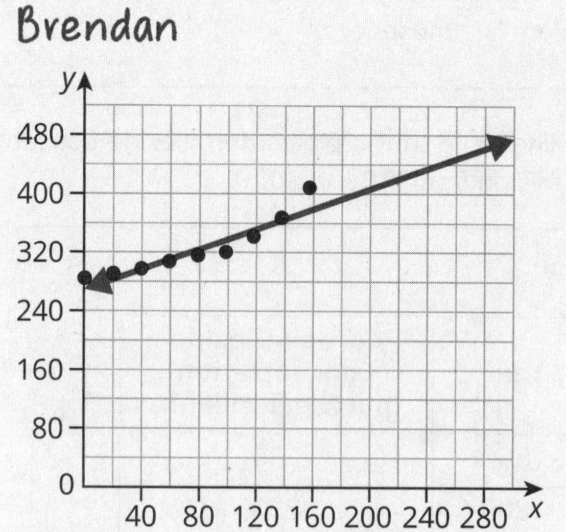

Linear Regression Equation

$f(x) = 0.7175x + 268.15$

$r = 0.9093$

$r^2 = 0.8268$

3 What other information would help you to make the decision as to whether a linear or exponential function is best to model this context and data?

© Carnegie Learning, Inc.

4 Why does the exponential function look very similar to the linear function?

5 Use each function to predict the concentration of carbon dioxide for each given year.

(a) During 2160

(b) During 2500

© Carnegie Learning, Inc.

6 According to the data, the concentration of carbon dioxide has been increasing over the past 157 years. What factors could have contributed to this behavior?

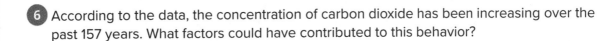

Making a List, Checking It Twice

> Reflect on the exponential situations and graphs you have encountered in past lessons.

1 Consider the contexts.

(a) Describe the contexts that you can model with an exponential function.

(b) What do the contexts have in common that identify them as being exponential functions?

2 Consider the graphs.

(a) How can you tell from a scatter plot that you can model it with an exponential function?

(b) Sketch four different possible graphs of an exponential function of the form $y = a \cdot b^x$. **Describe the *a*-value and common multiplier in each.**

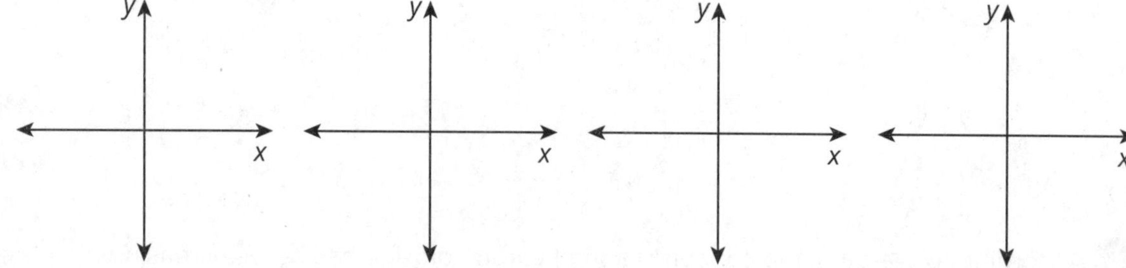

© Carnegie Learning, Inc.

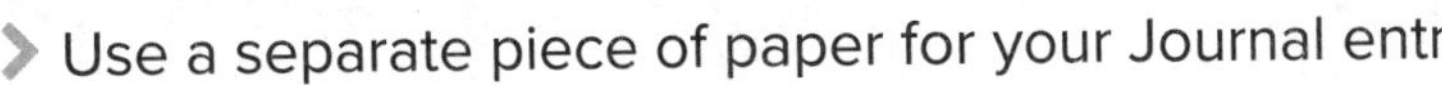

LESSON 3 ASSIGNMENT

> Use a separate piece of paper for your Journal entry.

JOURNAL

Describe the information that you can use to determine whether a linear or exponential function is best to model a context and data.

REMEMBER

You can use exponential functions to model scenarios that involve a percent increase or decrease, such as compound interest and population growth or decay.

In some cases, the scenario can help you determine whether a data set is best modeled by a linear or exponential function, while in other cases you may need more data points or information.

PRACTICE

1. The table shows the number of U.S. Post Offices at the beginning of each decade from 1900 to 2000.

Year	Number of U.S. Post Offices
1900	76,688
1910	59,580
1920	52,641
1930	49,063
1940	44,024
1950	41,464
1960	35,238
1970	32,002
1980	30,326
1990	28,959
2000	27,876

(a) Create a scatter plot of the data.

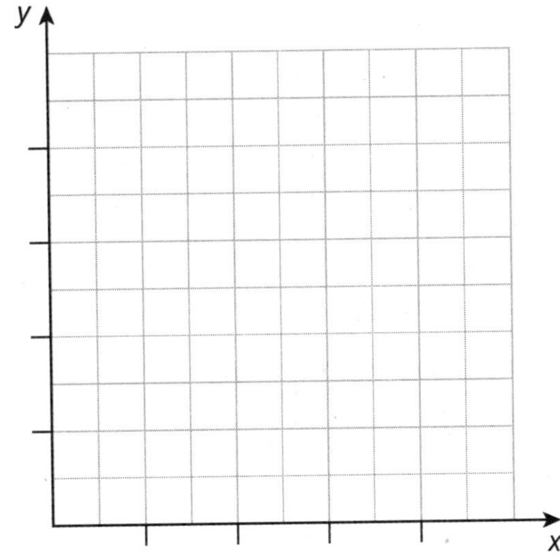

(b) Determine the exponential regression equation and the value of the correlation coefficient, r. Then, graph the equation on the grid with the scatter plot.

© Carnegie Learning, Inc.

Go to LiveHint.com for help on the PRACTICE questions.

(c) Predict the number of U.S. Post Offices in the year 2050.

(d) Predict when the number of U.S. Post Offices will reach 20,000.

(e) What do you think is causing the decline in the number of U.S. Post Offices?

STRETCH Optional

The number of fixed landline phone subscribers in the U.S. has been declining. The bar graph shows the decrease in the number of subscribers from 2010 to 2015.

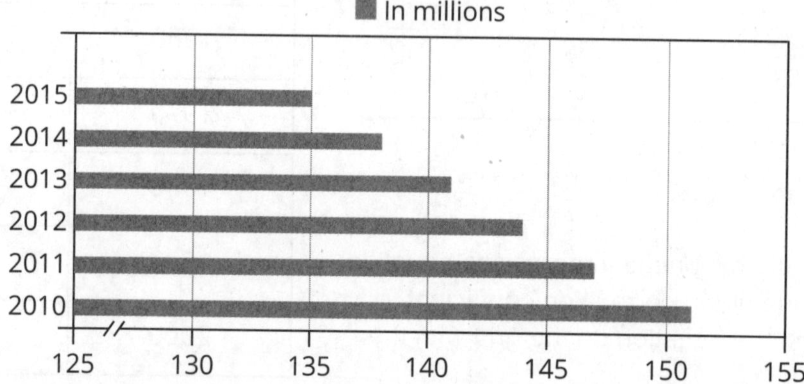

1 To estimate the number of subscribers per year, create a scatter plot of the ordered pairs, with x representing the number of years since 2010 and y representing the number of subscribers in millions.

2 Determine both an exponential and a linear regression function to model the situation.

3 Which model would you use from Question 2? Explain your reasoning.

© Carnegie Learning, Inc.

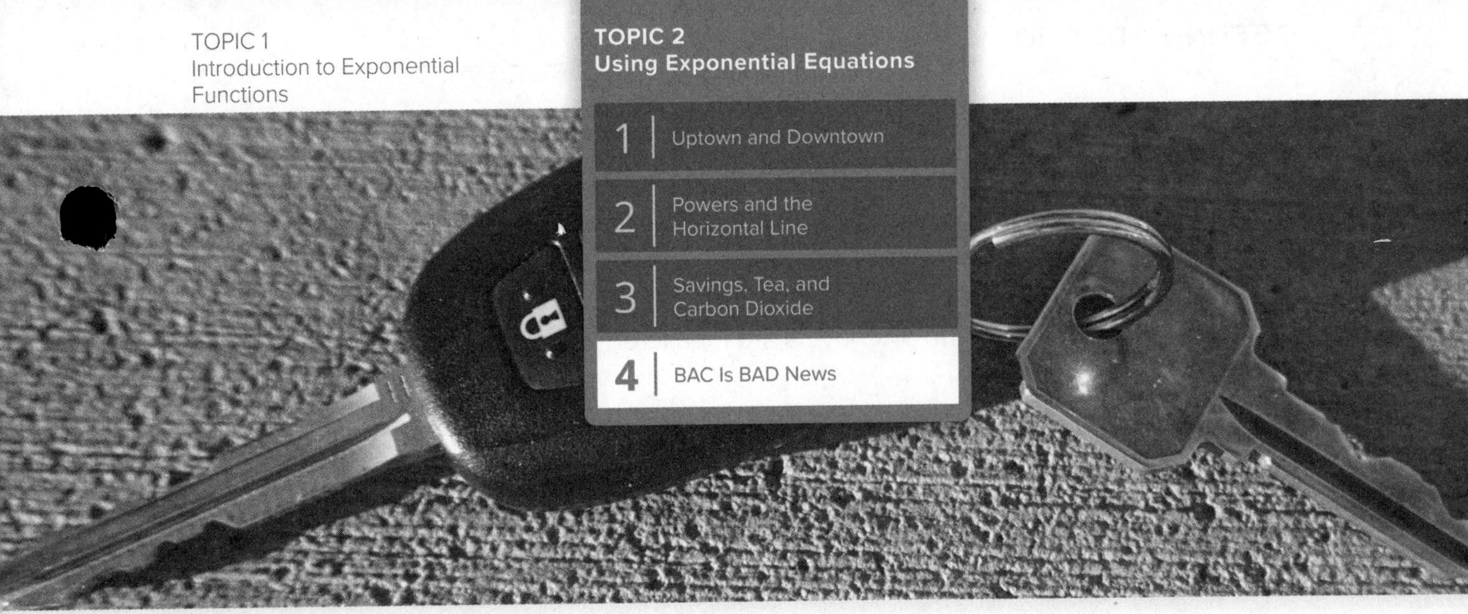

TOPIC 1
Introduction to Exponential Functions
TOPIC 2
Using Exponential Equations
1 Uptown and Downtown
2 Powers and the Horizontal Line
3 Savings, Tea, and Carbon Dioxide
4 BAC Is BAD News

LESSON 4

BAC Is BAD News

Choosing a Function to Model Data

Learning Goals

- Determine the appropriate regression equation for a data set.
- Solve a complex problem using the mathematical modeling process.
- Reflect upon the mathematical modeling process.

REVIEW (1–2 minutes)

> Use the scatter plot to answer each question.

1 Is this scatter plot best represented by a linear or exponential function? **Explain your answer.**

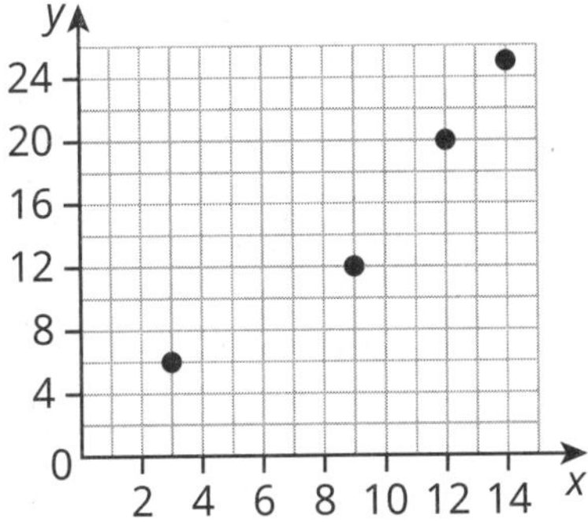

2 Determine a regression equation that best fits this data.

© Carnegie Learning, Inc.

You can determine a regression equation for a data set.

How can you use this knowledge to solve a real-world problem?

Drinking and Driving Don't Mix

Blood Alcohol Content (BAC) is a way of measuring the amount of alcohol in a person's blood stream. BAC levels are measured in percentages.

A recent study shows that a person with no alcohol in the blood system has a 1.8% chance of causing a car accident.

There is a relationship between the relative probability of a driver causing a car accident and a driver's BAC. The relative probability is the number of times more likely a driver with alcohol in their blood system is to cause a car accident than a driver with no alcohol in their blood system. For example, a relative probability of 2 for a driver with a BAC of 0.06% means that a car accident is twice as likely to occur as for a driver with a BAC of 0.00.

DID YOU KNOW?
A BAC of 0.08 means that 0.08% of a person's blood is alcohol.

1. Explain the difference in meaning between probability and relative probability using the values in this scenario.

2. Use the likelihood of a person with no alcohol in their blood system causing a car accident to answer each question.

   a. There is a relative probability of 2 that a person with a BAC of 0.06% causes an accident. What is the probability that this person will cause a car accident?

DID YOU KNOW?
It is illegal for anyone over the age of 21 to drive once their BAC reaches 0.08. For drivers under 21, any BAC level above 0.00 is illegal!

© Carnegie Learning, Inc.

(b) There is a relative probability of 5 that a person with a BAC of 0.10% causes an accident. What is the probability that this person will cause a car accident?

(c) There is a relative probability of 25 that a person with a BAC of 0.16% causes an accident. What is the probability that this person will cause a car accident?

3 Examine your answers from Question 2. **What do you notice about the rate at which alcohol affects a person's ability to drive?**

© Carnegie Learning, Inc.

Analyzing and Using Data to Make Predictions

HABITS OF MIND

- Reason abstractly and quantitatively.
- Construct viable arguments and critique the reasoning of others.

Different factors affect a person's BAC, including weight, gender, the duration of consuming alcohol, and the amount of food the person eats.

According to the Virginia Tech Alcohol Abuse Prevention website, a typical 140-pound male who has one drink over a 40-minute period will have a BAC of 0.03%. If he has another drink over the next 40 minutes, his BAC rises to 0.05%. If he has one more drink over the next 40-minute period, his BAC rises to 0.08%, which means he legally cannot drive.

BAC Level (percent)	Relative Probability of Causing an Accident (percent)
0.02	1
0.06	2
0.10	5
0.16	25

> Create a model to predict the likelihood of a person causing an accident based on their BAC. Include a table, a graph, and an equation in your model. **Be sure to define your variables.**

Include these elements in your analysis:

- Describe why the function type you chose is appropriate for this situation. How do you know that it's a good fit?
- Predict the probability that drivers with different BACs will cause an accident. Show all your work.
- How can you use your graph to write guidelines to communicate when a person is safe to drive, even when they can legally drive?

© Carnegie Learning, Inc.

© Carnegie Learning, Inc.

Summarizing the Results

HABITS OF MIND

- Reason abstractly and quantitatively.
- Construct viable arguments and critique the reasoning of others.

> Write an article to report your conclusions for the newsletter of the local chapter of S.A.D.D. (Students Against Destructive Decisions) that stresses the seriousness of drinking and driving.

Include tables and/or graphs to help the reader make sense of the issue. You may want to include these points:

- Facts about the rate at which a driver's probability of causing an accident increases as their BAC increases
- The definitions of legal limits in your state
- How a driver's motor skills are affected by alcohol

© Carnegie Learning, Inc.

What Have I Done?

By solving the problem in this lesson, you intuitively engaged in the mathematical modeling process.

The Modeling Process

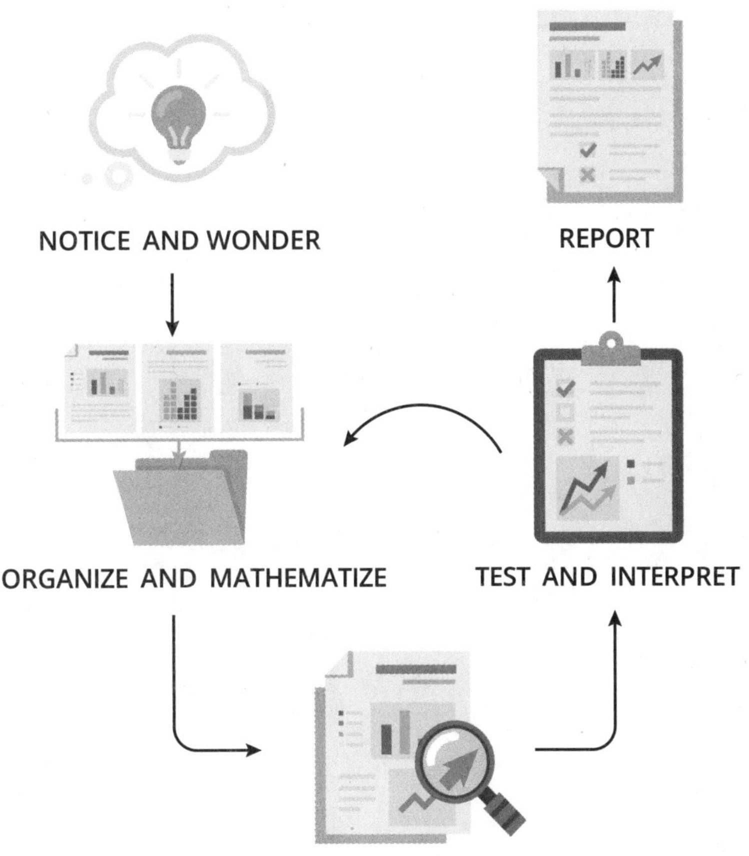

1. Reflect on your process by referencing the diagram and noting the type of thinking and work you engaged in next to each step.

© Carnegie Learning, Inc.

2. Were there instances where you looped back in the process? **Explain how you knew you needed to loop back and how you changed the direction in your thinking.**

© Carnegie Learning, Inc.

LESSON 4 ASSIGNMENT

> Use a separate piece of paper for your Journal entry.

JOURNAL

Describe the mathematical modeling process in your own words.

REMEMBER

Determining and using a regression equation is sometimes a step in the process of solving a more complex mathematical problem rather than the final solution.

PRACTICE

The table shows the purchasing value of the dollar, or the consumer price index, for consumers in the United States from 1955 to 2010. The table uses the year 1982 as a base period, so the consumer price index written in dollars and cents in 1982 is 1.00. For instance, in 1955, the consumer price index was 3.73. This means that a dollar in 1955 was worth 3.73 times what it was worth in 1982. Similarly, a dollar in 2010 was worth 0.46 times what it was worth in 1982.

Year	Consumer Price Index	Year	Consumer Price Index
1955	3.73	1985	0.93
1960	3.37	1990	0.77
1965	3.17	1995	0.66
1970	2.57	2000	0.58
1975	1.86	2005	0.51
1980	1.22	2010	0.46

The scatter plot shows the data in the table, where x represents the number of years since 1955 and y represents the consumer price index.

1. Describe how the consumer price index changes over time.

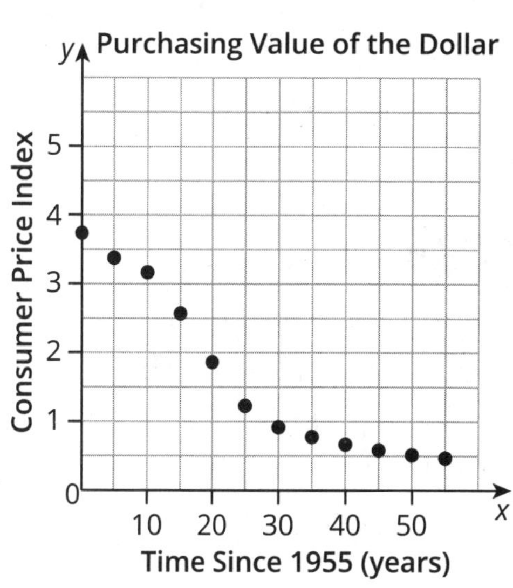

2. Which function best models this situation? Explain your reasoning.

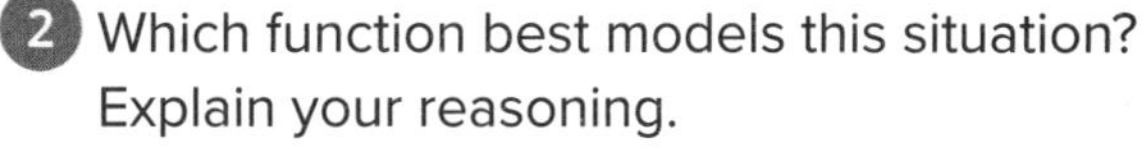

© Carnegie Learning, Inc.

Go to LiveHint.com for help on the PRACTICE questions.

3 Analyze the data and scatter plot.

(a) Determine the regression equation for the model that best represents the data. Explain how you determined your answer. Then, graph the model on the same grid as the scatter plot.

(b) Predict the consumer price index in 2025. Explain what your answer means in terms of the problem situation.

(c) Mr. Kratzer asks his students to calculate what the consumer price index was in 1950. Melina says that you must evaluate the function at $x = 5$ to determine the consumer price index in 1950. Dominque argues you must evaluate the function at $x = -5$ to determine the consumer price index in 1950. Who is correct? Explain your reasoning.

(d) Calculate the consumer price index for 1950. Show your work.

(e) The consumer price index in 1950 was actually 4.15. Compare this to the answer you calculated in part (d). Explain why these answers differ.

STRETCH Optional

> Analyze this scatter plot.

1 Determine the function that best models the graph.

2 Plot the point (8, 6) on the graph. Does your answer to Question 1 change? Why or why not?

3 If you were doing research and a situation arose in which a data point that gets added to the graph changes the model, what is one thing you might do to investigate further?

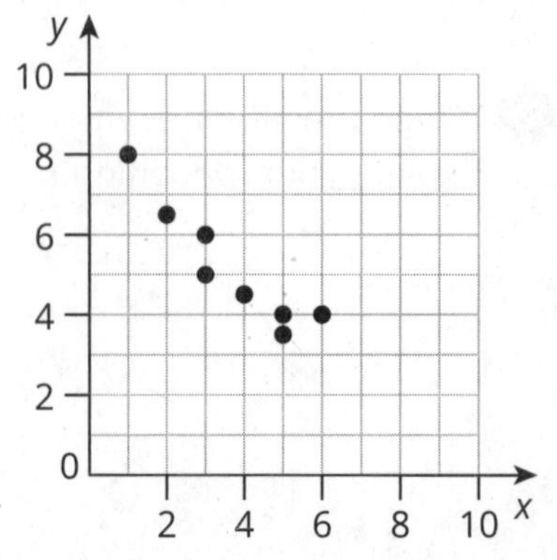

© Carnegie Learning, Inc.

MIXED PRACTICE

> This Mixed Practice worksheet includes two sections: Spaced Review and End-of-Topic Review. **Use a separate piece of paper to show your work.**

Spaced Review

> Practice concepts from previous topics.

1 Solve each linear absolute value equation. Show your work.

(a) $6 - 7|x - 4| = -36$

(b) $-8|-10x| + 1 = -79$

2 Rewrite each expression using the fewest terms.

(a) $4 - (2.3x - 7)$

(b) $10 - 8(2x - 7)$

3 Graph each system of linear inequalities to show the solution set.

(a) $\begin{cases} y > -\frac{5}{4}x - 2 \\ x \geq -5 \end{cases}$

(b) $\begin{cases} 2x - 3y > -3 \\ x + 3y > -6 \end{cases}$

4 Each function is a transformation of the linear basic function $f(x) = x$. Graph each transformation.

(a) $g(x) = \frac{1}{3}x - 2$

(b) $h(x) = -2x + 1$

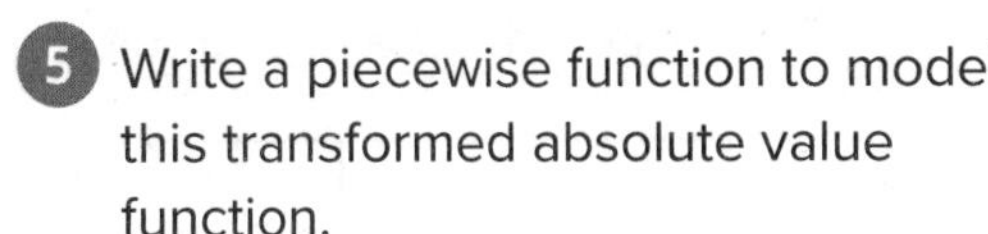

5 Write a piecewise function to model this transformed absolute value function.

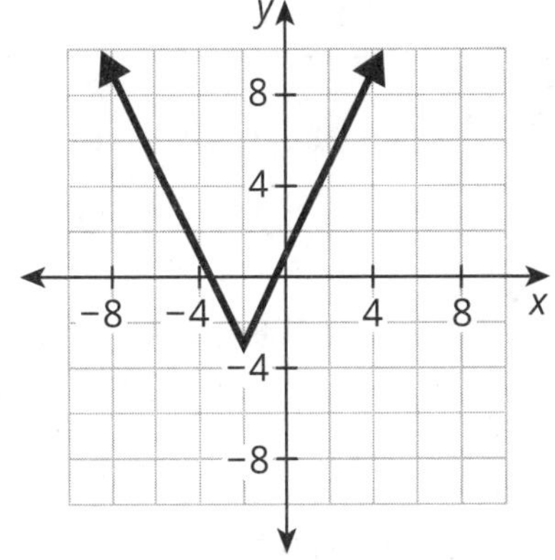

6 Each graph represents a form of the function $g(x) = Af(x) + D$ given $f(x) = x$. Determine A and D and then explain the transformations these values make on the linear basic function. Write the function in terms of the basic function.

(a)

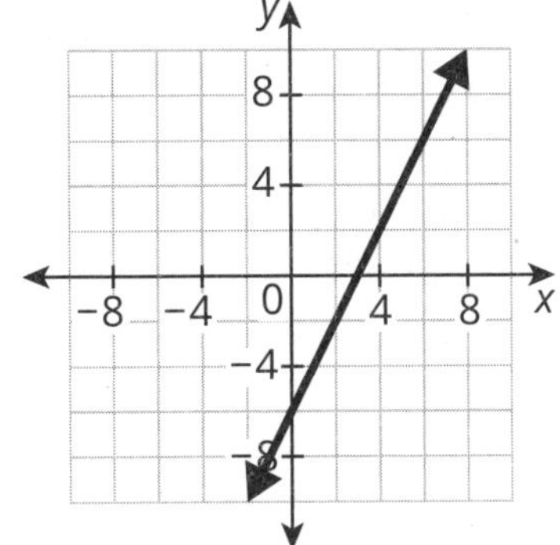

(b)

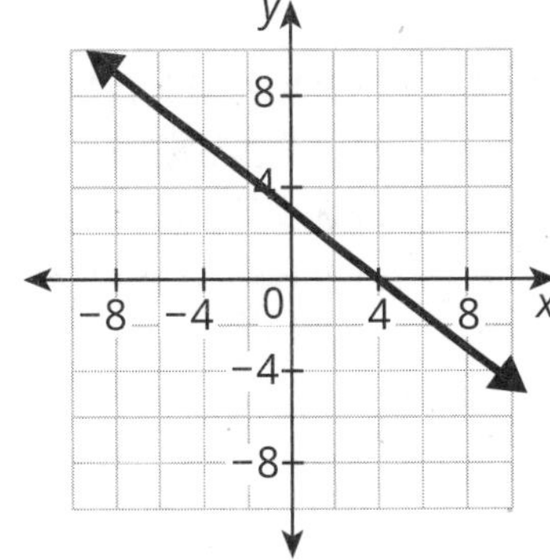

© Carnegie Learning, Inc.

End-of-Topic Review

AVAILABLE ONLINE

1. A **Topic Summary** reviews the main concepts for the topic.
2. A video of the **Worked Example** is provided.

> Practice concepts you learned in *Using Exponential Equations*.

7. An experiment begins with 400 bacteria. The bacteria population doubles each day. Write an equation in function notation to represent the number of bacteria as a function of the day number, x. Explain how you determined the equation.

8. Alejandra has $900 to open a bank account. She wants to put her money in the bank where she will earn the most money over time. Alejandra has a choice between the Platinum Bank that offers an account with 3% compound interest and the Diamond Bank that offers an account with 4% simple interest.

   (a) What is the function used to calculate the balance in each account based on the year, t? Describe each function.

   (b) In which bank should Alejandra deposit her money? Explain your reasoning.

9. The table shows an example of a rabbit population.

Year	0	1	2	3	4	5	6
Population	4	11	29	79	213	577	1557

   (a) Create a scatter plot of the data. Be sure to label the axes.

   (b) Write the regression equation that models the data. Graph the equation on the grid with the scatter plot.

   (c) How did you determine which type of function to use?

   (d) What do you predict the rabbit population will be in the 20th year? Explain your reasoning.

10. Eleanor receives $1500 for her birthday. She is going to spend $500 and wants to put the rest into an account that will earn interest. She is considering two different accounts. Account A earns 6.5% annual simple interest. Account B earns 4.5% annual compound interest.

   (a) Write a function for each account that can be used to determine the balance in the account based on the year, t.

   (b) Graph the functions for Accounts A and B using technology. Then, graph the functions. Be sure to label your graph.

   (c) If Eleanor plans on leaving the money in the account for 12 years, which account should she use to deposit her money? Explain your reasoning.

   (d) If Eleanor plans on leaving the money in the account for 25 years, which account should she use to deposit her money? Explain your reasoning.

© Carnegie Learning, Inc.

Describing Distributions

TOPIC 1
One-Variable Statistics

MATHbook

MATHia

Graphically Representing Data
- Creating Frequency Plots
- Describing Data Sets

Comparing Measures of Center and Spread
- Determining Appropriate Measures of Center
- Measuring the Effects of Changing Data Sets
- Creating Box Plots and Identifying Outliers
- Calculating Standard Deviation

Comparing Data Sets
- Comparing and Interpreting Measures of Center
- Comparing Data Sets Using Center and Spread

TOPIC 2
Two-Variable Categorical Data

MATHbook

MATHia

Two-Variable Categorical Data
- Creating Marginal Frequency Distributions
- Using Marginal Frequency Distributions
- Creating Marginal Relative Frequency Distributions
- Using Marginal Relative Frequency Distributions
- Creating Conditional Relative Frequency Distributions
- Using Conditional Relative Frequency Distributions

© Carnegie Learning, Inc.

Getting Ready for Module 4

Describing Distributions

You will continue to develop your understanding of data displays. You will expand your work with measures of variation to include standard deviation. You will create two-way frequency distributions, relative frequency distributions, and conditional relative frequency distributions. You will analyze the data for any possible trends or associations.

The lessons in this module build on your prior experiences with measures of center and variation, five-number summaries, and percents.

Review these key terms and five-number summaries to get ready to describe distributions.

KEY TERMS

measure of center

A measure of center tells you how data values cluster, or the location of the "center" of the data.

The data displayed on the dot plot has a mean of 30. The mean, median, and mode are all measures of center.

measure of variation

A measure of variation describes the spread of data values.

The data on the dot plot has a mean average deviation (MAD) of 10. The mean average deviation, interquartile range (IQR), and range are measures of variation.

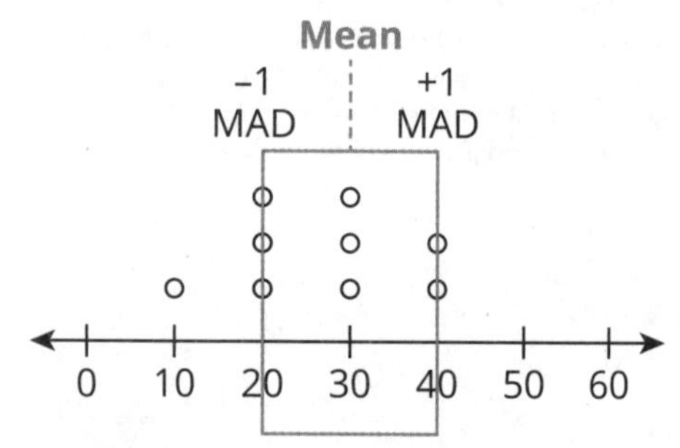

Brush up on your skills.
If you need more practice with these skills, ask your teacher for access to corresponding workspaces in MATHia.

SKILLS YOU WILL NEED

Determining a Five-Number Summary

The five-number summary of a data set includes the minimum, Q1, median, Q3, and maximum values.

Consider the data set:

24, 32, 14, 18, 30, 20, 15, 27, 19, 31

You can use a box-and-whiskers plot to represent the five-number summary.

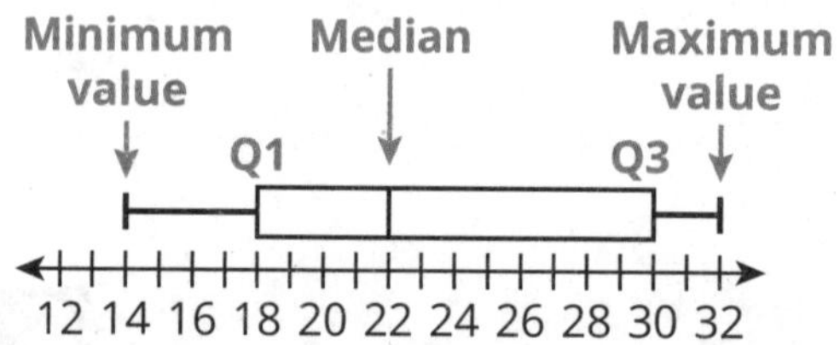

Using this data display, you know the median is 22. The interquartile range (IQR) is the difference between the third and first quartiles, Q3 – Q1, and represents the middle 50% of the data set. The IQR of this data set is 12.

REVIEW

> Rewrite each value as a percent.

1. $\frac{57}{100}$

2. 0.07

3. $\frac{31}{43}$

4. $\frac{17}{68}$

See Appendix on page 879 for answers.

© Carnegie Learning, Inc.

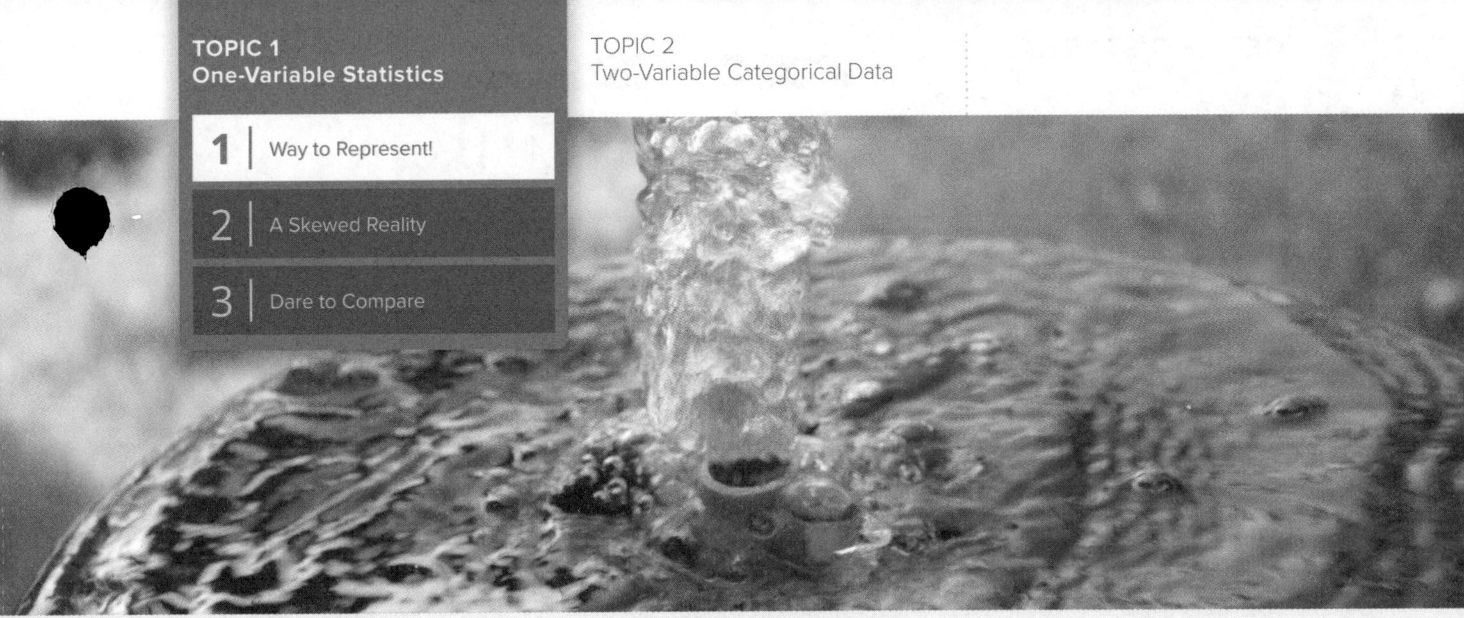

1 Way to Represent!
2 A Skewed Reality
3 Dare to Compare

LESSON 1

Way to Represent!

Graphically Representing Data

KEY TERMS

- **dot plot**
- **histogram**
- **bin**
- **frequency**
- **box-and-whisker plot**
- **five-number summary**

Learning Goals

- Represent and interpret data displayed on dot plots, histograms, and box-and-whisker plots.
- Determine whether a dot plot, a histogram, or a box-and-whisker plot is the best way to display a data set.
- Compare the box-and-whisker plots of two different data sets.

REVIEW (1–2 minutes)

> Consider the data set: 0.3, 0.7, 1.5, 1.9, 2.4, 3.0, 3.2, 5.3, 5.6, 5.8, 6.6, 7.5, 8.0, 9.1.

Determine which histogram best represents the data. **Explain your reasoning.**

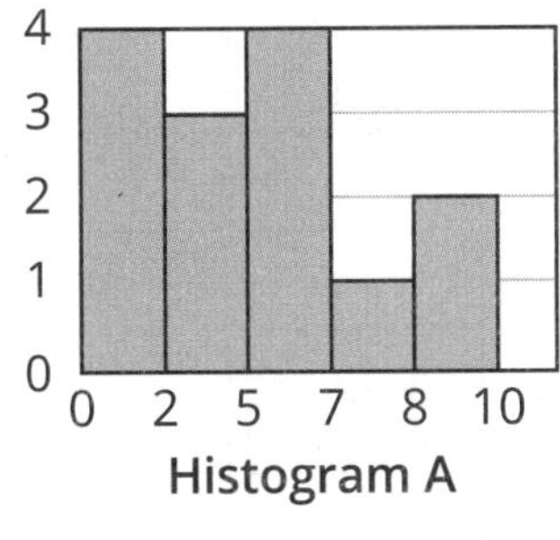

Histogram A

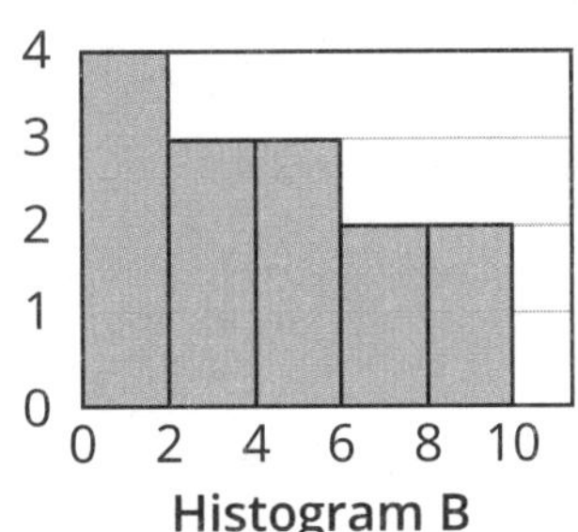

Histogram B

© Carnegie Learning, Inc.

You know how to represent and interpret data using dot plots, histograms, and box-and-whisker plots.

How can you determine which representation is most appropriate given a data set?

Get the Lead Out

Recall that there are four components of the statistical process:

- Formulating a statistical question
- Collecting appropriate data
- Analyzing the data graphically and numerically
- Interpreting the results of the analysis

ASK YOURSELF . . .
How is the statistical process similar to the modeling process?

Lead concentrations in drinking water should be fewer than 15 parts per billion (ppb). A water system technician took samples of the amounts of lead in the water in one neighborhood of the city of Greenville and recorded the data in this table.

Site Number	Amount of Lead in Water (ppb)
1	11
2	22
3	6
4	10
5	8
6	3
7	12
8	5
9	10
10	4
11	4
12	7
13	7
14	11
15	7
16	5
17	1
18	13
19	4
20	7

1. Analyze the data collected, using only the table. What conclusions can you draw about the amount of lead in the water at the different sites?

One way to better organize data in a table is to create a *dot plot*. A **dot plot** is a graph that shows the distribution of discrete data, or data that can only take on specific, individual values, using a number line. Dot plots are useful for organizing and displaying a small number of data points.

2. Construct a dot plot to represent the amount of lead in the water at each site. **Make sure to label your dot plot.**

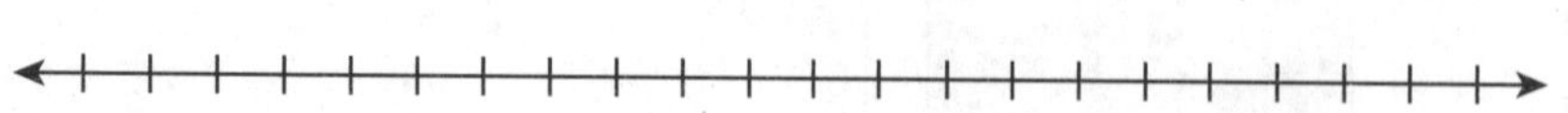

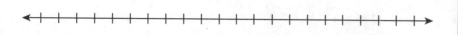

3. What conclusions can you draw about the amount of lead in the water of the neighborhood in Greenville from your dot plot?

© Carnegie Learning, Inc.

ACTIVITY 1

MATHia CONNECTION

- Creating Frequency Plots

Histograms

According to the Environmental Protection Agency, when more than 10% of tap water samples are greater than or equal to 15 parts per billion (ppb), the city must take action to reduce the levels.

HABITS OF MIND

- Reason abstractly and quantitatively.
- Construct viable arguments and critique the reasoning of others.

1 According to the data in the Getting Started, must the city take action to reduce the amount of lead in the water in the neighborhood? **Justify your response.**

TAKE NOTE . . . The fourth part of the statistical process is to interpret the results of your analysis.

The mayor of Greenville wants to analyze the lead levels for the water in the entire city. The frequency table displays the data for the amount of lead in drinking water samples taken from sites all over Greenville.

Amount of Lead in Water (ppb)	Frequency
0 up to 5	32
5 up to 10	48
10 up to 15	100
15 up to 20	47
20 up to 25	23

Another way to display quantitative data is to create a *histogram*. A **histogram** is a graphical way to display quantitative data using vertical bars.

- The width of a bar in a histogram represents an interval of data and is often referred to as a *bin*.
- The height of each bar indicates the **frequency**, which is the number of data values included in any given bin.
- Histograms are effective in displaying large amounts of continuous data, or data which can take any numeric value within a range.

2 Construct a histogram to display the data in the table.

TAKE NOTE . . . A **bin** represents an interval of data instead of individual data values. The value on the left side of the bin is the least data value in the interval.

© Carnegie Learning, Inc.

3 What conclusions can you draw from the histogram about the amount of lead in the drinking water of Greenville?

4 Marcel created a histogram to display the same data and claimed that Greenville did not have to take action to reduce lead levels in its drinking water. Is Marcel correct? **Explain why or why not.**

ASK YOURSELF . . .
Do more than 10% of the samples have amounts of lead greater than or equal to 15 ppb?

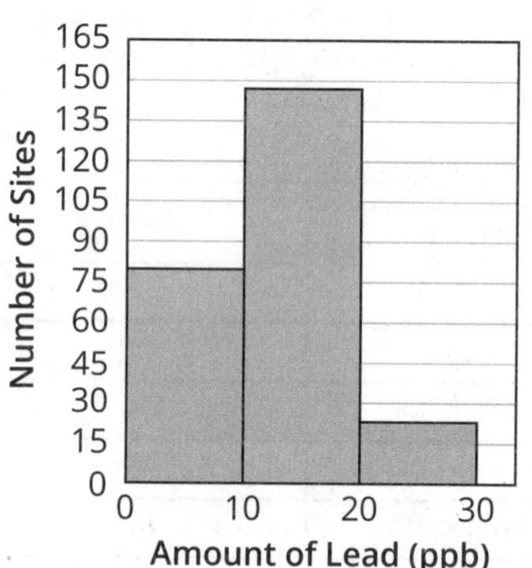

5 Does the water system management of Greenville need to take action to reduce the amount of lead in the water? **Explain your reasoning.**

6 Do you think a histogram is a good representation of the data? **Explain your reasoning.**

© Carnegie Learning, Inc.

Box-and-Whisker Plots

HABITS OF MIND
- Reason abstractly and quantitatively.
- Construct viable arguments and critique the reasoning of others.

You can visually compare two large data sets at a glance using *box-and-whisker plots*. A **box-and-whisker plot** is a graphical representation that displays the distribution of quantitative data based on a *five-number summary*. The **five-number summary** consists of the minimum value, the first quartile (Q1), the median, the third quartile (Q3), and the maximum value.

WORKED EXAMPLE

You can use the five-number summary to create a box-and-whisker plot. Each vertical line of the box-and-whisker plot represents a value from the summary.

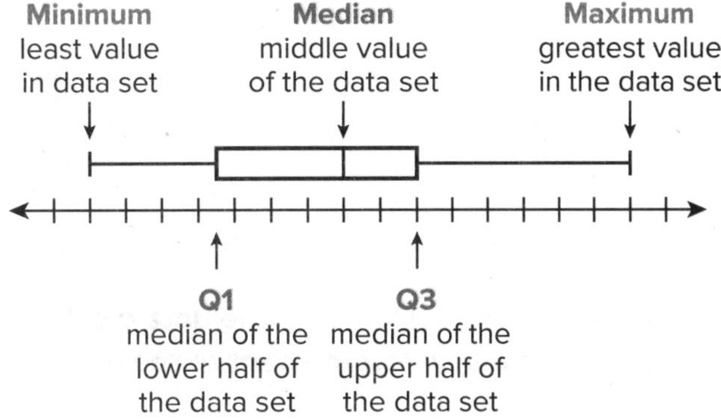

There are four sections of the graphical display: minimum to Q1, Q1 to median, median to Q3, and Q3 to maximum. Each section of the box-and-whisker plot represents 25 percent of the data set.

The governor wants to compare the amount of lead in the drinking water of different cities in her state to see where improvements in the water systems should be made.

The five-number summaries of the data for the amount of lead in drinking water samples taken from the cities of Greenville and Oaktown are given.

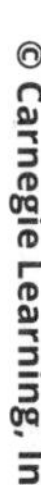
© Carnegie Learning, Inc.

Five-Number Summary	
Greenville	**Oaktown**
Minimum = 1	Minimum = 2
Q1 = 8	Q1 = 6
Median = 12	Median = 8
Q3 = 16	Q3 = 9
Maximum = 22	Maximum = 15

1 Construct a box-and-whisker plot of the data for each city on the same number line using the five-number summaries.

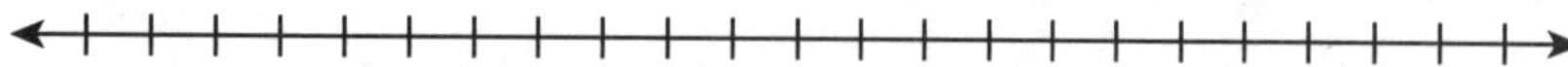

2 Suppose you work in the governor's office. **Compare the data displayed in your box-and-whisker plots and write an analysis to present to the governor.**

© Carnegie Learning, Inc.

Dots, Bins, or Boxes?

> Analyze each situation. Describe which representation you would use (dot plot, histogram, or box-and-whisker plot) to display and analyze the data set. **Explain your reasoning.**

1. Nick collects data about the one hundred tallest buildings in the United States. He wants to quickly determine between which two heights the top 25% of the data fall.

2. Lily conducted a school survey to determine how many problems each math teacher assigned for homework on Friday.

3. The National Wildlife Service records the migration ranges of the white deer and mule deer populations in Montana to compare them.

4. A school district wants to determine how many students in the entire district scored above 70 on a standardized test.

© Carnegie Learning, Inc.

5 What conclusions can you draw from each display?

(a)

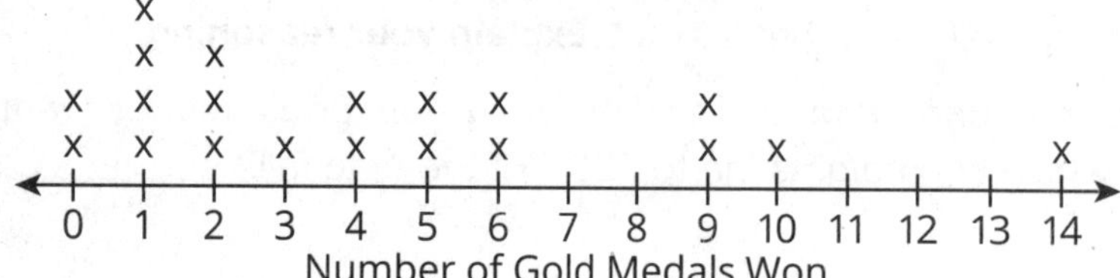

(b)

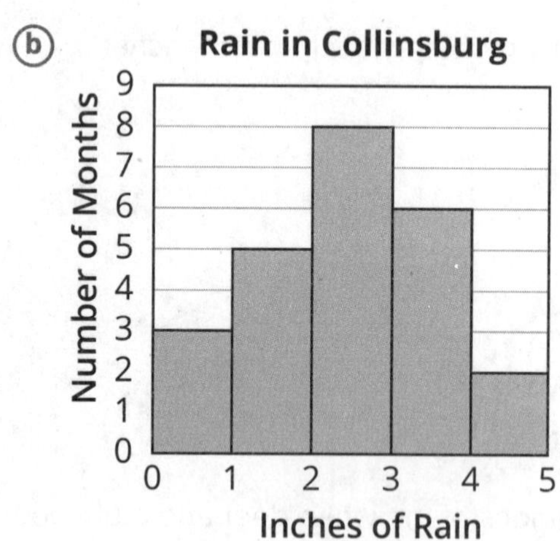

(c)

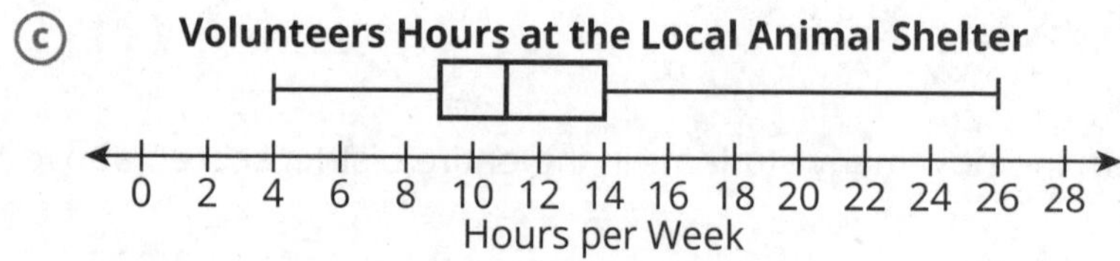

© Carnegie Learning, Inc.

LESSON 1 ASSIGNMENT

> Use a separate piece of paper for your Journal entry.

JOURNAL

> Complete each statement.

1. A ____________ is a graphical way to display quantitative data using vertical bars.
2. A ____________ displays the data distribution based on a five-number summary.
3. A ____________ is a graph that shows how data are distributed using a number line.
4. For a set of data, the ____________ consists of the minimum value, the first quartile, the median, the third quartile, and the maximum value.
5. The number of data values included in a given bin of a data set is the ____________.
6. The bar width in a histogram that represents an interval of data is often referred to as a ____________.

REMEMBER

A dot plot helps organize a small number of data points. A histogram is effective in displaying large amounts of data. Box-and-whisker plots are effective for visually comparing two data sets.

PRACTICE

1. Mr. Follweiller finished grading the quizzes for one of his Algebra 1 classes. The table shows the recorded grades of the class.

   a. Mr. Follweiller worries his students may not have understood the material covered on the quiz. He would like to get a better idea of how the class did as a whole. Would you recommend that he make a dot plot, a box-and-whisker plot, or a histogram to display this data? Explain your reasoning.

Student	Grade	Student	Grade
A	85	N	53
B	89	O	71
C	66	P	90
D	74	Q	65
E	77	R	55
F	72	S	98
G	64	T	53
H	55	U	62
I	61	V	55
J	52	W	64
K	81	X	62
L	61	Y	56
M	71	Z	87

© Carnegie Learning, Inc.

ⓑ Construct a dot plot and histogram of the data in the table.

ⓒ What information does the dot plot provide that the histogram does not?

ⓓ The students argue that more than half the students didn't pass the quiz, so they think Mr. Follweiller should let them retake it. A grade of 57 or higher is passing. Construct a box-and-whisker plot of the data. Are the students correct? Explain your reasoning.

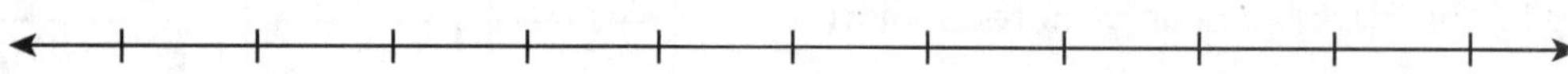

© Carnegie Learning, Inc.

STRETCH Optional

> George bowls in tournaments on the weekends. He recorded the scores of each game for his last two tournaments. A perfect score is 300.

Tournament 1: 182, 197, 178, 272, 180, 188, 202, 179, 191

Tournament 2: 188, 195, 177, 192, 180, 187, 201, 183, 197

1. Calculate the five-number summary and IQR for the two tournaments. Interpret your findings.

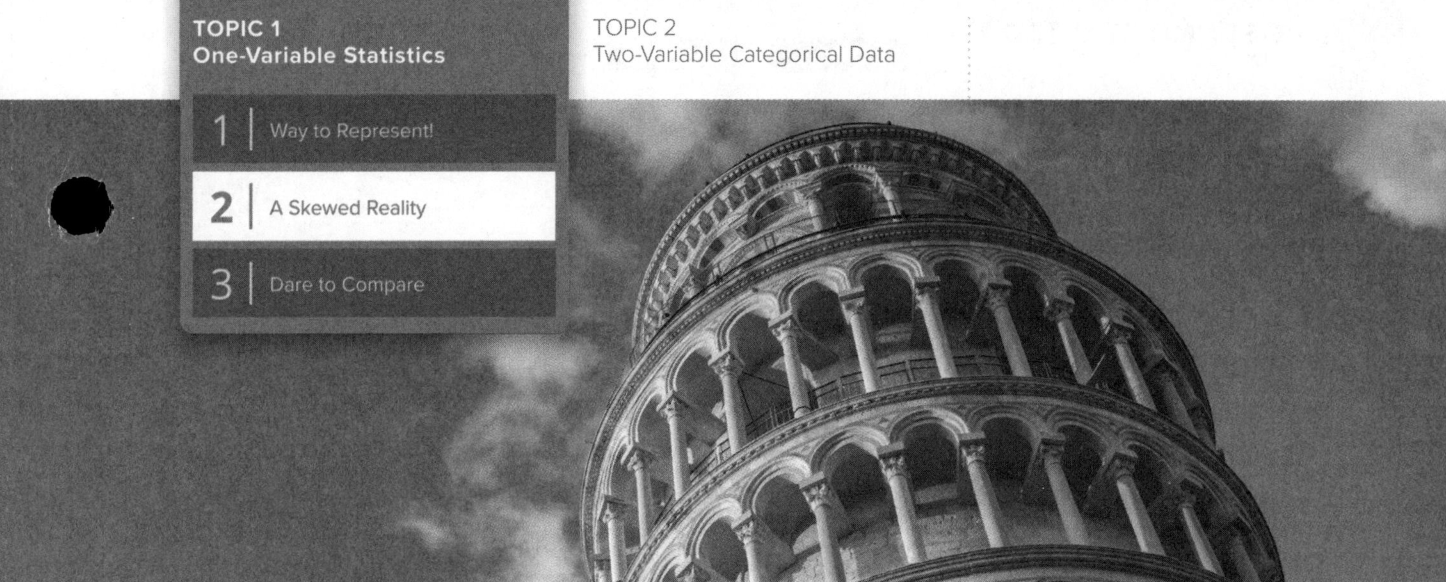

TOPIC 1
One-Variable Statistics
TOPIC 2
Two-Variable Categorical Data
1 | Way to Represent!
2 | A Skewed Reality
3 | Dare to Compare

LESSON 2

A Skewed Reality

Determining the Better Measure of Center and Spread for a Data Set

KEY TERMS

- statistics
- measure of central tendency
- interquartile range (IQR)
- data distribution
- outlier
- lower fence
- upper fence
- standard deviation

Learning Goals

- Calculate and interpret the mean and median of a data set.
- Determine which measure of central tendency is best to use for a data set.
- Calculate and interpret the interquartile range (IQR) of a data set.
- Determine whether a data set contains outliers.
- Calculate and interpret the standard deviation of a data set.
- Determine which measure of spread is best to use for a data set.

REVIEW (1–2 minutes)

> Calculate the mean of each data set.

1. 4, 4, 7, 7, 7, 8, 8, 8, 8, 9, 9, 9, 12, 12

2. 0, 2, 10, 10, 11, 11, 11, 12, 12, 12, 13, 13

3. 40, 60, 60, 70, 70, 70, 80, 80, 100

4. 20, 20, 22, 23, 23, 24, 24, 24, 42, 50

You have displayed and interpreted data sets using the statistical process.

How can you further describe a data set using center, shape, and spread?

© Carnegie Learning, Inc.

Make Your Mark

> Consider each data display.

Heights of Home Team Basketball Players

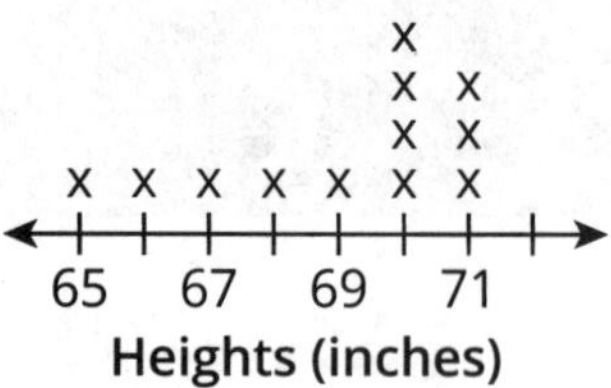

Amount of Grocery Purchases by Customer

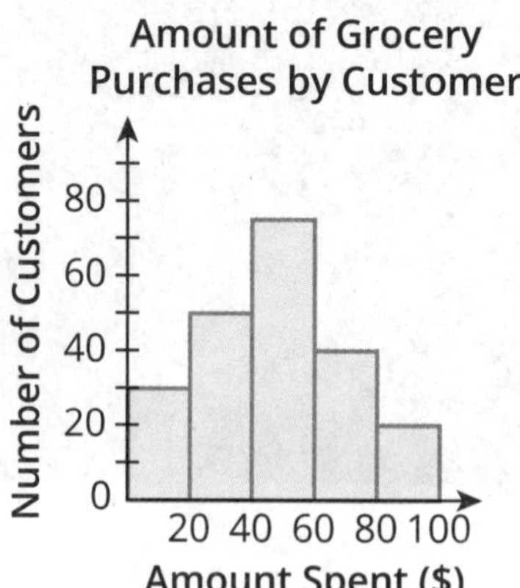

Daily Rainfall Amounts for Seattle April 2017

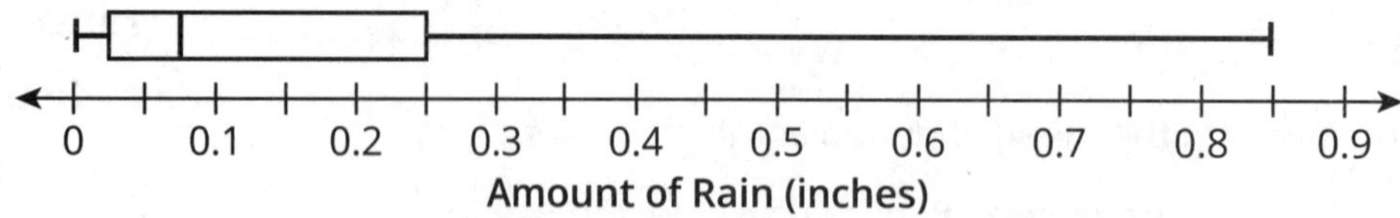

1. Without doing any calculations, predict whether the mean or median will be greater for the data set represented by each display. Indicate your predictions by marking and labeling each measure of center on the number lines of the dot plot and the box-and-whisker plot and within one or more bins of the histogram. **Explain your reasoning.**

© Carnegie Learning, Inc.

MATHia CONNECTION
- Determining Appropriate Measures of Center
- Measuring the Effects of Changing Data Sets

Median and IQR

HABITS OF MIND
- Look for and make use of structure.
- Look for and express regularity in repeated reasoning.

You can analyze a data set by describing numeric characteristics, or **statistics**, of the data. A statistic that describes the center of a data set is a *measure of central tendency*. A **measure of central tendency** is a numeric value that describes the overall clustering of data in a set. Mean and median are two measures of central tendency that you typically use to describe a set of data.

A gym surveys its members about the average number of hours they spend at the gym each week. The dot plot displays the recorded data.

THINK ABOUT . . .
Just as you analyze data presented in a scatter plot to determine which type of regression equation best fits the data, you can analyze data in a display to determine which measure of center best fits the data.

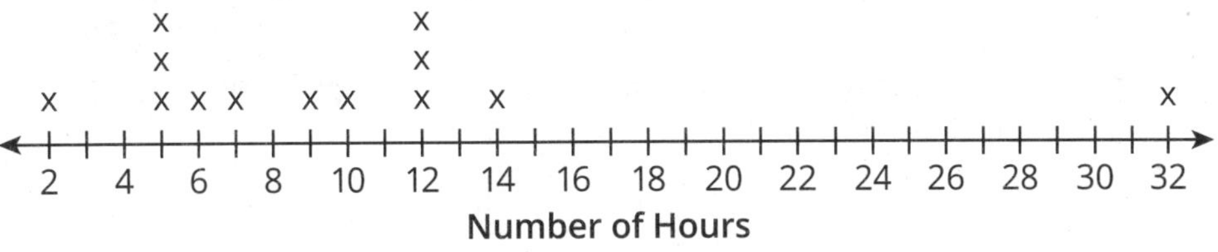

To describe the mean of a data set you need to calculate $\bar{x}$, which you read as "x bar."

WORKED EXAMPLE

This formula represents the mean of a data set.

$$\text{mean} \rightarrow \bar{x} = \frac{\Sigma x}{n}$$

(Σx: the sum of the data values; n: the number of data values)

You can write the mean of the data set 5, 10, 9, 7, 5 using this formula.

$$\bar{x} = \frac{5 + 10 + 9 + 7 + 5}{5}$$

$$\bar{x} = 7.2$$

The mean of this data set is 7.2.

DID YOU KNOW?
The E-like symbol is actually the Greek letter sigma and in mathematical terms it means the "summation" or "sum of."

© Carnegie Learning, Inc.

To describe the median of a data set, determine the middle number in a data set when you place the values in order from least to greatest or greatest to least.

The median of the data set from the Worked Example is 7 because the data in order from least to greatest are 5, 5, 7, 9, 10.

1 Analyze the data collected from the gym members in the dot plot.

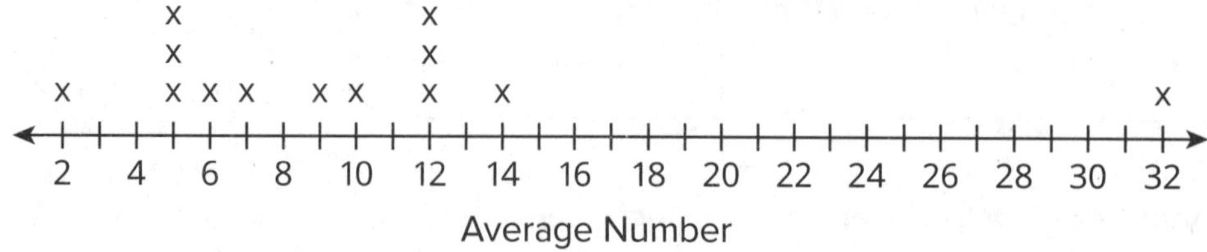

(a) Calculate the five-number summary for the data. Construct a box-and-whisker plot that displays the same data on top of the dot plot.

(b) Calculate the mean of the data. Mark $\bar{x}$ above the point on the number line.

(c) **What do you notice about how the data clusters?**

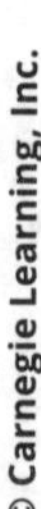

© Carnegie Learning, Inc.

The overall shape of a graph is the **data distribution**. Remember, there are three common distributions of data: skewed left, skewed right, and symmetric. The distribution of data can help you determine whether the mean or median is a better measure of center.

> Examine these diagrams.

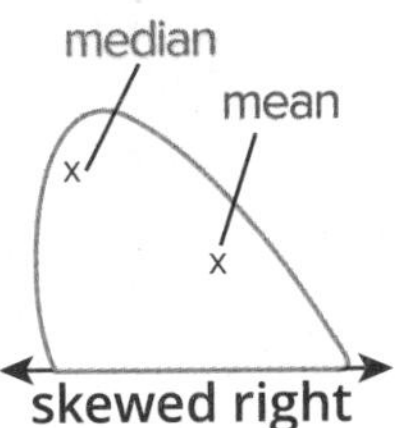

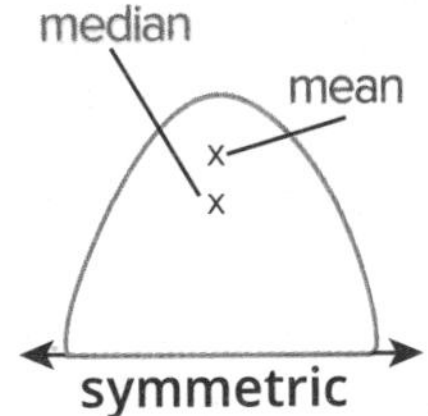

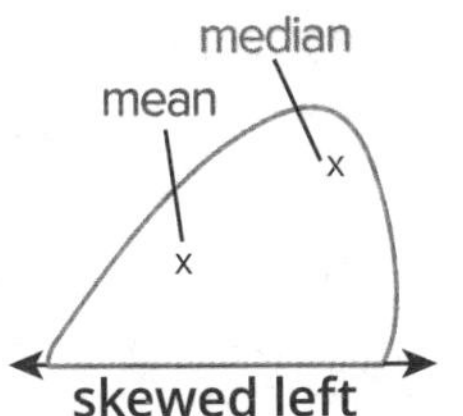

The **mean** of a data set is greater than the **median** when the data are skewed to the right.

The **median** is the best measure of center because very large data values do not affect it.

The **mean** and **median** are approximately equal when the data are symmetric.

The **mean** of a data set is less than the **median** when the data are skewed to the left.

The **median** is the best measure of center because very small data values do not affect it.

2. Which measure of central tendency would you choose to represent the data collected from the gym members? **Explain your reasoning. Then, interpret its meaning in this context.**

Another characteristic to consider when analyzing a graphical display is the spread, or variability, of the data. One common measure of spread is the *interquartile range* or *IQR*. The **interquartile range, IQR**, measures how far the data spread out from the median. You calculate it by subtracting Q3 from Q1 in the five-number summary.

When the median is the better measure of center to use to describe a data set, you should use the IQR to describe the spread. A box-and-whisker plot provides both of these pieces of information.

TAKE NOTE . . .
The IQR is the range of the middle 50% of the data.

3. Calculate the IQR of the data collected from the gym members. **Interpret its meaning in this context.**

© Carnegie Learning, Inc.

Another useful statistic when analyzing data is to determine whether there are any *outliers*. It is important to identify outliers because outliers can often affect the other statistics of the data set, such as the mean.

You identify an outlier by multiplying the IQR by 1.5 and then determining whether any data values are greater or less than that calculated distance away from Q1 or Q3. The value of Q1 − (IQR · 1.5) is the **lower fence** and the value of Q3 + (IQR · 1.5) is the **upper fence**. Any value outside these limits is an outlier.

REMEMBER . . .
An **outlier** is a data value that is significantly greater or lesser than other data values in a data set.

WORKED EXAMPLE

Let's analyze the data collected from the gym members to see how you can represent outliers on a box-and-whisker plot.

2, 5, 5, 5, 6, 7, 9, 10, 12, 12, 12, 14, 32

Given this data set, the five-number summary is:

Minimum = 2, Q1 = 5, Median = 9, Q3 = 12, Maximum = 32

IQR = 7

Using the five-number summary and IQR, calculate the upper and lower fence to determine whether there are any outliers in the data set.

Lower Fence

= Q1 − (IQR • 1.5)

= 5 − (7 · 1.5)

= −5.5

There are no values less than −5.5.

Upper Fence

= Q3 + (IQR • 1.5)

= 12 + (7 · 1.5)

= 22.5

The value 32 is greater than 22.5.

When there are outliers, the whisker will end at the lowest or highest value that is not an outlier.

Since 32 is an outlier, 14 is the greatest data value that is not an outlier.

Once the outlier is removed, the five-number summary is:

Minimum = 2, Q1 = 5, Median = 8, Q3 = 12, Maximum = 14

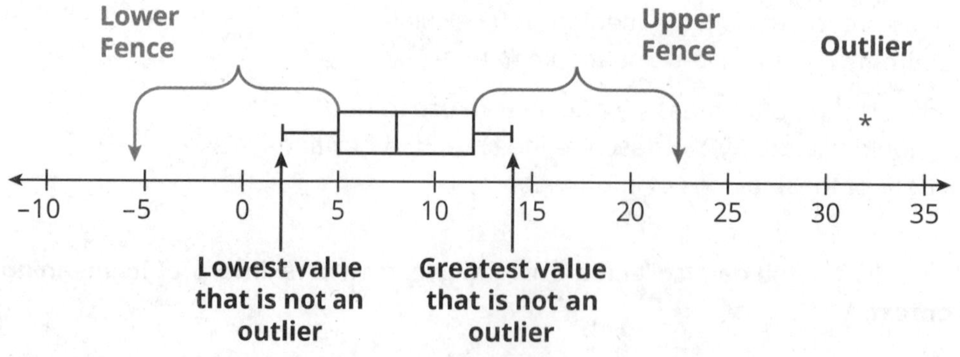

On a box-and-whisker plot, it is common to denote outliers with an asterisk.

© Carnegie Learning, Inc.

4 Recalculate the IQR of the data from Question 1 with the outlier removed.

5 Was the IQR affected by the outlier? **Do you think this is true in all cases?**

© Carnegie Learning, Inc.

Using IQR to Identify Outliers

Identifying and removing outliers from a data set is useful when analyzing and comparing two different data sets.

HABITS OF MIND
- Reason abstractly and quantitatively.
- Construct viable arguments and critique the reasoning of others.

Coach Petersen's Middletown High School football team is struggling to win games this season. He is trying to determine why his team has won only a few times this year. The table shows the points scored in games in 2018 and 2019. The box-and-whisker plots represent and compare the data in the table.

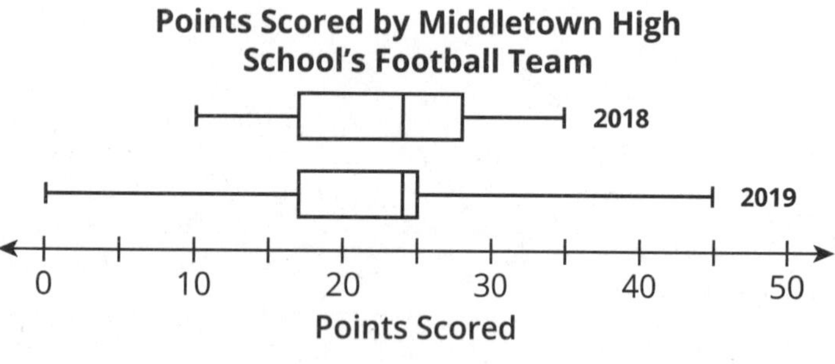

Points Scored (2018)	Points Scored (2019)
10	0
13	7
17	17
20	17
22	18
24	24
24	24
27	24
28	25
29	27
35	45

1 Which year do you think was better in terms of points scored?

2 Calculate and interpret the IQR for the points scored each year. **What does the IQR tell you about which year was better?**

REMEMBER . . .
When one data set appears symmetric and the other appears skewed, you should use the median and IQR to compare both data sets.

© Carnegie Learning, Inc.

3. Remove any outliers for the data sets and, if necessary, reconstruct and label the box-and-whisker plot(s). Compare the IQR of the original data to your new calculations. **What do you notice?**

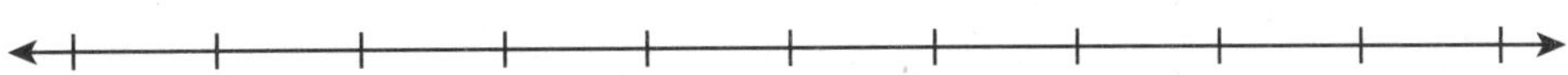

4. Analyze the box-and-whisker plots with the outliers removed and compare the number of points scored each year.

© Carnegie Learning, Inc.

Mean and Standard Deviation

HABIT OF MIND
• Attend to precision.

You have learned about the spread of data values from the median, or the IQR. When you know the mean of a data set, you can calculate the spread using *standard deviation*. **Standard deviation** is a measure of how spread out the data are from the mean.

Ms. Webb is determining which student she should add to the spelling bee roster that will represent Tyler High School. The table shows the 10 most recent scores for three students.

The box-and-whisker plots display each of the student's spelling bee scores.

Jack	Aleah	Tymar
33	20	5
32	42	10
30	45	12
50	51	40
49	49	45
50	47	55
35	58	88
73	53	60
71	55	90
77	80	95

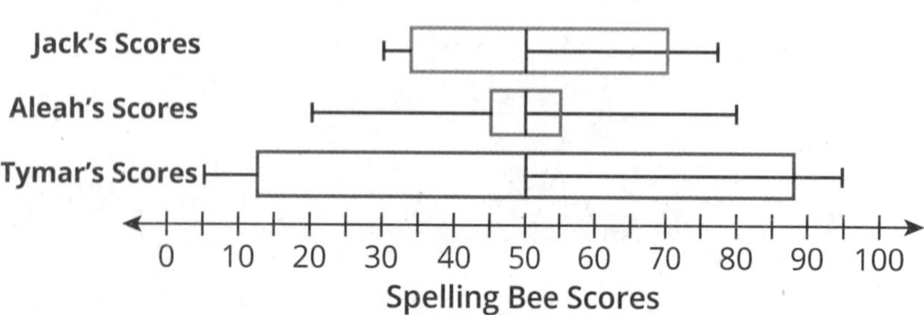

1 Describe the shape of each student's data set.

The formula to determine the standard deviation of a sample of a population is:

$$s = \sqrt{\frac{\sum_{i=1}^{n}(x_i - \bar{x})^2}{n-1}}$$

where s is the standard deviation, x_i represents each individual data value, $\bar{x}$ represents the mean of the data set, and n is the number of data points.

Let's look at each part of the standard deviation formula separately.

DID YOU KNOW?
The reason why $n - 1$ is used in the formula is that statisticians have determined that it calculates a statistic that more closely represents the population.

© Carnegie Learning, Inc.

WORKED EXAMPLE

Follow the steps to determine the standard deviation.
Let's use the data set 6, 4, 10, 8, where $\bar{x} = 7$.

First, think of each data value as its own term labeled as x_1, x_2, and so on.

$x_1 = 6$ $x_3 = 10$

$x_2 = 4$ $x_4 = 8$

The first part of the formula identifies the terms you add. Since n represents the total number of values and $i = 1$, add all the values that result from substituting in the first term to the fourth term.

$$\sum_{i=1}^{n}$$

Next, evaluate the expressions you are adding. Subtract $\bar{x}$ from each term and then square each difference.

$(x_1 - \bar{x})^2$

$(6 - 7)^2 = 1$

$(4 - 7)^2 = 9$

$(10 - 7)^2 = 9$

$(8 - 7)^2 = 1$

Now, determine the sum of the squared values and divide the sum by the number one fewer than the number of data values.

$$\frac{1 + 9 + 9 + 1}{4 - 1} = \frac{20}{3} \approx 6.7$$

Finally, calculate the square root of the quotient.

$s = \sqrt{6.7}$

$s \approx 2.6$

So, the standard deviation for the given data set is approximately 2.6. It is important to note that when the data values have a unit of measure, the standard deviation of the data set also uses the same unit of measure.

2. Do you think the standard deviation for each student's spelling bee scores will be the same? **If yes, explain your reasoning. If no, predict who will have a higher or lower standard deviation.**

THINK ABOUT . . .
The whole purpose of statistics is to make sense of a population using a sample. What is the sample in Ms. Webb's data and what is the population?

© Carnegie Learning, Inc.

When the mean is the better measure of center to use to describe a data set, you should use the standard deviation to describe the spread. Each student's data set shows a symmetric distribution, so the mean is the better measure of center. Therefore, the standard deviation is the better measure to use to describe the spread.

3 Use the standard deviation formula to determine the standard deviation of Jack's spelling bee scores.

(a) Determine the $\bar{x}$ value.

(b) Complete the table. The data values have been put in ascending order.

x_i	$x_i - \bar{x}$	$(x_i - \bar{x})^2$
30		
32		
33		
35		
40		
50		
50		
71		
73		
77		
Sum		

THINK ABOUT . . .

The mean represents the balance point of the data values in the set. What sum should you expect to get when you add all the values for $x_i - \bar{x}$?

(c) Determine the standard deviation for Jack's spelling bee scores and interpret the meaning.

© Carnegie Learning, Inc.

4 Complete each table for Aleah's and Tymar's spelling bee scores.

(a) Aleah

x_i	$x_i - \bar{x}$	$(x_i - \bar{x})^2$
20		
42		
45		
47		
49		
51		
53		
55		
58		
80		
Sum		

(b) Tymar

x_i	$x_i - \bar{x}$	$(x_i - \bar{x})^2$
5		
10		
12		
40		
45		
55		
60		
88		
90		
95		
Sum		

TOPIC 1

5 Determine the standard deviation of Aleah's and Tymar's spelling bee scores.

6 Was the prediction you made in Question 2 correct? What do the standard deviations tell you about each student's spelling bee scores?

REMEMBER . . .

To calculate the standard deviation:

- Calculate the mean of the data set.
- Calculate the deviations from the mean.
- Add the squared deviations.
- Divide by $n - 1$.
- Take the square root.

7 Which student do you think Ms. Webb should add to the spelling bee roster? **Use the mean and standard deviation for the student you recommend to add to the roster to justify your answer.**

© Carnegie Learning, Inc.

Interpreting Standard Deviation

> Use what you have learned about standard deviation to answer each question.

HABITS OF MIND

- Reason abstractly and quantitatively.
- Construct viable arguments and critique the reasoning of others.

The Mountain View High School basketball team has its first game of the season, and Coach Maynard is comparing the heights of the home team's top 10 players to the heights of the visiting team's top 10 players. The dot plots of the data are given.

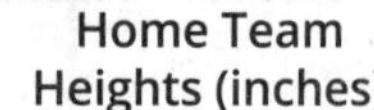

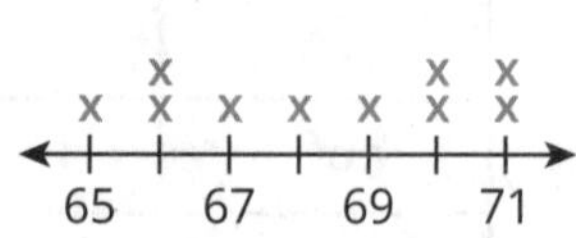

Visiting Team
Heights (inches)

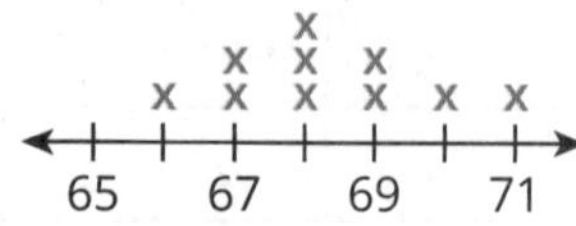

1. Predict which team has the greater standard deviation in their heights. **Explain how you determined your answer.**

2. Determine the standard deviation of the heights of each team. Describe what this means in terms of this problem situation. **How does this information help Coach Maynard?**

TAKE NOTE . . .

You can use technology to calculate the standard deviation of the data values for the sample of the population.

© Carnegie Learning, Inc.

Data on Display

> Consider the dot plot from the Getting Started.

1. Calculate the mean and median heights for the basketball players on the home team. Was your prediction correct?

> Consider the histogram from the Getting Started.

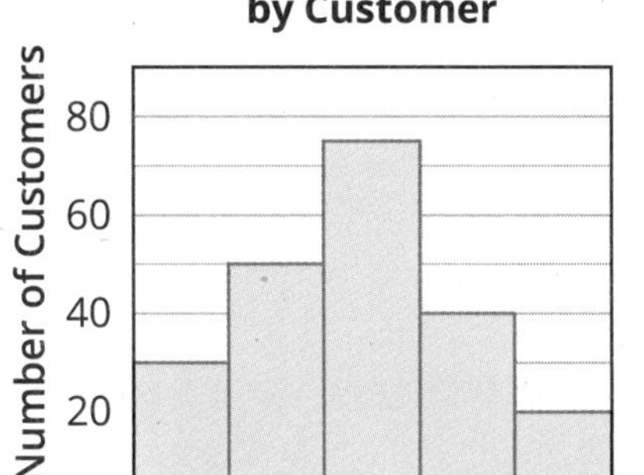

2. The mean of the data set is 51, and the median of the data set is 50. How do these values compare to your prediction?

© Carnegie Learning, Inc.

> Consider the box-and-whisker plot from the Getting Started.

Daily Rainfall Amounts for Seattle April 2017

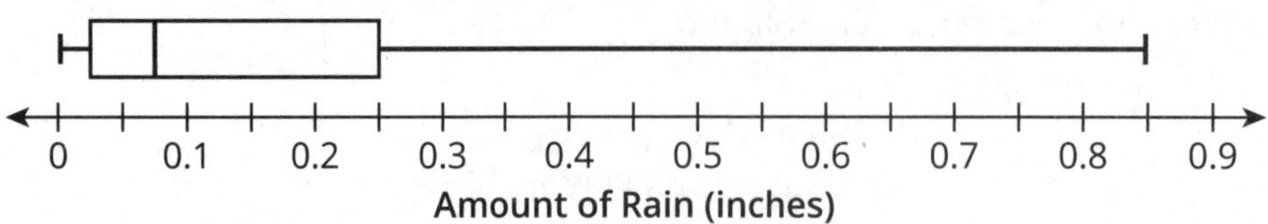

3 The median of the data set is 0.07, and the mean of the data set is 0.16. How do these values compare to your prediction?

4 Determine which measure of center and which measure of spread are most appropriate to use to describe each data set. **Explain your reasoning.**

5 How do you know which measure of center and measure of spread is most appropriate for a given data set?

© Carnegie Learning, Inc.

LESSON 2 ASSIGNMENT

> Use a separate piece of paper for your Journal entry.

REMEMBER

- The median is the better measure of central tendency, and the IQR is the better measure of spread to use to describe a data set that is skewed.
- The mean is the better measure of central tendency, and the standard deviation is the better measure of spread to use to describe a data set that is symmetric.
- You identify outliers in a data set using the formula Q1 − (IQR·1.5) to determine a lower fence and Q3 + (IQR·1.5) to determine an upper fence. Any value outside these limits is an outlier.

JOURNAL

> Match each definition to its corresponding term.

1. interquartile range (IQR)
2. standard deviation
3. lower fence
4. upper fence
5. statistic
6. measure of central tendency
7. outlier

(a) A value calculated using the formula Q1 − (IQR·1.5)
(b) Numeric characteristics of a data set
(c) A value that is much greater or lesser than other values in a data set
(d) A value calculated using the formula Q3 + (IQR·1.5)
(e) Measure of spread from the mean
(f) A value used to describe the overall clustering of data in a set
(g) A measure of spread from the median

PRACTICE

1. Consider each data set. Calculate the median, mean, IQR, and standard deviation of each set. Then, determine which measure of central tendency and which measure of spread is the most appropriate to use to describe the data set. Explain your reasoning.

   (a) 1, 2, 2, 4, 8, 8, 8, 9, 9, 9, 10, 10, 10

   (b) 5, 5, 6, 6, 6, 7, 7, 7, 8, 8, 8, 9, 9

© Carnegie Learning, Inc.

   (c) 0, 1, 2, 10, 12, 12, 16, 16, 16, 16, 18, 18, 20

   (d) 2, 2, 2, 3, 3, 4, 4, 8, 9, 9, 10, 10, 10

Go to LiveHint.com for help on the PRACTICE questions.

2 The five-number summaries for the average monthly precipitation in millimeters during the summer for the Western and Midwestern states are provided.

West	Midwest
Min = 7	Min = 68
Q1 = 22	Q1 = 81.5
Med = 33	Med = 99.5
Q3 = 49	Q3 = 102.5
Max = 107	Max = 111

ⓐ Construct box-and-whisker plots of each area's monthly precipitation using the same number line for each.

ⓑ Describe the distribution of both box-and-whisker plots and explain what they mean in terms of the problem situation.

ⓒ Determine whether there are outliers in either data set. Show your work and explain how you determined your answer.

ⓓ Chen is considering a long camping trip this summer and hopes to avoid the rain. Would you recommend that he camp in the West or the Midwest? Explain your reasoning.

© Carnegie Learning, Inc.

STRETCH Optional

1 Create a data set of 15 numbers where the mean and median are both 59 and the standard deviation is between 10 and 11. Then, add an outlier to your data set. How are the mean and standard deviation affected?

LESSON 3

Dare to Compare

Comparing Data Sets

Learning Goals

- Compare the standard deviation of data sets.
- Analyze and interpret data graphically and numerically.
- Determine which measure of central tendency and spread is most appropriate to describe a data set.

REVIEW (1–2 minutes)

> Determine whether the distribution of each data set is symmetric, skewed left, or skewed right.

1. 4, 4, 7, 7, 7, 8, 8, 8, 8, 9, 9, 9, 12, 12

2. 0, 2, 10, 10, 11, 11, 11, 12, 12, 12, 13, 13

3. 40, 60, 60, 70, 70, 70, 80, 80, 100

4. 20, 20, 22, 23, 23, 24, 24, 24, 42, 50

© Carnegie Learning, Inc.

You know how to determine the most appropriate measure of center and spread to describe a data set based on its distribution.

How can you use what you know to compare data sets in problem situations?

Stats on Cats

The Humane Society records the number of different visits from potential families a sample of 25 cats from each of their two locations received before being adopted. The box-and-whisker plots display the collected data.

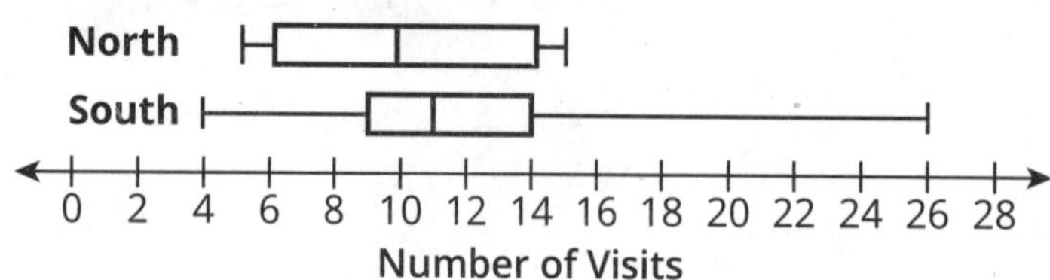

1 Yumi, Mia, and Sloane are trying to determine which shelter's cats receive fewer visits before being adopted. Yumi says the mean and standard deviation of the data for the North shelter should be compared to the median and IQR of the data from the South shelter. Mia says the median and IQR of the data from each shelter should be compared. Sloane says the mean and standard deviation of the data from each shelter should be compared. Who's correct? **Explain your reasoning.**

© Carnegie Learning, Inc.

ACTIVITY 1

MATHia CONNECTION

- Comparing and Interpreting Measures of Center
- Comparing Data Sets Using Center and Spread

Comparing Students

Let's compare the center and spread of two data sets to analyze a real-world situation.

HABITS OF MIND

- Reason abstractly and quantitatively.
- Construct viable arguments and critique the reasoning of others.

Ms. Webb, the spelling bee coach, prepares her class for their first spelling bee scrimmage. She needs to determine which student should be the spelling bee captain.

The table shows the two top spelling bee students' scores. Ms. Webb analyzes the scores and calculates the approximate mean score and standard deviation for each student.

1. Advise Ms. Webb whom she should choose to captain the spelling bee team. **Explain your reasoning**.

Maria	Heidi
81	81
73	68
94	60
86	109
70	82
68	88
97	60
93	102
81	78
67	69
85	84
77	103
79	92
103	60
90	108

© Carnegie Learning, Inc.

Comparing Airlines

You may need to analyze the distribution of two different data sets before you can compare them.

HABITS OF MIND

- Reason abstractly and quantitatively.
- Construct viable arguments and critique the reasoning of others.

A travel website collected data from two rival airlines measuring the difference in the stated departure times and the times the flights actually departed. It recorded the average departure time differences for each month for one year as shown in the table.

1 You are scheduling a flight for an important meeting and you must be there on time. Which airline would you schedule with? **Explain your reasoning**.

Differences in Departure Times (minutes)	
My Air Airlines	**Fly High Airlines**
26	14
15	32
40	29
0	8
20	24
33	45
20	7
5	30
19	15
34	49
11	16
33	27

© Carnegie Learning, Inc.

Comparing Garages

You may need to identify outliers before comparing two data sets.

HABITS OF MIND

- Reason abstractly and quantitatively.
- Construct viable arguments and critique the reasoning of others.

Brenda needs to get the oil changed in her car, but she hates to wait! Quick Change and Speedy Oil are two garages near Brenda's house. She decides to check an online site that allows customers to comment on the service at different local businesses and record their wait times. Brenda chooses 12 customers at random for each garage. This table consists of wait times for each garage.

Wait Times (minutes)	
Quick Change	**Speedy Oil**
10 60 22 15	5 60 45 24
12 24 20 18	40 26 55 30
16 23 22 15	32 85 45 30

1. Based on the data gathered, which garage should Brenda choose when she is in a hurry?

© Carnegie Learning, Inc.

Which Came First—the Data or the Display?

1. Analyze these box-and-whisker plots.

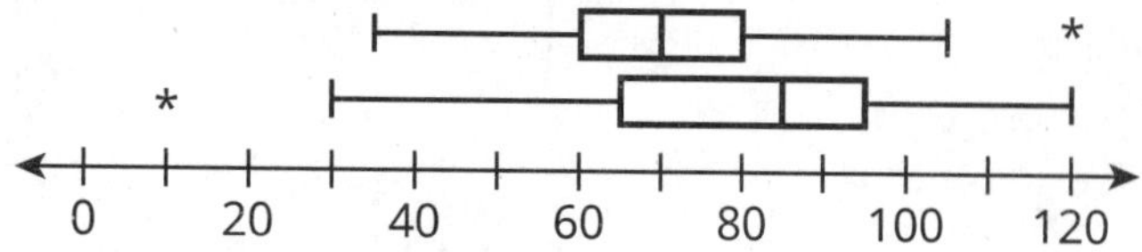

(a) Create a possible data set for each box-and-whisker plot.

(b) Create a possible scenario that compares the two data sets.

(c) Write at least two questions that you can answer using your scenario and data sets.

2. A data set ranges from 10 to 20. You add a value of 50 to the data set.

(a) Explain how the new value affects the mean and median.

(b) Which measure of central tendency and spread would you use to describe the original data set before you added the new value? **Explain your reasoning.**

(c) Which measure of central tendency and spread would you use to describe the data set after you add the new value? **Explain your reasoning.**

© Carnegie Learning, Inc.

LESSON 3 ASSIGNMENT

> Use a separate piece of paper for your Journal entry.

JOURNAL

Describe in your own words how to compare two data sets.

REMEMBER

When comparing two data sets, when at least one of the data sets is skewed, you should use the median and IQR to compare the data.

PRACTICE

1. Dannette and Alphonso work for a computer repair company. They must include the time it takes to complete each repair in their repair log book. The dot plots show the number of hours each of their last 12 repairs took.

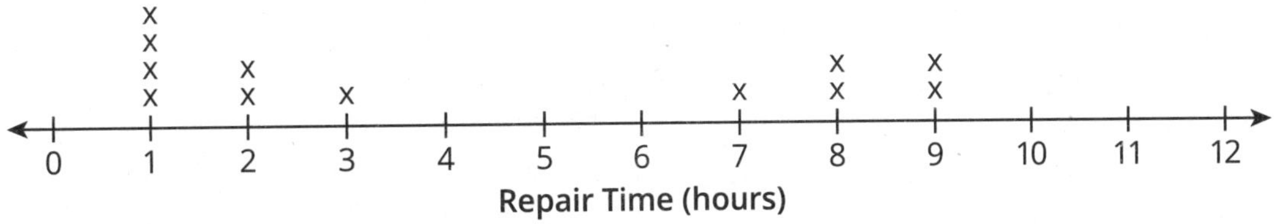

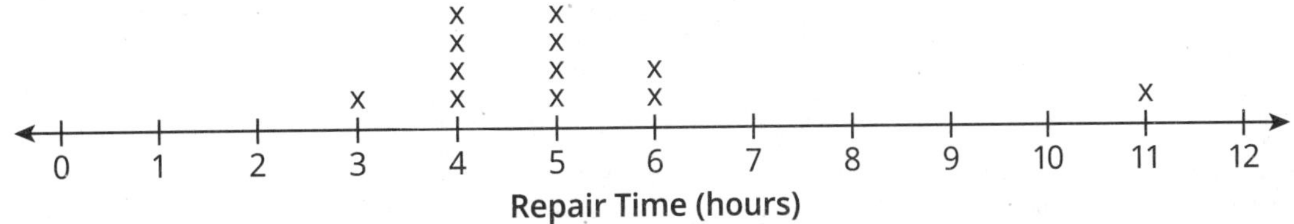

   a. Calculate the median, mean, IQR, and standard deviation of each data set.

   b. Which measure of central tendency and spread should you use to compare the two data sets? Explain your reasoning.

© Carnegie Learning, Inc.

Go to LiveHint.com for help on the PRACTICE questions.

(c) Determine whether there are any outliers in either data set and recalculate the IQR, if necessary.

(d) Which repair person would you ask to fix your computer when you are in a hurry to have it repaired? Explain your reasoning.

STRETCH Optional

A normal curve is a bell-shaped curve that is symmetric about the mean of the data.

Normal curves *A*, *B*, and *C* represent the battery lives of a population of cell phones of comparable models from three different companies. The normal curves represent distributions with standard deviations of 0.1, 0.4, and 0.5.

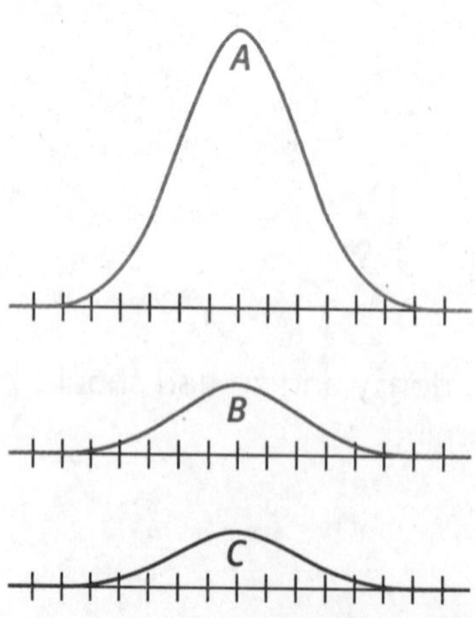

1 Match each standard deviation value with one of the normal curves and explain your reasoning.

© Carnegie Learning, Inc.

MIXED PRACTICE

> This Mixed Practice worksheet includes two sections: Spaced Review and End-of-Topic Review. **Use a separate piece of paper to show your work.**

Spaced Review

> Practice concepts from previous topics.

1. Rewrite the expression $(\sqrt[6]{16})^5$ using a rational exponent.

2. Rewrite the expression $7^{\frac{3}{4}}$ using a radical.

3. Solve each system of linear equations.

   a. $\begin{cases} 2x - 3y = 4 \\ 4x + y = 8 \end{cases}$

   b. $\begin{cases} -5x + 6y = 10 \\ 2x - 3y = 15 \end{cases}$

4. Solve each equation for x.

   a. $8^{3x} = 262{,}144$

   b. $2^{-x} = 1{,}048{,}576$

5. A home recently experienced an infestation of insects. The table displays the insect population over time. Write the function that represents the insect population over time.

Day	Number of Insects
1	240
2	360
3	540
4	810

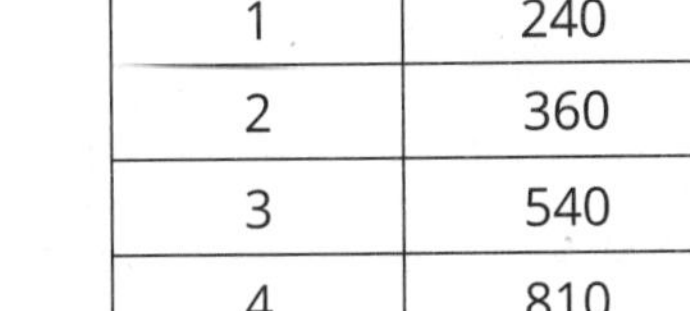

6. Write a function, $h(x)$, and sketch a graph that is translated 2 units down from $f(x) = -3^x$ and is a reflection of $f(x) = -3^x$ across the line $x = 0$.

7. Patrick recorded the number of emails he sent over two weeks: 11, 5, 6, 9, 10, 5, 4, 2, 9, 10. What is the median of his data?

8. Given $f(x) = |x|$.

   a. Sketch the graph of $g(x) = f(x - 2)$.

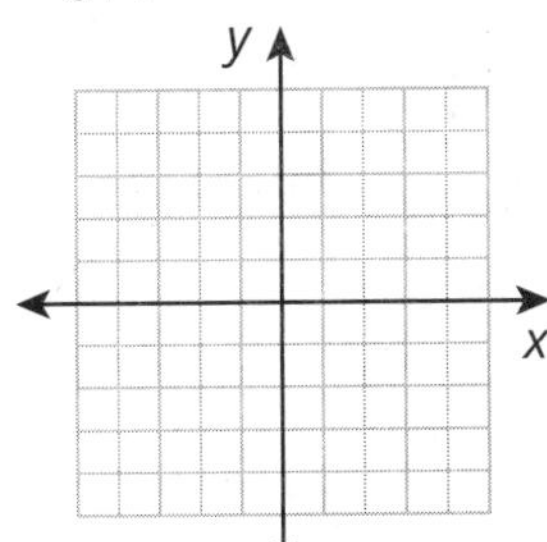

   b. Sketch the graph of $h(x) = -2f(x + 3) + 5$.

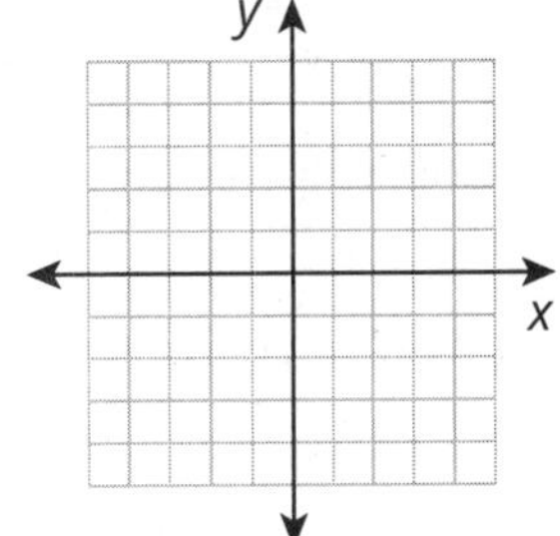

© Carnegie Learning, Inc.

End-of-Topic Review

AVAILABLE ONLINE
1. A **Topic Summary** reviews the main concepts for the topic.
2. A video of the **Worked Example** is provided.

> Practice concepts you learned in *One-Variable Statistics*.

9 This is a list of seconds it takes swimmers to swim 50 yards freestyle.

29, 27, 28, 24, 32, 30, 28, 29, 32, 26, 34, 30, 25, 27, 30, 29, 25, 28, 29, 32

(a) Construct a box-and-whisker plot based on the list of swimmers' times.

(b) What does the distribution of the box-and-whisker plot mean in terms of the swimmers' times?

10 Consider the data set: 6, 7, 7, 10, 12, 16, 16, 17, 20, 22, 22, 22, 23, 24, 24, 24, 24, 24, 25, 40.

(a) What is the five-number summary and the IQR for the data set?

(b) Are there outliers for the data set? If so, what are they?

11 A group of 45 adults were asked how many times they dined out the previous week. The dot plot displays the responses.

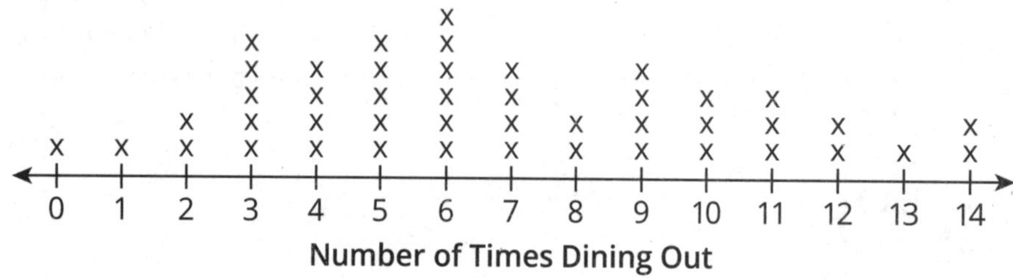

(a) Describe the distribution of the dot plot.

(b) How do you think the mean and median of the data set compare? Explain your reasoning.

(c) Calculate the mean and median. Explain what they mean in terms of the problem situation.

(d) Which measure of center do you think best represents these data? Explain your reasoning.

12 The five-number summaries for the heights in inches of male soccer and basketball players for a school district are provided.

Players	Min	Q1	Med	Q3	Max
Soccer	61	63	66	68	71
Basketball	65	69	71	73	78

(a) Construct box-and-whisker plots of each type of player's heights using a single number line.

(b) Describe each distribution and explain what they mean in terms of the problem situation.

(c) Determine whether there are outliers in either data set. Explain how you determined your answer.

© Carnegie Learning, Inc.

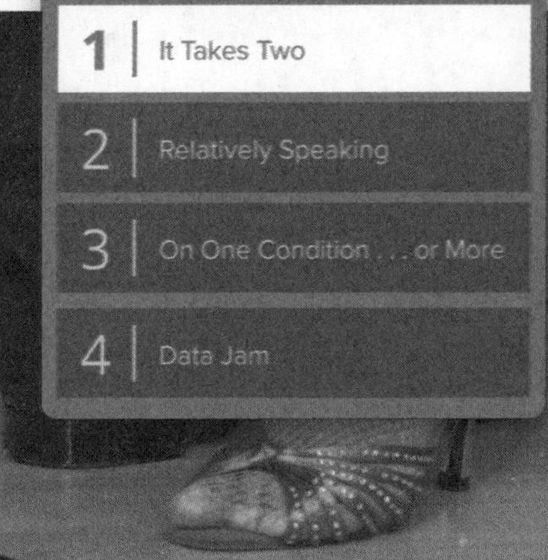

TOPIC 2
Two-Variable Categorical Data
1 It Takes Two
2 Relatively Speaking
3 On One Condition . . . or More
4 Data Jam

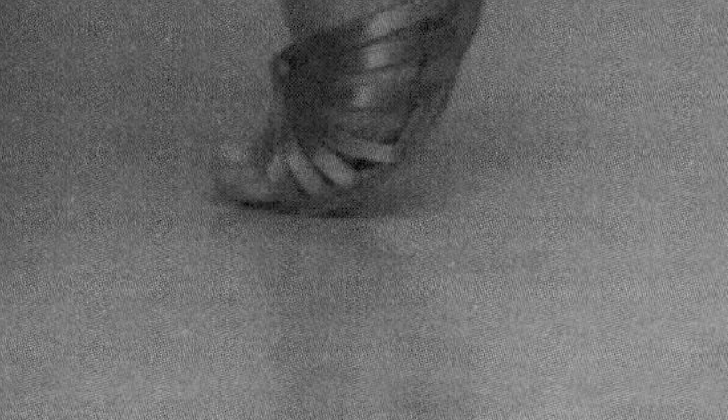

LESSON 1

It Takes Two

Creating and Interpreting Frequency Distributions

KEY TERMS

- categorical data
- two-way frequency table
- frequency distribution
- joint frequency
- marginal frequency distribution

Learning Goals

- Construct and interpret frequency and marginal frequency distributions displayed in two-way tables for two-variable categorical data.
- Create and interpret graphs of frequency distributions displayed in two-way tables.

REVIEW (1–2 minutes)

> Create a bar graph to display the data in the frequency table.

Favorite School Subjects in Mr. Luft's Class	
Subject	**Frequency**
Math	𝍸 |||
History	||||
Science	𝍸 |
Art	𝍸 ||

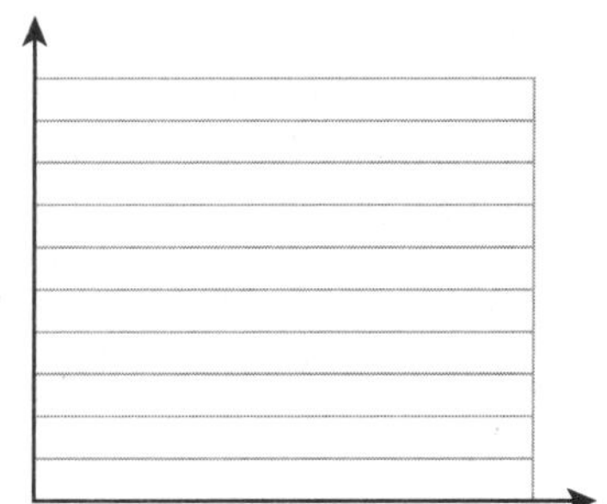

© Carnegie Learning, Inc.

You have explored the relationship between two variables of numeric data.

How can you determine whether there are any associations between two variables of categorical data?

Survey Says . . .

Recall that the first step of the statistical process is to formulate a question. A statistical question anticipates an answer based on data that vary.

> Cut out the survey questions located on page 621. Read each question and consider how you and other people might answer it. Sort the questions into groups based on the types of answers that could be given for each.

GETTING STARTED CUTOUTS

Survey Questions

A How many pets do you own?	B What is your favorite color?
C What is your favorite sport?	D What score did you earn on the last math test?
E How many texts do you send per day?	F What type of music do you prefer?
G How many glasses of water do you drink each day?	H How far do you live from school in miles?
I What is your favorite snack?	J How many hours do you watch television per day?
K What mascot would you prefer for a sports team?	L Which grade are you in?

© Carnegie Learning, Inc.

Lesson 1 > It Takes Two 13

1 Record your groups and the questions in each group.

2 What observations can you make about the types of data that you can collect using the questions?

Two types of variable data that you can collect from a statistical question are numeric and *categorical data*. **Categorical data** are data that you can group into categories. Numeric data are data that you can place on a numeric scale and compare.

3 For the survey questions that have categorical answers, is there a way to group the data collected by the question into more than one category? **Explain your reasoning.**

© Carnegie Learning, Inc.

Categorical Data in Two Variables

In this activity, you will analyze categorical data recorded in a data table.

HABITS OF MIND
- Reason abstractly and quantitatively.
- Construct viable arguments and critique the reasoning of others.

Ms. Seymour is the school cafeteria supervisor at Williams High School. She has been asked to cut her food budget for the upcoming school year. One idea she has is to cut the number of meal choices during the week. Ms. Seymour decides to survey the students in Mr. Kolbe's gym class, which consists of 9th- and 10th-graders. She recorded the results of her survey in this table.

Grade	Favorite Meal	Grade	Favorite Meal	Grade	Favorite Meal
9	Salad bar	10	Pizza	10	Salad bar
10	Burgers	9	Salad bar	9	Burgers
10	Pizza	9	Burgers	9	Pizza
10	Chicken nuggets	10	Burgers	10	Chicken nuggets
10	Chicken nuggets	9	Chicken nuggets	10	Salad bar
9	Burgers	9	Salad bar	9	Salad bar
10	Salad bar	10	Chicken nuggets	10	Pizza
9	Salad bar	10	Chicken nuggets	9	Pizza
10	Chicken nuggets	10	Salad bar	10	Chicken nuggets
9	Burgers	10	Burgers	9	Pizza

The first step of the statistical process is to formulate a statistical question. The second step is to collect the data.

1. Consider the table.

   a. What type of collection method did Ms. Seymour use?

   b. What questions did she ask the students?

© Carnegie Learning, Inc.

(c) Describe the data she collected as either numeric or categorical. **Explain your reasoning.**

The third step of the statistical process is to analyze the data.

2. Analyze Ms. Seymour's data table. Can you see any trends in the data just by looking at her data table? **Explain why or why not.**

© Carnegie Learning, Inc.

Frequency Distribution Tables

HABITS OF MIND
- Reason abstractly and quantitatively.
- Construct viable arguments and critique the reasoning of others.

Previously, you analyzed two-variable data sets that were quantitative, or numeric. You displayed those as a scatter plot and modeled them with a regression curve. In this topic, you will explore the relationship between two-variable data sets that are qualitative, or categorical.

One method of organizing categorical data is to use a *two-way frequency table*. A **two-way frequency table** displays categorical data by representing the number of occurrences that fall into each group for two variables. The table divides one variable into rows and the other into columns.

TAKE NOTE . . .
Categorical data are the same as qualitative data.

> Consider the favorite meal data collected by Ms. Seymour in the previous activity.

1. The first variable is the grade level. Identify the groups for this variable.

REMEMBER . . .
There is a difference between the variables in a data set and the groups in a data set.

2. The second variable is the favorite meal. Identify the groups for this variable.

© Carnegie Learning, Inc.

The third step of the statistical process is to analyze the data numerically and graphically. Creating a two-way frequency table helps to organize the data set so that you can analyze it numerically.

Grade	Favorite Meal
9	Salad bar
10	Burgers
10	Pizza
10	Chicken nuggets
10	Chicken nuggets
9	Burgers
10	Salad bar
9	Salad bar
10	Chicken nuggets
9	Burgers
10	Pizza
9	Salad bar
9	Burgers
10	Burgers
9	Chicken nuggets
9	Salad bar
10	Chicken nuggets
10	Chicken nuggets
10	Salad bar
10	Burgers
10	Salad bar
9	Burgers
9	Pizza
10	Chicken nuggets
10	Salad bar
9	Salad bar
10	Pizza
9	Pizza
10	Chicken nuggets
9	Pizza

3 Create a two-way frequency table of the data.

(a) Enter the name of each group.

Favorite Meals of Students

Grade Level

(b) Record the favorite meal for each student in the appropriate row using tally marks. Then, write the frequency of each meal for each grade level.

4 Are there any associations between grade level and favorite meal? **If so, explain what trends you think exist in these data.**

The table you created is a *frequency distribution*. A **frequency distribution** displays the frequencies for categorical data in a two-way table. Each time you determined the frequency of one favorite meal of one of the grade levels, you recorded a *joint frequency*. Any frequency you record within the body of a two-way frequency table is known as a **joint frequency**.

A two-way frequency table is helpful in organizing each group's frequency in an efficient way. However, it is common to determine the total number of people surveyed just to ensure that a good survey was taken. Determining this total is also helpful to ensure that you recorded the data accurately within the table. For example, if you know 50 people took part in the survey, and the sum of the joint frequencies is 47, then you know that you are missing three data points from the data set.

© Carnegie Learning, Inc.

5 Use the data from your frequency distribution to determine the total number of 9th-graders and 10th-graders, and to determine the total number of frequencies for each favorite meal category.

Favorite Meals of Students

Grade Level		Burgers	Chicken Nuggets	Pizza	Salad Bar	Total
	9th grade					
	10th grade					
	Total					

You just created a *marginal frequency distribution* of the data by determining the totals for each group.

TAKE NOTE . . .

A **marginal frequency distribution** displays the total of the frequencies of the rows or columns of a frequency distribution.

6 Analyze the marginal frequency distribution to answer each question.

(a) How many 9th-graders participated in the survey?

(b) How many students prefer burgers?

(c) How many students prefer chicken nuggets?

(d) How many 10th-graders participated in the survey?

(e) How many students prefer the salad bar?

© Carnegie Learning, Inc.

7 How can you use the totals to determine whether you correctly created the frequency distribution?

8 Use the marginal frequency distribution to answer each question.

(a) Which meal did the least number of students say was their favorite meal?

(b) Which meal did the least number of 9th-grade students say was their favorite meal?

(c) Which meal is the most favorite of all students?

(d) Which meal is the most favorite of the 10th-graders?

© Carnegie Learning, Inc.

Representing Data

While a two-way table shows a numeric summary of the data, a graph can help relay information about a survey in a visual way. Remember, every graph tells a story.

HABITS OF MIND
- Reason abstractly and quantitatively.
- Construct viable arguments and critique the reasoning of others.

Recall that Ms. Seymour is trying to determine ways to cut the cafeteria budget for the upcoming school year. She would like to use a graph to visually display the ideas she has for cutting the cafeteria budget.

> Consider the frequency distribution table that organizes the data Ms. Seymour gathered.

Favorite Meals of Students

Grade Level	Burgers	Chicken Nuggets	Pizza	Salad Bar
9th grade	4	1	3	5
10th grade	3	7	3	4

1. Analyze the frequency distribution table.

   (a) Determine which graphical display(s) would be appropriate to represent Ms. Seymour's data. **Justify your response.**

THINK ABOUT . . .
You are still completing the third step of the statistical process, but now you are analyzing the data graphically by creating a display.

   (b) Determine which graphical displays are not appropriate to represent Ms. Seymour's data. **Justify your response.**

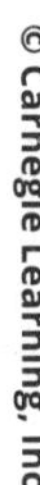
© Carnegie Learning, Inc.

2 Construct two bar graphs of the frequencies. Be sure to include a key to identify what each bar represents.

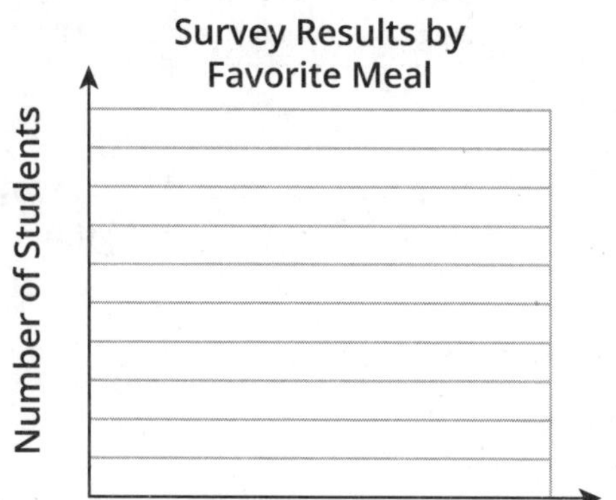

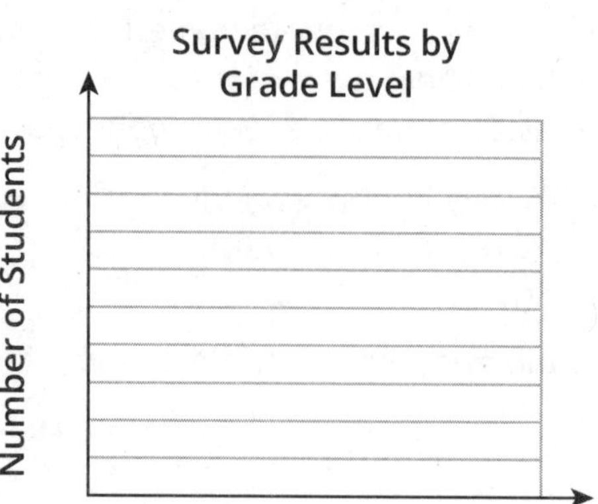

3 What conclusions can you draw by examining the graphs?

4 Use the graphs to determine whether you represented the data from the frequency distribution table accurately. **Explain how you verified that the data in the graphs match the data in the frequency distribution table.**

5 Does it matter which graph Ms. Seymour's uses to display her survey data? **Explain your reasoning.**

© Carnegie Learning, Inc.

Ms. Seymour must decide on a plan for the upcoming school year. The principal of the school would like Ms. Seymour to present her data and a graph to justify her decision to cut costs.

6 Which meal choice would you cut, according to the data? **Explain why you would discontinue that meal choice and which graph you would recommend Ms. Seymour use when she presents her plan.**

REMEMBER . . .
The fourth step of the statistical process is to interpret the data.

Ms. Seymour just thought of an idea, and she thinks it will help cut the cafeteria costs. She is recommending that the school create two lunch periods—one for the 9th-graders and one for the 10th-graders. She thinks that if two lunch periods exist, she can keep all four meal choices, but just cook a lesser amount of certain choices.

7 Do you think Ms. Seymour should present this idea to the principal? **Use the data to justify your reasoning.**

© Carnegie Learning, Inc.

8 Which graph would you recommend Ms. Seymour use to justify her solution? **Explain your reasoning.**

Frequent Favorites

An art teacher asks his students to state their favorite season and their favorite color. The results are displayed in the table.

Favorite Season	Favorite Color
Summer	red
Winter	blue
Spring	blue
Fall	red
Spring	green
Winter	blue
Fall	red
Summer	red
Summer	green
Spring	green
Summer	red
Winter	blue
Summer	red
Fall	red
Spring	blue
Winter	blue

1. Explain how the art teacher can represent these data in a way that others could interpret it.

2. List some advantages and disadvantages of using a table, a marginal frequency distribution, and a graphical display to represent categorical data.

   Table

   Marginal frequency distribution

   Graphical display

© Carnegie Learning, Inc.

Survey Questions

A How many pets do you own?	**B** What is your favorite color?
C What is your favorite sport?	**D** What score did you earn on the last math test?
E How many texts do you send per day?	**F** What type of music do you prefer?
G How many glasses of water do you drink each day?	**H** How far do you live from school in miles?
I What is your favorite snack?	**J** How many hours do you watch television per day?
K What mascot would you prefer for a sports team?	**L** Which grade are you in?

© Carnegie Learning, Inc.

Why is this page blank?

So you can cut out the survey questions on the other side

© Carnegie Learning, Inc.

LESSON 1 ASSIGNMENT

> Use a separate piece of paper for your Journal entry.

JOURNAL

Describe the difference between a *frequency distribution* and a *marginal frequency distribution* in your own words.

REMEMBER

A frequency distribution table is helpful in organizing categorical data in two variables to see any associations and trends in the data.

You can use a double bar graph to visualize categorical data in two variables.

PRACTICE

1. Forty workers arriving at an office building in a city were asked how they got to work that day. They were also asked if they were less than 40 years old or older. The table displays the survey results.

   (a) Identify the variables for this survey. Are the variables categorical or quantitative? Explain your reasoning.

Age	Transportation Method	Age	Transportation Method
< 40	Subway	< 40	Bus
< 40	Bus	< 40	Bus
40 +	Walk	< 40	Subway
< 40	Bus	40 +	Car
< 40	Subway	< 40	Walk
40 +	Car	40 +	Taxi
40 +	Car	40 +	Walk
40 +	Walk	< 40	Subway
< 40	Subway	40 +	Car
40+	Taxi	< 40	Taxi
< 40	Walk	40 +	Taxi
< 40	Bus	< 40	Bus
< 40	Subway	< 40	Bus
40 +	Bus	< 40	Subway
< 40	Bus	40 +	Walk
40 +	Walk	40 +	Car
40 +	Taxi	40 +	Subway
< 40	Subway	40 +	Bus
40 +	Car	< 40	Subway
< 40	Car	40 +	Taxi

© Carnegie Learning, Inc.

Go to LiveHint.com for help on the PRACTICE questions.

ⓑ Construct a marginal frequency distribution for the survey data.

ⓒ Construct two bar graphs of the frequencies. In one, let the *x*-axis represent the transportation method, and in the other, let the *x*-axis represent the age levels. Let the *y*-axis represent the number of workers in both graphs. What conclusion(s) can you draw by examining each graph?

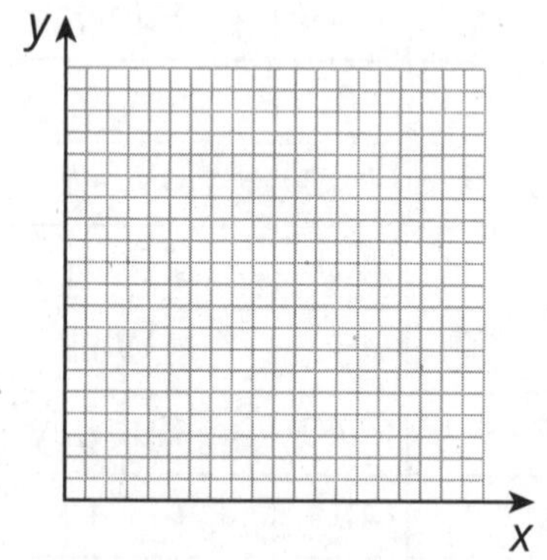

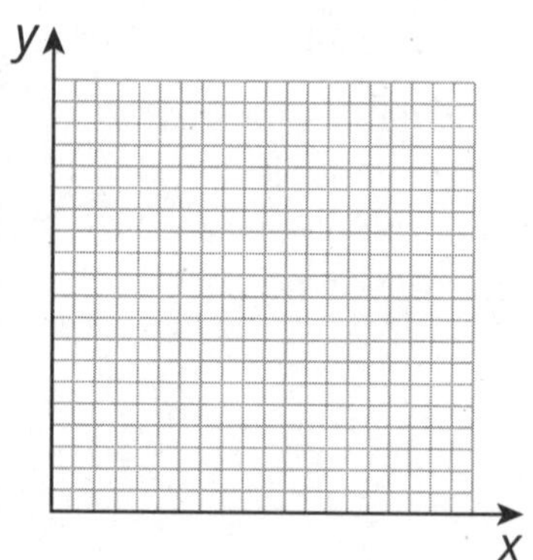

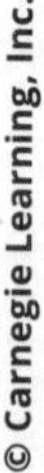
© Carnegie Learning, Inc.

STRETCH Optional

> Analyze the transportation survey data from the marginal frequency distribution in the Practice.

1. Complete a table to show the percent of the total in each category that used the different forms of transportation.

2. Construct a bar graph of the percents. Let the *x*-axis represent the transportation method, and let the *y*-axis represent the percent of workers. What conclusions can you make based on the graph?

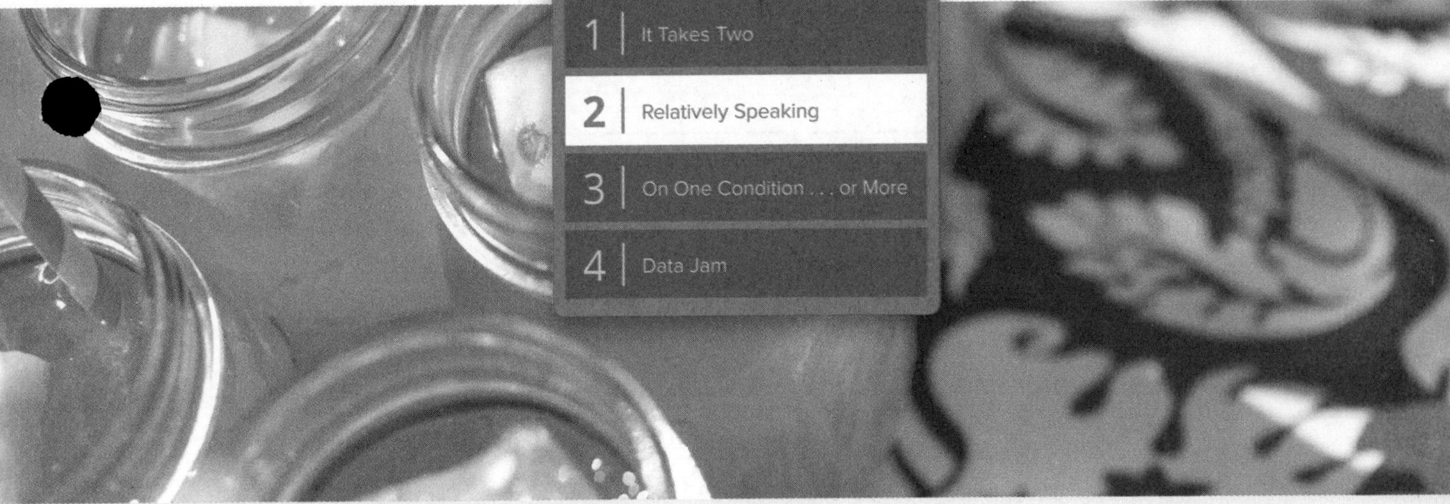

1 It Takes Two
2 Relatively Speaking
3 On One Condition . . . or More
4 Data Jam

LESSON 2

Relatively Speaking

Relative Frequency Distribution

KEY TERMS

- relative frequency distribution
- marginal relative frequency distribution

Learning Goals

- Construct and interpret relative frequency distribution and marginal relative frequency distributions displayed in two-way tables for categorical data.
- Analyze and use marginal relative frequency distributions to make decisions for a problem situation.

REVIEW (1–2 minutes)

> Rewrite each ratio as a percent.

1. $\frac{39}{100}$

2. $\frac{3}{8}$

3. $\frac{7}{12}$

4. $\frac{13}{25}$

5. $\frac{77}{80}$

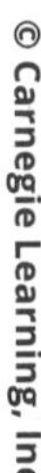
© Carnegie Learning, Inc.

You have organized and analyzed data using marginal frequency distribution tables.

How can you use percents to analyze the same data set?

Sour Statements

A sample of 9th- and 10th-grade students at Valley High School were surveyed about their favorite things to drink on a hot day. There were a total of five groups recorded for the variable *favorite drink*, including *water*, *sports drinks, iced coffee, lemonade,* and *iced tea*. The frequency distribution shows the results for the group *lemonade*.

Two students used the table to make percent statements.

Favorite Drink

Grade Level		Lemonade
	9th	7
	10th	7

Analyze Chris's and Brad's statements.

Chris

Seven percent of 9th-graders and seven percent of 10th-graders prefer lemonade.

Brad

Since 7 = 7, the same percent of 9th- and 10th-graders prefer lemonade.

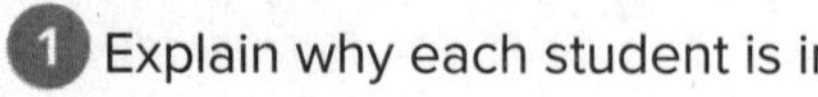

1. Explain why each student is incorrect.

© Carnegie Learning, Inc.

Relative Frequency Distribution

In this activity, you will use a marginal frequency table to determine ratios.

HABITS OF MIND
- Reason abstractly and quantitatively.
- Construct viable arguments and critique the reasoning of others.

The Northpointe community outreach director wants to plan special summer activities for the members of Northpointe. He selects a random sample of members of the community, and each of those members responds to his survey. Participants identify their age and then chose from four given activities. The marginal frequency table shows the responses gathered from the survey.

THINK ABOUT . . .
Is there an association between a person's age and their preferred activity?

Activities Preferred During Hot Weather

Age Group	Sports	Movies	Reading	Walking	Total
Students Age 18 Years Old and Under	20	30	22	8	80
Adults Age 19 Through 50 Years Old	10	32	25	43	110
Adults Over 50 Years Old	5	20	35	30	90
Total	35	82	82	81	280

While the raw data provide some information, it is often more efficient to use percents when analyzing data. The relative frequencies of each data entry can provide that information.

A representation of the relative frequencies for joint data displayed in a two-way table is a *relative frequency distribution*. The **relative frequency distribution** provides the ratio of occurrences for each category to the total number of occurrences.

A representation that displays the relative frequencies for the rows or columns is a *marginal relative frequency distribution*. The **marginal relative frequency distribution** provides the ratio of total occurrences for each category to the total number of occurrences.

© Carnegie Learning, Inc.

1 Construct a marginal relative frequency distribution of the data. Represent each ratio as a percent.

Activities Preferred During Hot Weather

		Sports	Movies	Reading	Walking	Total
Age Group	Students Age 18 Years Old and Under					
	Adults Age 19 Through 50 Years Old					
	Adults Over 50 Years Old					
	Total					

> Analyze Isaac's and Aaron's statements.

Isaac

58.6% of participants in the survey prefer watching movies or reading in hot weather.

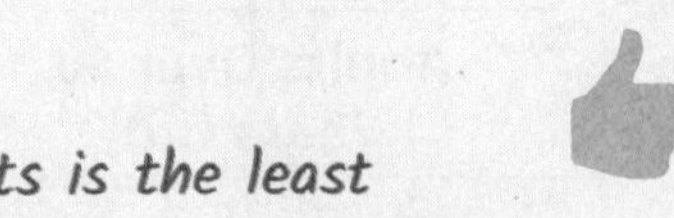

Aaron

Playing sports is the least popular activity in hot weather, according to the survey results.

2 Explain why each student is correct.

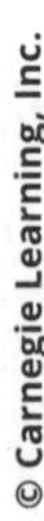

© Carnegie Learning, Inc.

> Analyze Shane's, Olivia's, and Marie's statements.

Shane

1.07% of adults over age 50 prefer walking in hot weather.

Olivia

More adults over 50 responded to the survey than any other age group.

Marie

Out of all survey participants that prefer playing sports in hot weather, 7.1% of those are students age 18 years old and under.

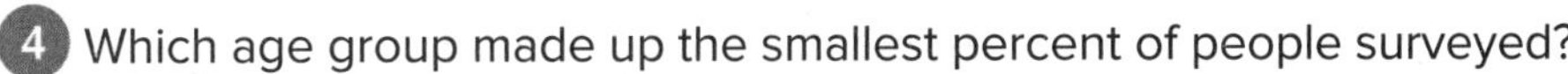

3. Explain why each student is incorrect and rewrite each as a correct statement.

4. Which age group made up the smallest percent of people surveyed?

5. Which activity was preferred by the largest percent of people surveyed?

6. Does there appear to be an association between age and preferred activity? **If so, explain what trends you notice in these data.**

© Carnegie Learning, Inc.

Analyzing Data Ratios

HABITS OF MIND
- Reason abstractly and quantitatively.
- Construct viable arguments and critique the reasoning of others.

You have previously used a bar graph to visually represent data. Another way to represent data is to use a stacked bar graph in which the bars stack on top of each other as opposed to sitting next to each other.

> Consider the marginal relative frequency distribution from the previous activity. The stacked bar graph represents the activities preferred during hot weather by age group.

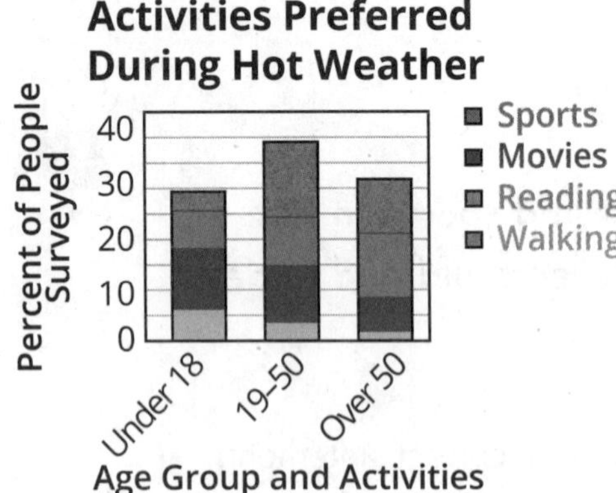

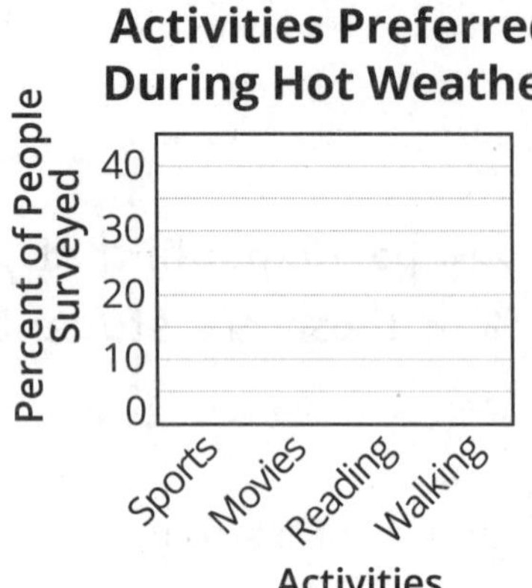

1. Construct a stacked bar graph using the marginal relative frequency distribution by activities. Be sure to include a legend.

2. How do the graphs compare to the relative frequency distribution table you completed in the previous activity?

3. What conclusions can you draw by examining the graphs?

4. Name some advantages of graphing the data by age group. Name some advantages of graphing the data by activity.

© Carnegie Learning, Inc.

Interpreting Data Ratios

HABITS OF MIND
- Reason abstractly and quantitatively.
- Construct viable arguments and critique the reasoning of others.

Now that you have organized and analyzed the data about preferred activities in hot weather using tables and graphs, let's interpret the ratios in the data.

1 Analyze each of the given activities. Determine whether you think the activity would be a good idea to have during the summer. **Use the data to justify your answer.**

(a) A walking club for community members age 19 to 50

(b) A soccer tournament for community members over the age of 50

(c) An ultimate Frisbee league for community members aged 18 or younger

The community outreach director wants to offer one summer activity each week that will appeal to all ages of the community.

2 Write a letter to the community outreach director recommending one activity and tell why the other activities may not be the best activities during the summer. **Use the data to support your idea.**

© Carnegie Learning, Inc.

A Hot Topic

Drama club members and game club members were surveyed to determine their favorite drink on a cold day. The table displays the results.

Favorite Drink on a Cold Day

Club		Coffee	Tea	Hot Cocoa	Total
	Drama	10	2	4	16
	Game	5	7	4	16
	Total	15	9	8	32

1. Construct a marginal relative frequency distribution of the data.

Favorite Drink on a Cold Day

Club		Coffee	Tea	Hot Cocoa	Total
	Drama				
	Game				
	Total				

2. Write a paragraph interpreting the marginal relative frequency distributions for the data.

3. Does there appear to be an association between club participation and favorite drink on a cold day? **Justify your answer.**

© Carnegie Learning, Inc.

LESSON 2 ASSIGNMENT

> Use a separate piece of paper for your Journal entry.

JOURNAL

Write a brief explanation of the difference between a relative frequency distribution and a marginal relative frequency distribution.

REMEMBER

A relative frequency distribution table provides the ratio of occurrences in each category to the total number of occurrences and allows you to use percents to analyze categorical data in two variables. You can use a stacked bar graph to visually represent the marginal relative frequencies of a data set.

PRACTICE

1. The principal of Umber Elementary School (Grades K–4) would like to reward his students for recent good test scores on a standardized test. He thinks of four different types of assemblies. In order to please the most students, the principal asks his teachers to survey the students in their classes. The students from each grade are asked which assembly they would most want to see. The table shows the responses gathered from the surveys.

	Wild Animals	Hip Hop Show	Magic Show	Puppet Show
Grade K	18	5	8	33
Grade 1	26	10	21	15
Grade 2	21	19	17	12
Grade 3	22	28	20	8
Grade 4	19	44	7	2

(a) Construct a marginal relative frequency distribution of the data.

	Wild Animals	Hip Hop Show	Magic Show	Puppet Show	Total
Grade K					
Grade 1					
Grade 2					
Grade 3					
Grade 4					
Total					

© Carnegie Learning, Inc.

Go to LiveHint.com for help on the PRACTICE questions.

ⓑ The principal wants to choose one assembly that he can show to all the students. Construct two stacked bar graphs of the marginal relative frequency distribution. Then, tell which assembly he should choose for the students. Explain how you determined your answer.

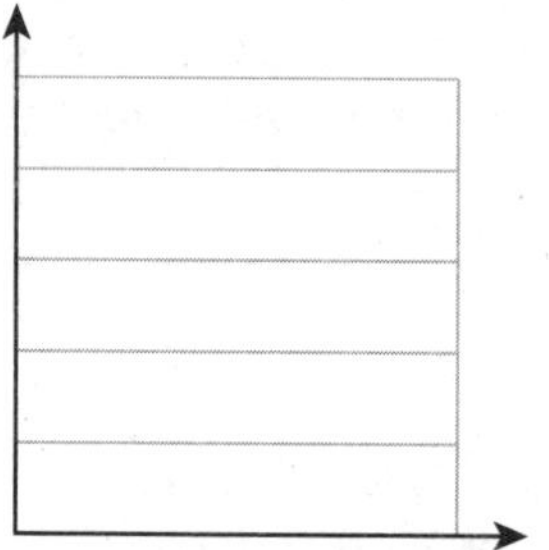

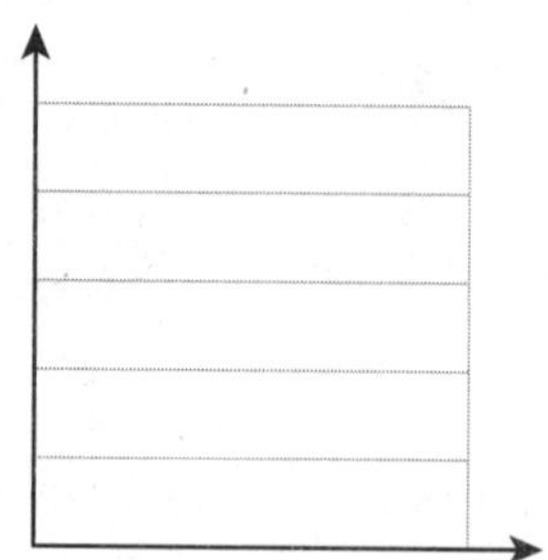

ⓒ The principal has come up with an idea to hold a hip hop assembly for Grades 1 through 4 and a puppet show for Kindergarten. Do you think this is a good idea? Explain your reasoning.

STRETCH Optional

A teacher at the Umber Elementary School decides to organize the data from the students differently. She decides to calculate percents of the assembly types the students want within each grade, not out of the total.

1. Use the data from Umber Elementary School to create a table showing the percents for each preferred assembly type by grade.
2. Construct a stacked bar graph of the percents for each grade. How does this graph compare to the stacked bar graph of the marginal relative frequency distribution that you constructed in the Practice to show the assembly choice by grade?

© Carnegie Learning, Inc.

LESSON 3

On One Condition . . . or More

Conditional Relative Frequency Distribution

KEY TERM

conditional relative frequency distribution

Learning Goals

- Construct and interpret conditional relative frequency distributions displayed in two-way tables for categorical data.
- Recognize possible associations and trends in categorical data.

REVIEW (1–2 minutes)

> Identify which fraction is greater. **Explain your reasoning.**

1. $\frac{6}{55}, \frac{6}{19}$

2. $\frac{2}{12}, \frac{2}{5}$

3. $\frac{15}{23}, \frac{15}{91}$

4. $\frac{7}{9}, \frac{7}{8}$

5. $\frac{67}{100}, \frac{67}{200}$

© Carnegie Learning, Inc.

You have created and interpreted relative frequency distributions for categorical data in two variables.

How can you compare relative frequencies within a single variable?

Did They Pass the Class?

Mr. Lewis teaches three science classes at Matthews High School. He wants to compare the grades of the three classes of his students. He creates this marginal frequency distribution table.

Grades of Mr. Lewis's Science Students

Science Classes		A	B	C	D	F	Total
	Biology	6	6	5	1	2	20
	Chemistry	4	8	12	4	2	30
	Physics	2	5	6	1	1	15
	Total	12	19	23	6	5	65

1. Complete the marginal relative frequency distributions for the data. Round each percent to the nearest tenth of a percent.

Grades of Mr. Lewis's Science Students

Science Classes		A	B	C	D	F	Total
	Biology						
	Chemistry						
	Physics						
	Total						

2. Explain what each percent means in the marginal relative frequency distribution table.

   (a) 12.3% (b) 23.1% (c) 35.4%

© Carnegie Learning, Inc.

Conditional Relative Frequency Distribution

HABITS OF MIND
• Model with mathematics.
• Use appropriate tools strategically.

> Analyze the marginal relative frequency distribution table you completed in the Getting Started.

1 Campbell claims that Mr. Lewis's chemistry class is the smartest because it has the greatest percent of students passing. Is Campbell's statement correct? **Explain your reasoning**.

TAKE NOTE . . .
At Matthews High School, passing grades are As, Bs, or Cs.

You can use a *conditional relative frequency distribution* to determine which class is doing the "best." A **conditional relative frequency distribution** is the percent or ratio of occurrences of a category given the specific value of another category.

Let's construct a conditional relative frequency distribution of grades given the classes using the information from the Getting Started.

2 Analyze the three conditional relative frequencies given in the table. **Describe why the denominator of each ratio is different.**

Grades of Mr. Lewis's Science Students

Science Classes	A	B	C	D	F	Total
Biology	$\frac{6}{20} = 30\%$					
Chemistry			$\frac{12}{30} = 40\%$			
Physics				$\frac{1}{15} \approx 6.7\%$		

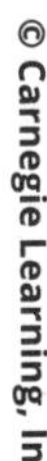

© Carnegie Learning, Inc.

3 Complete the remaining conditional relative frequencies in the table.

4 Interpret the conditional relative frequency distributions of each class.

5 Use the conditional relative frequency distribution to answer each question.

(a) What percent of the biology students are passing?

(b) What percent of the chemistry students are passing?

(c) What percent of the physics students are passing?

(d) Which science class is doing the best according to their grades? **Explain your reasoning**.

(e) How does this compare to the statement Campbell made?

6 Which science class has the greatest percent of students failing?

© Carnegie Learning, Inc.

Let's look at these data a different way. You can construct a different conditional relative frequency distribution for each class given the grades.

7 Use the information from the Getting Started activity to determine the relative frequency for each class given that particular grade.

Grades of Mr. Lewis's Science Students

Science Classes	A	B	C	D	F
Biology	$\frac{6}{12} = 50\%$				
Chemistry					$\frac{2}{5} = 40\%$
Physics			$\frac{6}{23} \approx 26.1\%$		
Total					

8 Campbell claims that 80% of the students who received a grade of F were in Biology and Chemistry. Is Campbell's statement correct? **Explain your reasoning.**

9 Does there appear to be an association between the science class and the grades of Mr. Lewis's science students? **Justify your answer.**

© Carnegie Learning, Inc.

Down to a Science

Mr. Lewis also teaches two general science classes. He wants to teach his students about a topic they have the most interest in. He surveys his students and records the data in this table.

Science Topics

Science Classes	Matter	Plants and Animals	Astronomy	Anatomy	Genetics	Total
Class 1	5	3	10	3	4	25
Class 2	9	5	3	7	6	30
Total	14	8	13	10	10	55

1. Mr. Lewis wants to teach the same topic to both classes. Which topic would you recommend Mr. Lewis teach? **Use conditional relative frequencies to explain why you made your suggestion to Mr. Lewis.**

© Carnegie Learning, Inc.

LESSON 3 ASSIGNMENT

> Use a separate piece of paper for your Journal entry.

JOURNAL

Describe how a marginal relative frequency compares to a conditional relative frequency.

REMEMBER

A conditional relative frequency distribution is the percent or ratio of occurrences of a category given the specific value of another category.

PRACTICE

1. Angie is taking a broadcast communications class at her local college. The professor presents the students with the results of a survey conducted to determine where different age groups of people get their news. This table shows the results of the survey.

News Source

Age Group	Local TV	National TV	Radio	Neswpaper	Internet	Total
Under 35	95	72	74	53	110	404
35–49	110	107	100	78	84	479
50+	136	129	111	106	71	553
Total	341	308	286	237	265	1436

(a) Angie claims that overall more people get their news from local TV than any other source. Is she correct? Explain your reasoning.

(b) Angie's classmate claims that the under 35 age group must use local TV less than the 35 to 49 age group because 95 is less than 110. Is she correct? Explain your reasoning.

(c) Construct a conditional relative frequency distribution of news source given the age group.

News Source

Age Group	Local TV	National TV	Radio	Local Newspaper	Internet	Total
Under 35						
35–49						
50+						

© Carnegie Learning, Inc.

Go to LiveHint.com for help on the PRACTICE questions.

ⓓ Which age group has the fewest number of people who receive their news from local TV? How does this compare to the claim made in part (b)?

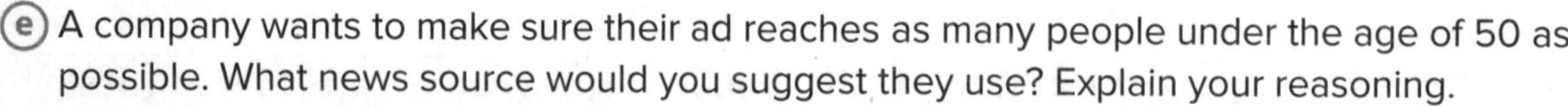

ⓔ A company wants to make sure their ad reaches as many people under the age of 50 as possible. What news source would you suggest they use? Explain your reasoning.

STRETCH Optional

> A study is done to see if there is a difference between the colors of cars that teenagers and adults prefer to drive. The colors in the study are black, white, gray, red, and blue. The researcher receives this incomplete information about the 100 total people that were surveyed.

- The ratio of the number of teenagers who prefer red cars to the number of teenagers is $\frac{15}{57}$.
- The ratio of the number of teenagers who prefer white cars to the number of people who prefer white cars is $\frac{3}{20}$.
- The ratio of the number of adults who prefer black cars to the number of adults is $\frac{6}{43}$.
- The ratio of the number of adults who prefer blue cars to the number of people who prefer blue cars is $\frac{8}{10}$.
- A total of 37 teenagers and adults prefer black cars.
- A total of 17 teenagers and adults prefer red cars.

1. Use the information to construct a two-way frequency table.

© Carnegie Learning, Inc.

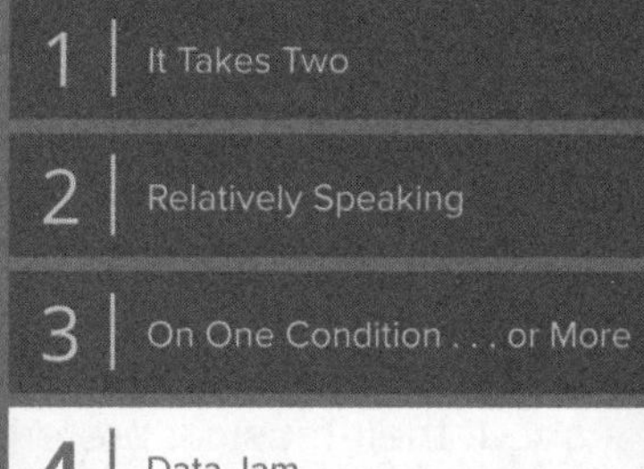

1 It Takes Two
2 Relatively Speaking
3 On One Condition . . . or More
4 Data Jam

LESSON 4

Data Jam

Drawing Conclusions from Data

Learning Goals

- Recognize possible associations and trends in categorical data.
- Use categorical data to make decisions.
- Recognize possible associations and trends in data sets.

REVIEW (1–2 minutes)

> Consider this scatter plot.

1 Should the owner of the music store plan to spend extra money on advertising during a week of temperatures over 24°C? **Explain your reasoning.**

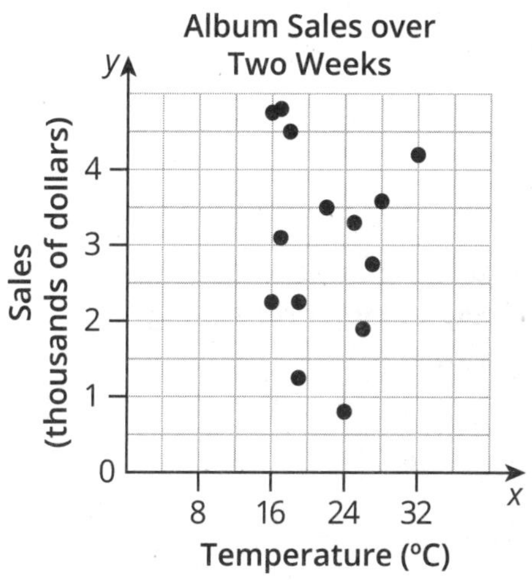

© Carnegie Learning, Inc.

You have analyzed categorical data in two variables by creating marginal frequency distributions, stacked bar graphs, and conditional relative frequency distributions.

How can you use these representations to make decisions in a problem situation?

I'm a Little Bit Country

A survey was conducted at Rawlings High School and 38 students in one 9th-grade classroom were asked two questions about their musical preferences: "Do you like country?" and "Do you like rock?" The marginal frequency distribution summarizes the responses.

	Likes Country	Doesn't Like Country	Total
Likes Rock	18	7	25
Doesn't Like Rock	5	8	13
Total	23	15	38

1. What percent of the students in the classroom like rock?

2. Does there appear to be an association between liking country and liking rock? **Use the data to justify your response.**

3. Is this a random sample that fairly represents the opinions of all students at Rawlings High School? **Explain your reasoning.**

© Carnegie Learning, Inc.

Interpreting a Whole Data Set

Let's use everything you have learned about organizing and analyzing two-variable categorical data to interpret data in a real-world problem.

HABITS OF MIND
- Reason abstractly and quantitatively.
- Construct viable arguments and critique the reasoning of others.

Andres is a new radio station general manager at KYWN. Currently, the station features country music. However, Andres is considering changing the genre of music to make the station more popular. He wants to target one of the highest demographics in radio listening—teenagers—so he decides to sponsor the next dance at Rawlings High School. Prior to the dance, Andres surveys the students.

> Analyze the survey results located on pages 649 and 650.

1. Organize the data in a table and represent them using a graph to help Andres determine which music genre is most popular at Rawlings High School according to the survey he conducted.

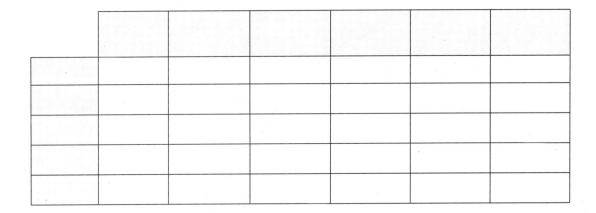

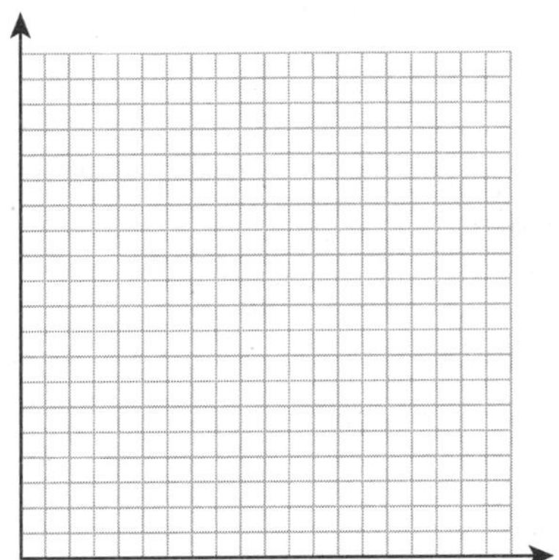

© Carnegie Learning, Inc.

2 Analyze the table you created to organize Andres's data.

(a) How many students did Andres survey for the dance? How did you determine that you organized the data correctly?

(b) Can you determine which genre of music was the most popular from the representations you created? **Explain why or why not.**

(c) Do you think the results might be the same or different if Andres conducted another random survey at Rawlings High School? **Explain your reasoning**.

(d) Based on the data you have analyzed, would you advise Andres to change the format of his station? **If so, explain why. If not, explain why not.**

© Carnegie Learning, Inc.

Interpreting a Subset of a Data Set

HABITS OF MIND
- Reason abstractly and quantitatively.
- Construct viable arguments and critique the reasoning of others.

> Consider the data set from Activity 1.

Andres wants to target the age 18 to 35 group to get advertisers to buy more air time. He decides to use only the data he gathered from the seniors he surveyed at Rawlings High School.

ASK YOURSELF . . .
Is there only one way to analyze and interpret data?

1. Analyze the tables and graphs you created in the previous activity and predict which music genre is the most popular for the Rawlings High School seniors. **Explain how you came to your conclusion.**

Suppose Andres decides to suggest a music format change for KYWN to dance music.

2. What information would you advise Andres use to strengthen his suggestion? Use any of the data and supply any graphs you think may strengthen Andres's suggestion. **Finally, explain why you chose the information.**

3. Based on the information you analyzed regarding the seniors, would you change KYWN's music format to match the Rawlings High School seniors' survey results? **If yes, use the data to explain why. If not, explain why not.**

© Carnegie Learning, Inc.

Pass the Aux Cord

Tanya surveyed people about the genre of the most played song on their playlist and also asked if they drive a car or a truck.

1 Construct a marginal relative frequency distribution of the data using the bar graph provided.

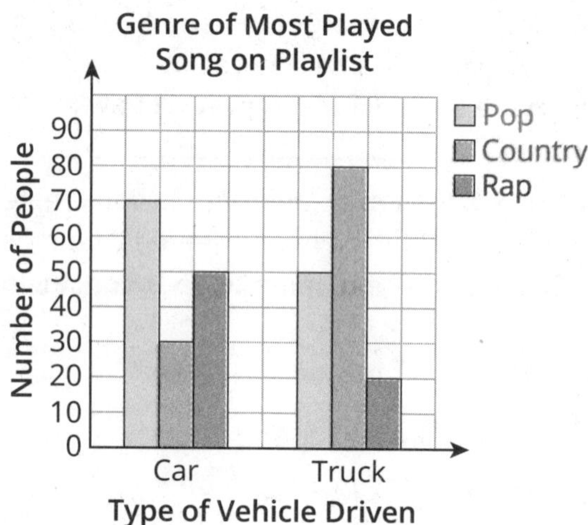

Genre of Most Played Song on Playlist

Type of Vehicle Driven

2 Write a paragraph interpreting the relative frequency distributions and marginal relative frequency distributions for the data. Include an explanation of whether there appears to be an association between the genre of the most played song on someone's playlist and the type of vehicle they drive.

© Carnegie Learning, Inc.

ACTIVITY 1 DATA TABLE

	Music Genre				
Grade Level	Rock (Classic/ Alternative)	Classical	Hip-Hop/ Rap	Dance	Country
12				X	
9		X			
10				X	
10					X
9					X
11			X		
12		X			
10	X				
9					X
9				X	
10		X			
12				X	
11	X				
12				X	
11			X		
9	X				
9	X				
10					X
11	X				
9	X				
12				X	
12			X		
11			X		
10		X			
9			X		
12			X		
11				X	

TOPIC 2

© Carnegie Learning, Inc.

	Music Genre				
Grade Level	Rock (Classic/ Alternative)	Classical	Hip-Hop/Rap	Dance	Country
9			X		
10	X				
10	X				
12					X
9				X	
9				X	
9					X
10		X			
12	X				
12	X				
12		X			
10		X			
10			X		
10				X	
11			X		
9				X	
9					X
10		X			
10		X			
12				X	
11	X				
12	X				
11	X				
11		X			
12				X	
12				X	
12		X			
11			X		
11					X

© Carnegie Learning, Inc.

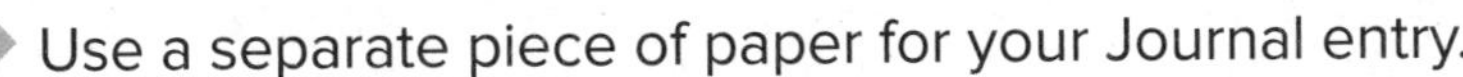

LESSON 4 ASSIGNMENT

› Use a separate piece of paper for your Journal entry.

JOURNAL

Describe how you can determine whether there is an association between two-variable categorical data.

REMEMBER

For categorical data in two variables, organizing and representing data in frequency distributions, marginal relative frequency distributions, conditional relative frequency distributions, and bar graphs are useful in formulating conclusions and using statistics to support your conclusions.

PRACTICE

People were surveyed to determine their favorite vehicle. This table displays the results.

Favorite Vehicle

Age		Sedan	SUV	Convertible	Total
	40+	88	115	34	237
	<40	73	62	102	237

Suppose you were the general sales manager of a car dealership and you were planning a big car sale.

› Use the information in the frequency table to answer each question. Support your answers with tables and/or graphs.

1. Which type of car would you have on display in the showroom if you anticipate that most people shopping for a car would be under 40 years of age?

© Carnegie Learning, Inc.

2 Which type of car would you have on display in the showroom if you anticipate that most people shopping for a car would be people 40 years of age or older?

3 Which type of car would you have on display in the showroom if you want to promote sales of cars that appeal to both age groups?

STRETCH Optional

In statistics, you can use the frequencies in two-way tables to help determine whether the frequency counts are distributed identically across populations. Using probability theory, you can determine expected frequencies when the counts are distributed identically. These frequencies are calculated for each cell by multiplying the row total by the column total and dividing by the grand total of frequencies.

1 Complete the table of expected frequencies for age and favorite vehicle.

Expected Frequencies	Sedan	SUV	Convertible	Row Total
40+	$\frac{(237)(161)}{474} = 80.5$			237
<40				237
Column Total	161	177	136	474

2 Does there seem to be a difference between the frequencies that were observed in the survey and those that would be expected if counts are distributed identically? What conclusion can you make?

© Carnegie Learning, Inc.

MIXED PRACTICE

> This Mixed Practice worksheet includes two sections: Spaced Review and End-of-Topic Review. **Use a separate piece of paper to show your work.**

Spaced Review

> Practice concepts from previous topics.

1. Stefan has been drinking protein shakes to try to improve his performance in basketball. In the last five games, Stefan's percent of successful shooting attempts has increased. Stefan concludes that protein shakes have caused him to shoot better. Determine whether Stefan reached a valid conclusion. Explain your reasoning.

2. The formula for the area of a triangle is $A = \frac{1}{2}bh$. Convert the equation to solve for b.

3. Consider the explicit formula $a_n = \frac{3}{2} + \frac{1}{2}(n - 1)$.
   a. Write the formula in function notation.
   b. Graph the function on a coordinate plane. Label the first three values of the sequence on the graph.

4. The population of a sunflower field is initially 60 plants. Each year the population grows 14%. Use an explicit formula to determine how many sunflower plants will be in the field in 6 years.

End-of-Topic Review

AVAILABLE ONLINE
1. A **Topic Summary** reviews the main concepts for the topic.
2. A video of the **Worked Example** is provided.

> Practice concepts you learned in *Two-Variable Categorical Data*.

5. A grocery store surveys customers by age group to determine what is most important to them when shopping. The table shows the customer responses.

	Self-Checkout Option	Good Customer Service	Good Selection of Produce	Butcher Available
20–29	52	8	20	14
30–39	44	11	23	16
40–49	34	15	26	17
50–59	25	31	32	2
60–69	5	35	27	25

   a. Construct a marginal relative frequency distribution of the data.
   b. The manager wants to concentrate on one area of the store to improve customer satisfaction. In which area should the manager concentrate? Explain your reasoning.

© Carnegie Learning, Inc.

6 Two hundred residents of Grapeville City are asked in a survey where they get their prescription medicine filled. The residents are categorized by age group: young adult, adult, and senior. The results from the survey are shown in the table.

Prescription Source

Age Group	Drugstore	Grocery Store	Big Box Store	Online	Total
Young Adult	2	4	15	44	65
Adult	18	25	19	10	72
Senior	26	22	10	5	63
Total	46	51	44	59	200

(a) Construct a conditional relative frequency distribution of age group given source of prescription.

(b) A lot of young adults are currently moving to the city. Which prescription source should be most concerned? Explain your reasoning.

7 People who prefer cats or dogs were surveyed to find out what their favorite season is. Construct a marginal relative frequency table from the bar graph provided and answer each question.

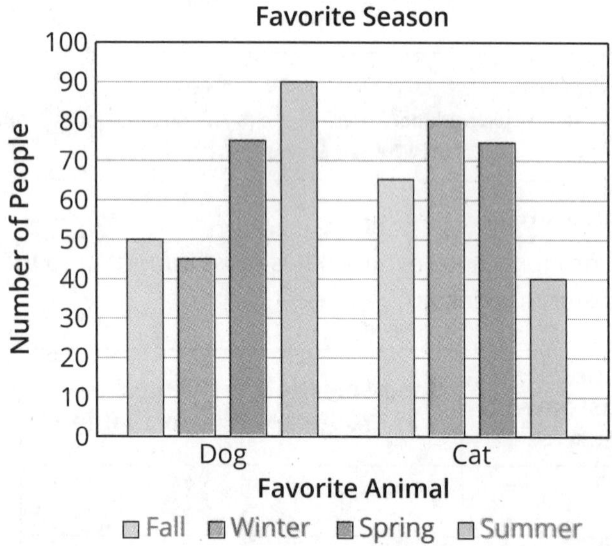

(a) Which season would a cat lover most likely prefer? Justify your response.

(b) Is there a season a dog and cat lover both prefer equally? If so, what season? Justify your response.

(c) What is the total percent of people that like the fall?

© Carnegie Learning, Inc.

Maximizing and Minimizing

TOPIC 1
Introduction to Quadratic Functions

TOPIC 2
Solving Quadratic Equations

MATHbook

TOPIC 3
Applications of Quadratics

MATHia

Exploring Quadratic Functions
- Introduction to a Quadratic Function
- Modeling Area as Product of Monomial and Binomial or Two Binomials
- Modeling Projectile Motion
- Recognizing Key Features of Vertical Motion Graphs
- Interpreting Maximums of Quadratic Models

Key Characteristics of Quadratic Functions
- Recognizing Quadratic Functions from Tables
- Identifying Properties of Quadratic Functions

Transformations of Quadratic Functions
- Vertically and Horizontally Translating Quadratic Functions
- Reflecting and Dilating Quadratic Functions Using Graphs
- Transforming Quadratic Functions Using Tables
- Multiple Transformations of Quadratic Functions

Sketching and Comparing Quadratic Functions
- Comparing Increasing Linear, Exponential, and Quadratic Functions
- Sketching Quadratic Functions
- Comparing Quadratic Functions in Different Forms

Adding, Subtracting, and Multiplying Polynomials
- Introduction to Polynomial Arithmetic
- Identifying Parts of Complex Algebraic Expressions
- Operating with Functions on the Coordinate Plane
- Adding and Subtracting Polynomials
- Using a Factor Table to Multiply Binomials
- Multiplying Binomials

Representing Solutions to Quadratic Equations
- Making Sense of Roots and Zeros
- Factoring Using Difference of Squares

Solutions to Quadratic Equations in Vertex Form
- Using Properties of Equality to Solve Quadratic Equations

Factoring and Completing the Square
- Introduction to Factoring
- Factoring Trinomials
- Factoring Quadratic Expressions
- Solving Quadratic Equations by Factoring
- Problem Solving Using Factoring
- Completing the Square
- Problem Solving Using Completing the Square

The Quadratic Formula
- Deriving the Quadratic Formula
- Solving Quadratic Equations

Using Quadratic Functions to Model Data
- Using Quadratic Models
- Introduction to Inverses
- Recognizing Graphs of Inverses

© Carnegie Learning, Inc.

Getting Ready for Module 5

Maximizing and Minimizing

You will investigate the structure and symmetry of quadratic functions. You will apply your knowledge of transformations to transform quadratic functions. You will explore operations with polynomials. Building on your work with equations, you will solve quadratics using various methods, including the Quadratic Formula. You will investigate complex numbers and solve problems involving quadratic inequalities.

The lessons in this module build on your prior experiences with lines of symmetry, rate of change, and the Distributive Property.

Review these key terms and the Distributive Property to get ready to maximize and minimize.

KEY TERMS

line of symmetry

A line of symmetry is an imaginary line that passes through a shape or object and divides it into two identical halves.

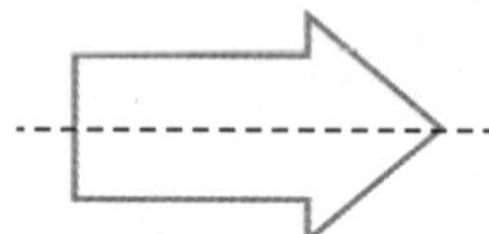

rate of change

The rate of change for a situation describes the amount that the dependent variable changes compared with the amount that the independent variable changes.

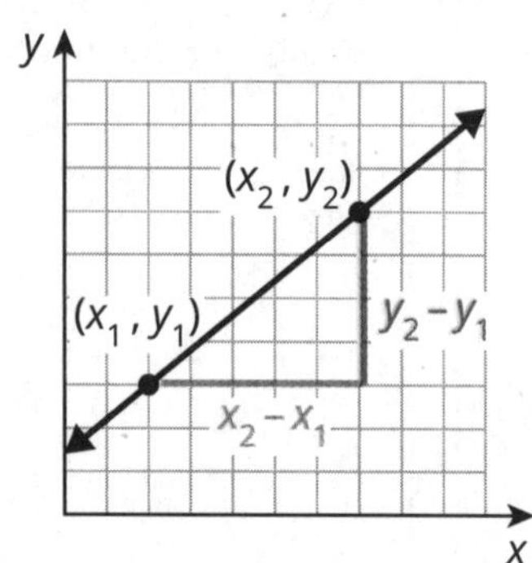

Rate of change = $\frac{y_2 - y_1}{x_2 - x_1}$

MATHia

Brush up on your skills.
If you need more practice with these skills, ask your teacher for access to corresponding workspaces in MATHia.

SKILLS YOU WILL NEED

Applying the Distributive Property

The Distributive Property states for any numbers a, b, and c, $a(b + c) = ab + ac$.

Consider the expression $-3(x + 7)$. Apply the Distributive Property to generate an equivalent expression.

$$-3(x + 7) = (-3)(x) + (-3)(7)$$
$$= -3x - 21$$

You can also apply the Distributive Property to write an expression like $6x + 30$ as a product of two factors.

$$6x + 30 = (6)(x) + (6)(5)$$
$$= 6(x + 5)$$

REVIEW

Solve each equation.

1. $x^2 = 81$
2. $x^2 = 25$
3. $x^2 = 121$
4. $x^2 = 49$
5. $2(x + 5) = 0$
6. $2x + 5 = 0$

See Appendix on page 879 for answers.

© Carnegie Learning, Inc.

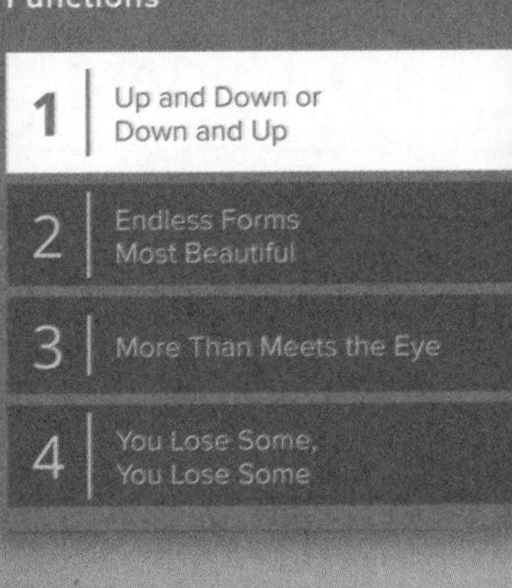

1 Up and Down or Down and Up
2 Endless Forms Most Beautiful
3 More Than Meets the Eye
4 You Lose Some, You Lose Some

LESSON 1

Up and Down or Down and Up

Exploring Quadratic Functions

KEY TERMS

parabola

vertical motion model

root

Learning Goals

- Write quadratic functions to model contexts.
- Graph quadratic functions using technology.
- Interpret the key features of quadratic functions in terms of a context.
- Identify the domain and range of quadratic functions and their contexts.

REVIEW (1–2 minutes)

> Evaluate $f(x) = x^2 + 3x + 4$ for each given value.

1. $f(1)$

2. $f(-1)$

3. $f(2)$

4. $f(-2)$

© Carnegie Learning, Inc.

You have used linear functions to model situations with constant change, and you have used exponential functions to model growth and decay situations.

What type of real-world situations can you model with quadratic functions?

Squaring It Up

Maddie is using pennies to create a pattern.

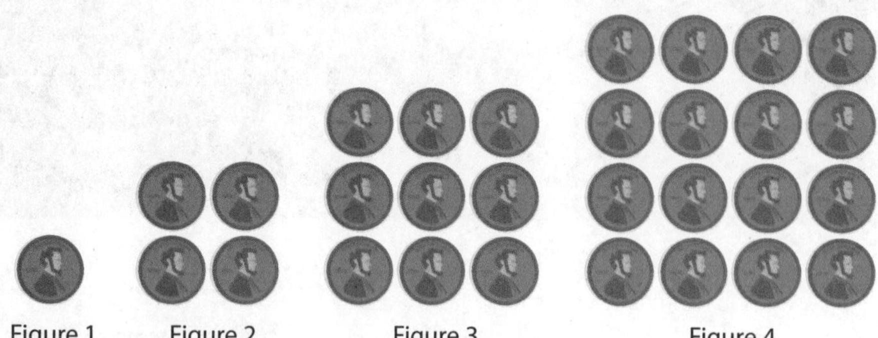

Figure 1 Figure 2 Figure 3 Figure 4

1. Analyze the pattern and explain how to create Figure 5.

2. How many pennies would Maddie need to create Figure 5? Figure 6? Figure 7?

3. Write an equation to determine the number of pennies for any figure number. **Define your variables.**

4. Which figure would Maddie create with exactly $4.00 in pennies?

5. Describe the function family to which this equation belongs.

© Carnegie Learning, Inc.

ACTIVITY 1

MATHia CONNECTION

- Introduction to a Quadratic Function
- Modeling Area as Product of Monomial and Binomial
- Modeling Area as Product of Two Binomials

Using Area to Investigate Quadratic Functions

HABITS OF MIND
- Model with mathematics.
- Use appropriate tools strategically.

Remember that in the *Quantities and Relationships* topic, you compared and sorted graphs to identify the family of quadratic functions.

In this activity, you will explore quadratic functions through the context of area.

A dog trainer is fencing in an enclosure, represented by the shaded region in the diagram. The trainer will also have two square-shaped storage units on either side of the enclosure to store equipment and other materials. She can make the enclosure and storage units as wide as she wants, and the total length must be 100 feet.

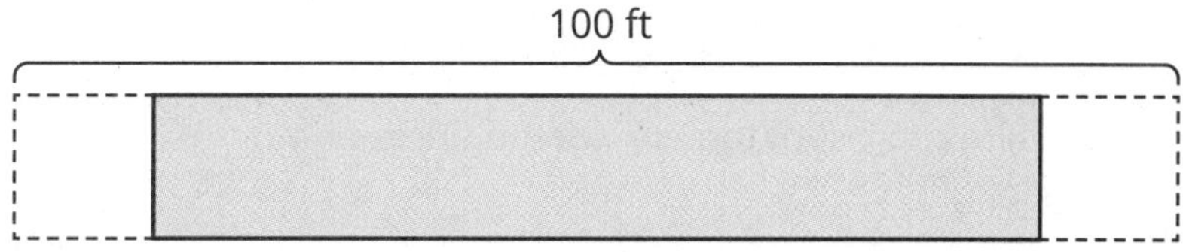

1. Let s represent a side length, in feet, of one of the storage units.

   a. Label the length and width of the enclosure in terms of s.

   b. Write the function $L(s)$ to represent the length of the enclosure as a function of side length, s.

   c. Sketch and label a graph of the function on the given coordinate plane. **Identify any key points.**

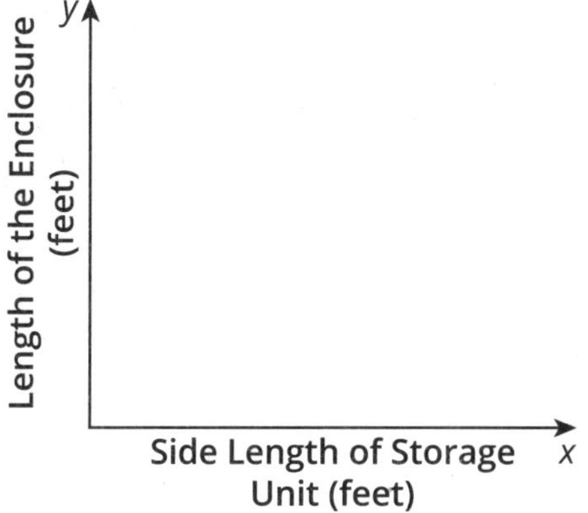

ASK YOURSELF . . .
To identify key points on the graph, think about the function you are representing. Are there any intercepts? Are there any other points of interest?

2. Describe the domain and range of the context and of the function.

© Carnegie Learning, Inc.

3. Identify each key characteristic of the graph. **Then, interpret the meaning of each in terms of the context.**

   a. Slope

   b. *y*-intercept

   c. Increasing or decreasing

   d. *x*-intercept

4. Write the function $A(s)$ to represent the area of the enclosure as a function of side length, s.

5. Describe how the area of the enclosure changes as the side length increases.

6. Consider the graph of the function, $A(s)$.

   a. Predict what the graph of the function will look like.

   b. Use technology to graph the function $A(s)$. Then, sketch the graph and label the axes.

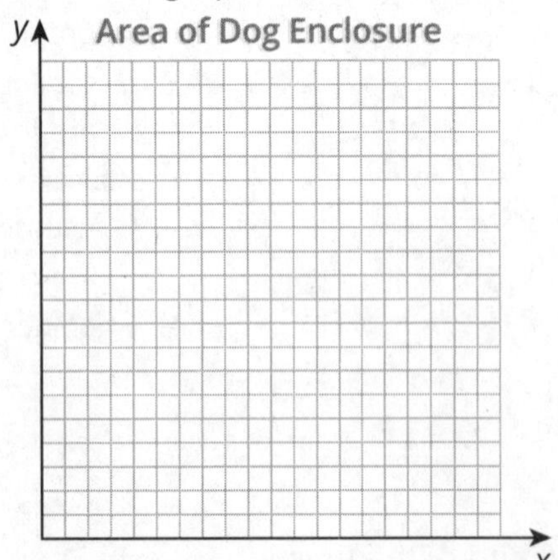

THINK ABOUT . . .

The diagrams show how the area of the enclosure, $A(s)$, changes as the side length, s, of each square storage unit increases.

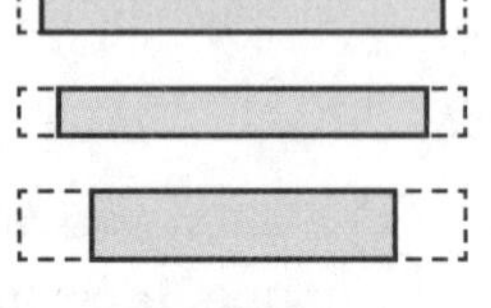

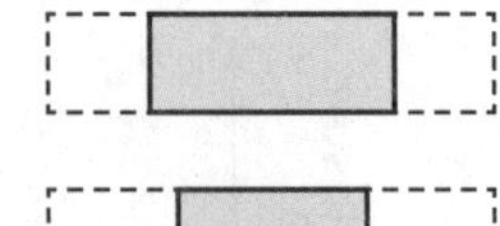

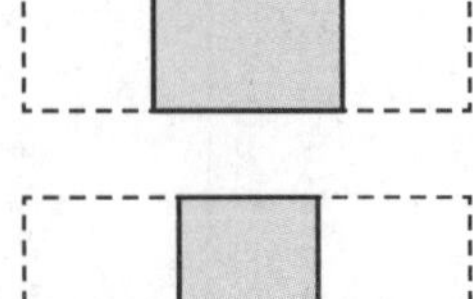

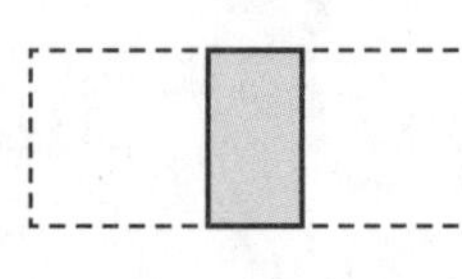

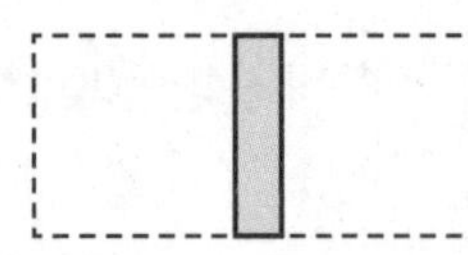

© Carnegie Learning, Inc.

7 Describe what all the points on the graph represent.

The function $A(s)$ that you wrote to model area is a quadratic function. The shape that a quadratic function forms when graphed is a **parabola**.

THINK ABOUT . . .
Quadratic functions model area because you measure area in square units.

8 Think about the possible areas of the enclosure.

(a) Is there a maximum area that the enclosure can contain? **Explain your reasoning in terms of the graph and in terms of the context.**

(b) Use technology to determine the maximum point of $A(s)$. **Describe what the *x*- and *y*-coordinates of the maximum point represent in this context.**

(c) Determine the dimensions of the enclosure that will provide the maximum area. **Show your work and explain your reasoning.**

© Carnegie Learning, Inc.

9 Identify the domain and range of the context and of the function.

10 Identify each key characteristic of the graph. **Then, interpret the meaning of each in terms of the context.**

(a) *y*-intercept

(b) Increasing and decreasing intervals

(c) Symmetry

(d) *x*-intercepts

© Carnegie Learning, Inc.

TOPIC 1

Writing and Interpreting a Quadratic Function

HABITS OF MIND

- Model with mathematics.
- Use appropriate tools strategically.

Let's consider a different real-world situation that you can represent with a quadratic function.

Suppose that there is a monthly meeting at CIA headquarters for all employees. How many handshakes will it take for every employee at the meeting to shake the hand of every other employee at the meeting once?

1 Use these figures to determine the number of handshakes that occur between 2 employees, 3 employees, and 4 employees.

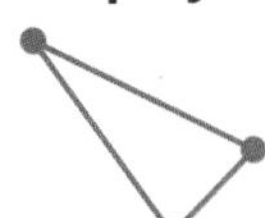

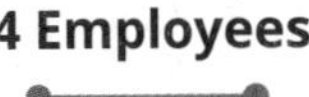

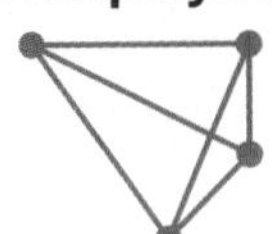

2 Draw figures to represent the number of handshakes that occur between 5 employees, 6 employees, and 7 employees and determine the number of handshakes that occur in each situation.

3 Enter your results in the table.

Number of Employees	2	3	4	5	6	7	n
Number of Handshakes							

ASK YOURSELF . . .
What will the shape of the graph be?

4 Write a function to represent the number of handshakes given any number of employees. Enter your function in the table.

© Carnegie Learning, Inc.

5 Use technology to graph the function you wrote in Question 4. Sketch the graph and label the axes.

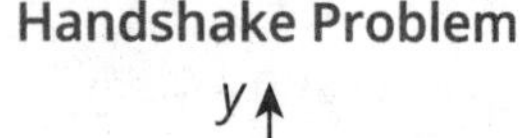

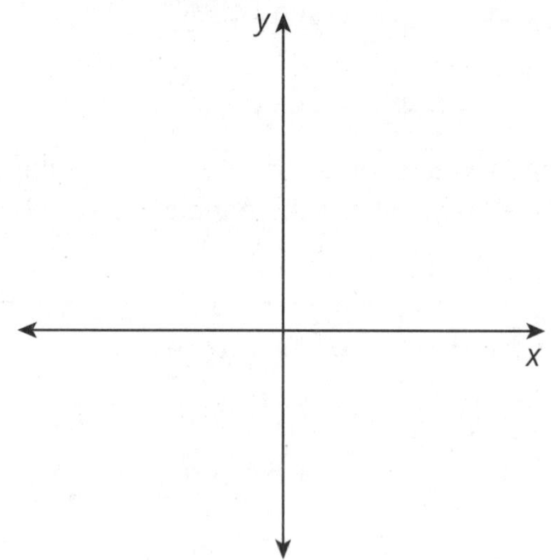

ASK YOURSELF . . .
What do all the points on this graph represent?

6 How is the orientation of this parabola different from the parabola for the area of the dog enclosure? How is this difference reflected in their corresponding equations?

7 Determine the minimum of your function. **Then, describe what the *x*- and *y*-coordinates of this minimum represent in this problem situation.**

8 Identify the domain and range of the problem situation and of the function.

© Carnegie Learning, Inc.

ACTIVITY 3

MATHia CONNECTION

- Modeling Projectile Motion
- Recognizing Key Features of Vertical Motion Graphs

Using a Quadratic Function to Model Vertical Motion

HABITS OF MIND
- Model with mathematics.
- Use appropriate tools strategically.

You can model the motion of a pumpkin released from a catapult using a vertical motion model. A **vertical motion model** is a quadratic equation that models the height of an object at a given time.

> Consider the equation for a vertical motion model.

$$y = -16t^2 + v_0t + h_0$$

In this equation, y represents the height of the object in feet, t represents the time in seconds that the object has been moving, v_0 represents the initial vertical velocity (speed) of the object in feet per second, and h_0 represents the initial height of the object in feet.

1. Which characteristics of this situation indicate that you can model it using a quadratic function?

Suppose that a catapult hurls a pumpkin from a height of 68 feet at an initial vertical velocity of 128 feet per second.

2. Write a function for the height of the pumpkin, $h(t)$, in terms of time, t.

3. Does the function you wrote have a minimum or maximum? **How can you tell from the form of the function?**

4. Use technology to graph the function. Sketch your graph and label the axes.

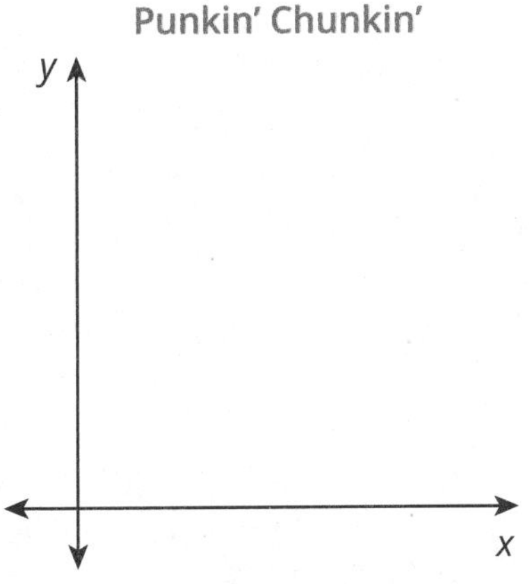

ASK YOURSELF . . .
What do all the points on this graph represent?

© Carnegie Learning, Inc.

5 Use technology to determine the maximum or minimum point and label it on the graph. **Explain what it means in terms of the problem situation.**

6 Determine the *y*-intercept and label it on the graph. **Explain what it means in terms of the problem situation.**

7 Use a horizontal line to determine when the pumpkin reaches each height after being catapulted. Label the points on the graph.

(a) 128 feet

(b) 260 feet

(c) 55 feet

8 Explain why the *x*- and *y*-coordinates of the points where the graph and each horizontal line intersects are solutions.

9 When does the catapulted pumpkin hit the ground? Label this point on the graph. **Explain how you determined your answer.**

© Carnegie Learning, Inc.

The time when the pumpkin hits the ground is one of the *x*-intercepts, (*x*, 0). When you use an equation to model a situation, you refer to the *x*-coordinate of the *x*-intercept as the *root*. The **root** of an equation indicates where the graph of the equation crosses the *x*-axis.

REMEMBER . . .
The zeros of a function are the *x*-values when the function equals 0.

Expressing a Quadratic Function as the Product of Two Linear Functions

HABITS OF MIND
- Model with mathematics.
- Use appropriate tools strategically.

Now, let's consider a real-world situation that you can model with a quadratic function in a different form.

> The Jacobson brothers own and operate their own ghost tour business. They take tour groups around town on a bus to visit the most notorious "haunted" spots throughout the city. They charge \$50 per tour. Each summer, they book 100 tours at that price.
>
> The brothers are considering a decrease in the price per tour because they think it will help them book more tours. They estimate that they will gain 10 tours for every \$1 decrease in the price per tour.

1. According to the scenario, how much money do the Jacobson brothers currently generate each summer with their ghost tour business?

Revenue is the amount of money regularly coming into a business. In the ghost tour business, the revenue is the number of tours multiplied by the price per tour. You can refer to your response to Question 1 as revenue. Because the Jacobson brothers are considering different numbers of tours and prices per tour, you can model the revenue using a function.

2. Write a function, $r(x)$, to represent the revenue for the ghost tour business.

   a. Let x represent the decrease in the price per tour. Write an expression to represent the number of tours booked if the decrease in price is x dollars per tour.

   b. Write an expression to represent the price per tour if the brothers decrease the price x dollars per tour.

   c. Use your expressions from parts (a) and (b) to represent the revenue, $r(x)$, as the number of tours times the price per tour.

   Revenue = Number of Tours • Price per Tour

   $r(x)$ = ________ • ________

THINK ABOUT . . .
You can always check your function by testing it with values of x. What is the value of $r(x)$ when $x = 0$? Does it make sense?

© Carnegie Learning, Inc.

3 Use technology to graph the function $r(x)$. Sketch your graph and label the axes.

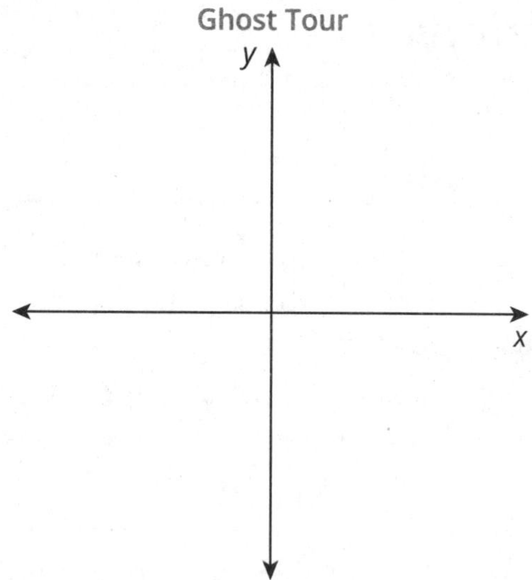

REMEMBER . . .
Don't forget to label key points!

4 Assume that the Jacobson brothers' estimate that for every $1 decrease in the price per tour, they will gain 10 tours is accurate.

(a) What is the maximum revenue that the Jacobson brothers could earn for the summer?

(b) Katie and Bryce are calculating the number of tours that would yield the maximum revenue. Who is correct? **Explain your reasoning.**

Katie

According to the graph, a tour should cost $20. Since $9000 ÷ $205 = 450, the number of tours would be 450.

Bryce

The cost of a tour should be $30, and $9000 divided by $30 per tour is 300 tours.

© Carnegie Learning, Inc.

ⓒ Would you advise the Jacobson brothers to adjust their cost per tour to make the maximum revenue? **Why or why not?**

5 Identify each key characteristic of the graph. **Then, interpret its meaning in terms of the context.**

ⓐ *x*-intercepts

ⓑ *y*-intercept

ⓒ Increasing and decreasing intervals

© Carnegie Learning, Inc.

Making Connections

> Analyze the graphs of the four quadratic functions in this lesson.

1 Summarize what you know about the graphs of quadratic functions. Include a sketch or sketches and list any characteristics.

2 Compare your sketch or sketches and list with your classmates. Did you all sketch the same parabola? **Why or why not?**

© Carnegie Learning, Inc.

LESSON 1 ASSIGNMENT

> Use a separate piece of paper for your Journal entry.

REMEMBER

The graph of a quadratic function is a parabola. Parabolas are smooth curves that have an absolute maximum or minimum point, both increasing and decreasing intervals, up to two *x*-intercepts, and symmetry.

JOURNAL

Complete each sentence with a key term from the lesson.

1. A quadratic equation that models the height of an object at a given time is a _______.
2. The shape that a quadratic function forms when graphed is a _______.
3. The _______ of an equation indicate where the graph of the equation crosses the *x*-axis.

PRACTICE

1. The citizens of Herrington County have an existing dog park for dogs to play but have decided to build another one so that one park will be for small dogs and the other will be for large dogs. The plan is to build a rectangular fenced in area adjacent to the existing dog park, as shown in the sketch. The county has enough money in the budget to buy 1000 feet of fencing.

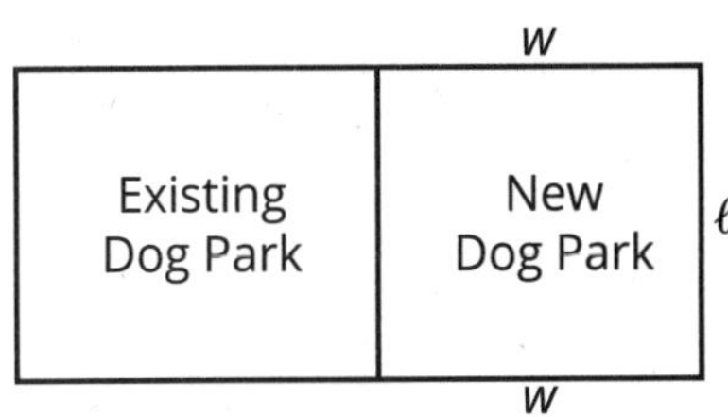

   a. Determine the length of the new dog park, *l*, in terms of the width, *w*.

   b. Write the function $A(w)$ to represent the area of the new dog park as a function of the width, *w*. Does this function have a minimum or a maximum point? Explain your answer.

   c. Determine the *x*-intercepts of the function. Explain what each means in terms of the problem situation.

© Carnegie Learning, Inc.

Go to LiveHint.com for help on the PRACTICE questions.

(d) What should the dimensions of the dog park be to maximize the area? What is the maximum area of the park?

(e) Sketch the graph of the function. Label the axes, the maximum or minimum point, the x-intercepts, and the y-intercept.

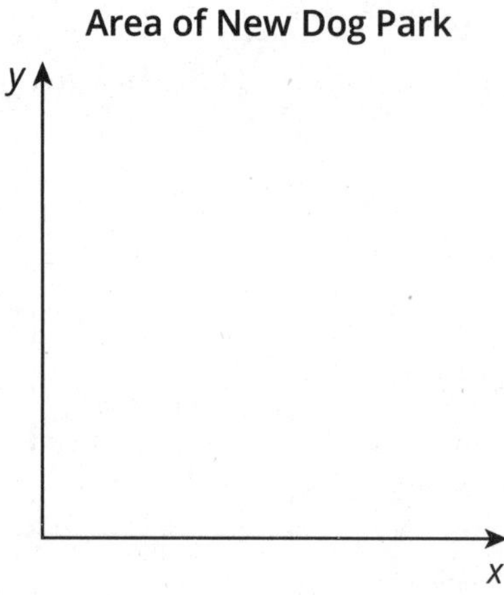

(f) Use the graph to determine the dimensions of the park if they restrict the area to 105,000 square feet.

© Carnegie Learning, Inc.

STRETCH Optional

1. Sketch a graph of a quadratic function that has a maximum point at (0, 2) and x-intercepts when $x = \pm 2$.
2. What is the quadratic function of your graph? Explain your reasoning.

LESSON 2

Endless Forms Most Beautiful

Key Characteristics of Quadratic Functions

KEY TERMS

- **second differences**
- **concave up**
- **concave down**
- **general form of a quadratic function**
- **factored form**
- **vertex of a parabola**
- **axis of symmetry**

Learning Goals

- Identify the factored form and general form of an equation for a quadratic function.
- Determine the equation for the axis of symmetry of a quadratic function, given the equation in general form or factored form.
- Determine the absolute minimum or absolute maximum point on the graph of a quadratic function and identify this point as the vertex.
- Describe intervals of increase and decrease in relation to the axis of symmetry on the graph of a quadratic function.
- Use key characteristics of the graph of a quadratic function to write an equation in factored form.

REVIEW (1–2 minutes)

> Determine the slope and *y*-intercept of each linear function.

1. $h(x) = 3x$

2. $g(x) = \frac{1}{2}(x - 5)$

3. $m(x) = \frac{8x}{4} + 1$

You have identified key characteristics of linear and exponential functions.

What are the key characteristics of quadratic functions?

© Carnegie Learning, Inc.

Dogs, Handshakes, Pumpkins, Ghosts

> Consider the four quadratic models you investigated in the previous lesson. There are multiple equivalent ways to write the equation to represent each situation and a unique parabola to represent the equivalent equations. You can also represent the function using a table of values.

Area of Dog Enclosure

$A(s) = -2s^2 + 100s$

$= -2(s)(s - 50)$

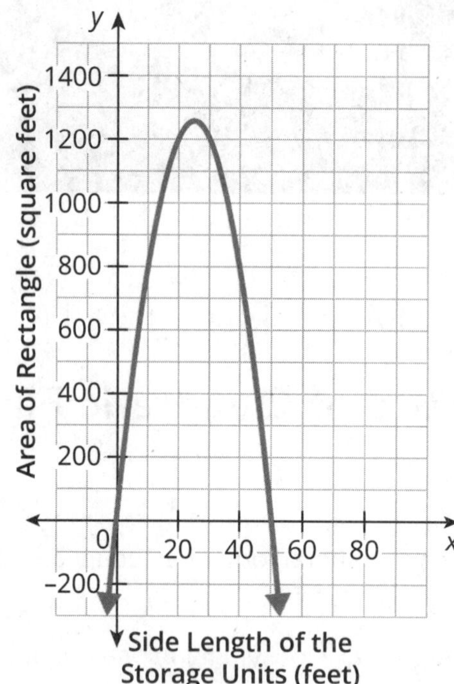

s	$A(s)$
0	0
1	98
2	192
3	282
4	368

Handshake Problem

$f(n) = \frac{1}{2}n^2 - \frac{1}{2}n$

$= \frac{1}{2}(n)(n - 1)$

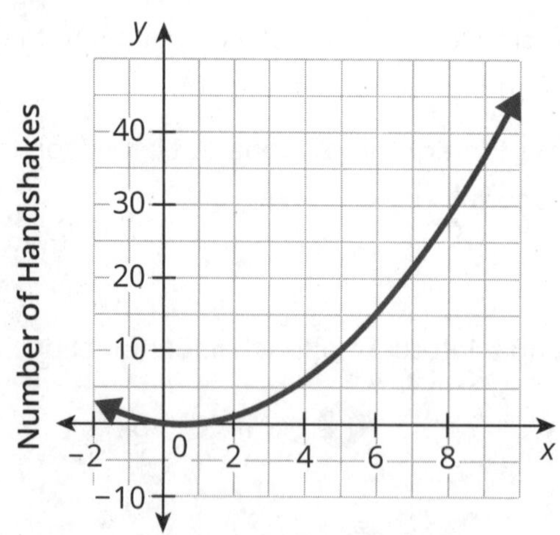

n	$f(n)$
0	0
1	0
2	1
3	3
4	6

© Carnegie Learning, Inc.

Punkin' Chunkin'

$h(t) = -16t^2 + 128t + 68$

$= -16\left(t - \frac{17}{2}\right)\left(t + \frac{1}{2}\right)$

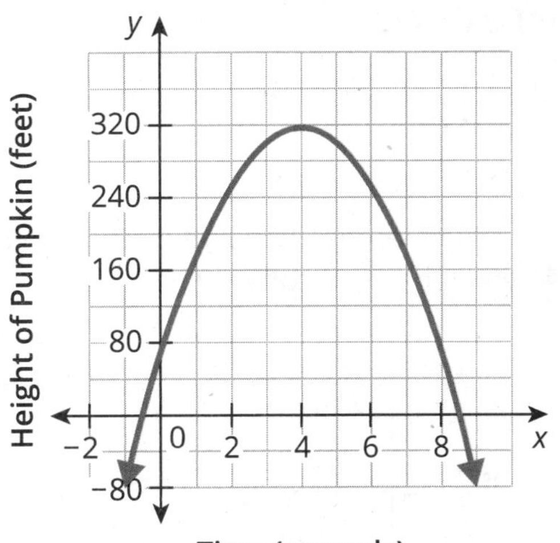

t	$h(t)$
0	68
1	180
2	260
3	308
4	324

Ghost Tour

$r(x) = -10(x + 10)(x - 50)$

$= -10x^2 + 400x + 5000$

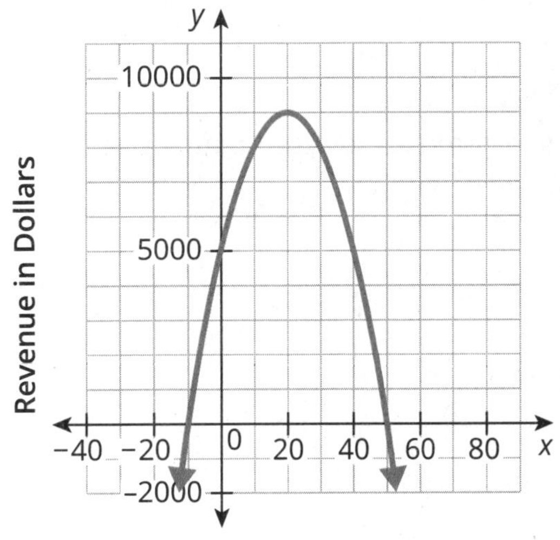

x	$r(x)$
0	5000
1	5390
2	5760
3	6110
4	6440

1. Consider each representation.

   (a) How can you tell from the structure of the equation that it is quadratic?

   (b) How can you tell from the shape of the graph that it is quadratic?

   (c) How can you tell from the table that the relationship is quadratic?

© Carnegie Learning, Inc.

Second Differences

Let's explore how a table of values can show that a function is quadratic.

HABITS OF MIND

- Look for and make use of structure.
- Look for and express regularity in repeated reasoning.

Consider the table of values represented by the basic quadratic function. This table represents the first differences between seven consecutive points.

x	$f(x)$
−3	9
−2	4
−1	1
0	0
1	1
2	4
3	9

First Differences

4 − 9 = −5
1 − 4 = −3
0 − 1 = −1
1 − 0 = 1
4 − 1 = 3
9 − 4 = 5

REMEMBER . . .

You can tell whether a table represents a linear function by analyzing first differences. First differences imply the calculation of $y_2 - y_1$ for consecutive values of x.

1. What do the first differences tell you about the relationship of the table of values?

Let's consider the *second differences*. The **second differences** are the differences between consecutive values of the first differences.

2. Calculate the second differences for $f(x)$. **What do you notice?**

© Carnegie Learning, Inc.

You know that with linear functions, the first differences are constant. For quadratic functions, the second differences are constant.

Let's consider the graph of the basic quadratic function, $f(x) = x^2$, and the distances represented by the first and second differences. Graph 1 shows the distances between consecutive values of $f(x)$. The blue line segments are different lengths because the first differences are not the same.

Graph 1

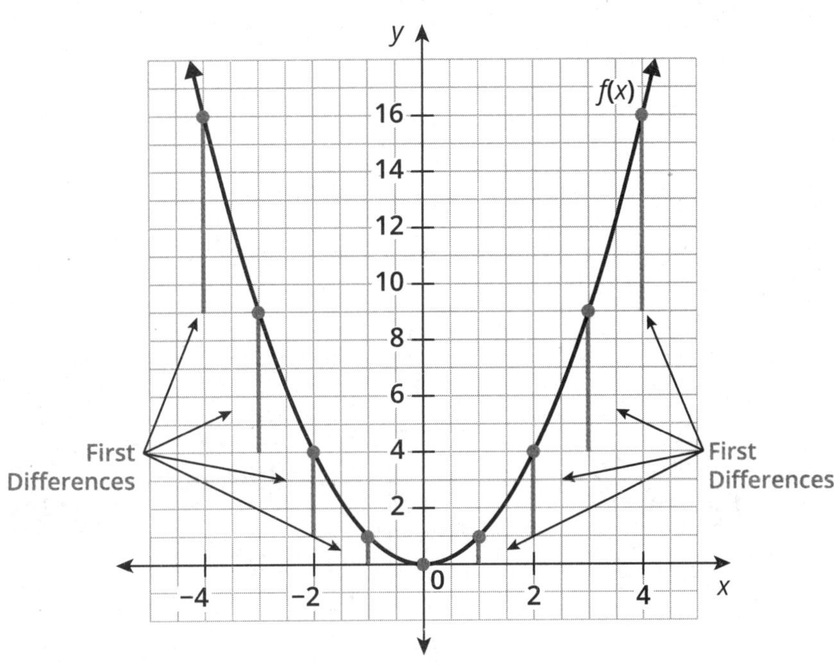

Graph 2 shows the lengths of the first differences repositioned to align along the x-axis. By comparing these lengths, you can see the second differences.

Graph 2

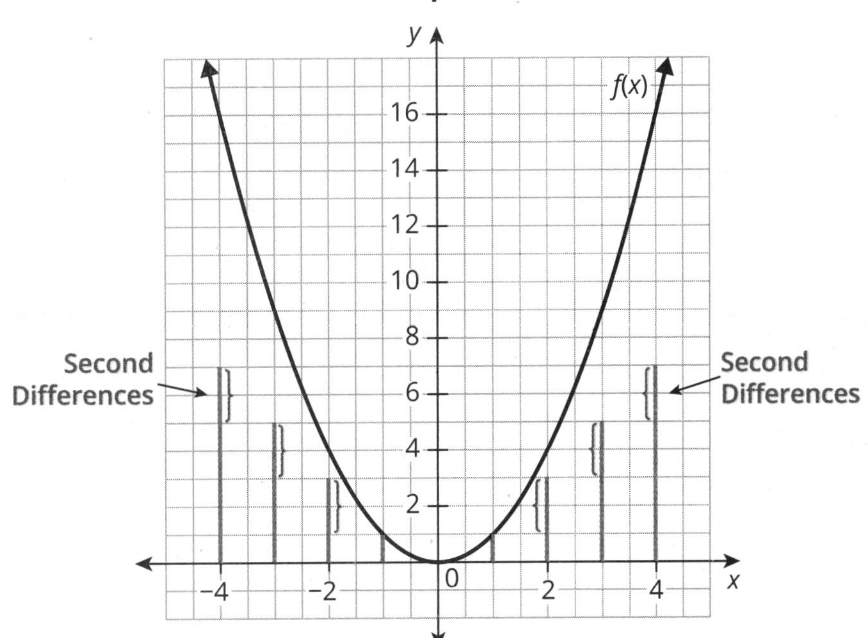

REMEMBER . . .
Quadratic equations are polynomials with a degree of 2. Their second differences are constant. Linear functions are polynomials with a degree of 1, and their first differences are constant.

© Carnegie Learning, Inc.

3 How does the representation in Graph 1 support the first differences calculated from the table of values?

4 How does the representation in Graph 2 support the second differences you calculated in the table?

5 Identify each equation as linear or quadratic. Complete the table to calculate the first and second differences. Then, sketch the graph.

(a) $y = 2x$ ______________

x	y	First Differences	Second Differences
–3	–6		
–2	–4		
–1	–2		
0	0		
1	2		
2	4		
3	6		

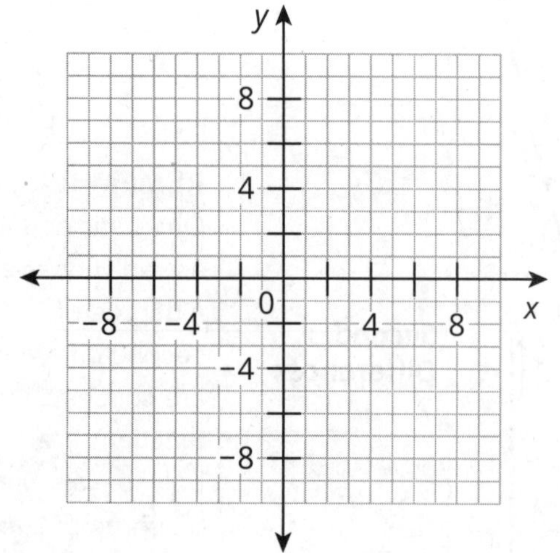

(b) $y = 2x^2$ ______________

x	y	First Differences	Second Differences
–3	18		
–2	8		
–1	2		
0	0		
1	2		
2	8		
3	18		

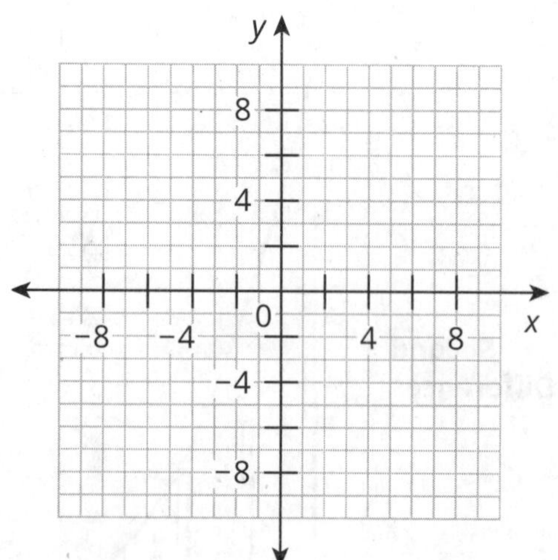

© Carnegie Learning, Inc.

ⓒ $y = -x + 4$ ________________

x	y	First Differences	Second Differences
-3	7		
-2	6		
-1	5		
0	4		
1	3		
2	2		
3	1		

ⓓ $y = -x^2 + 4$ ________________

x	y	First Differences	Second Differences
-3	-5		
-2	0		
-1	3		
0	4		
1	3		
2	0		
3	-5		

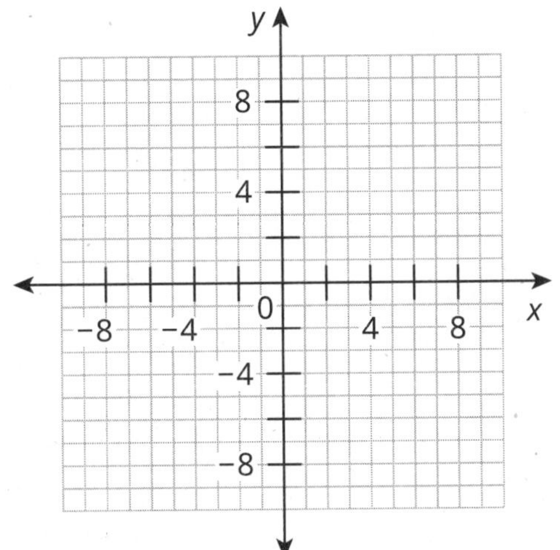

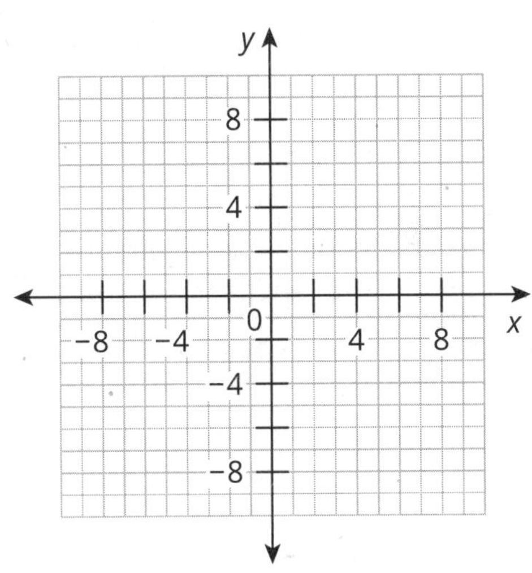

6 Compare the signs of the first and second differences for each function and its graph.

ⓐ How do the signs of the first differences for a linear function relate to the graph either increasing or decreasing?

ⓑ How do the signs of the second differences for quadratic functions relate to whether the parabola is opening upward or downward?

TAKE NOTE . . .

A graph that opens upward is **concave up**. A graph that opens downward is **concave down**.

© Carnegie Learning, Inc.

Analyzing the Leading Coefficient

HABITS OF MIND
- Look for and make use of structure.
- Look for and express regularity in repeated reasoning.

You know that different forms of an equation can reveal different characteristics about functions. You can write quadratic functions in different forms.

A quadratic function written in the form $f(x) = ax^2 + bx + c$, where $a \neq 0$, is in **general form**, or standard form. In this form, a and b are numeric coefficients and c is a constant.

A quadratic function written in **factored form** is in the form $f(x) = a(x - r_1)(x - r_2)$, where $a \neq 0$.

REMEMBER . . .
The leading coefficient of an equation is the numeric coefficient of the term with the greatest power.

1 Identify the general form and factored form of each equation in the Getting Started.

2 Consider the leading coefficient of each function equation in both general form and factored form.

(a) What does the leading coefficient tell you about the graph of each function?

TAKE NOTE . . .
The graph of a quadratic function has either an absolute maximum point or an absolute minimum point.

(b) How does the leading coefficient help you identify whether the function has an absolute minimum or maximum point?

(c) How can you determine the y-intercept of the graph using general form?

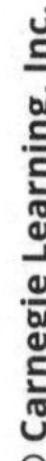
© Carnegie Learning, Inc.

3 Determine from the equation whether each quadratic function has an absolute maximum or absolute minimum point. **Explain how you know.**

(a) $f(n) = 2n^2 + 3n - 1$

(b) $g(x) = -2x^2 - 3x + 1$

(c) $r(x) = -\frac{1}{2}x^2 - 3x + 1$

(d) $b(x) = -0.009(x + 50)(x - 250)$

(e) $f(t) = \frac{1}{3}(x - 1)(x - 1)$

(f) $j(x) = 2x(1 - x)$

© Carnegie Learning, Inc.

Axis of Symmetry

HABITS OF MIND
- Look for and make use of structure.
- Look for and express regularity in repeated reasoning.

The **vertex of a parabola** is the lowest or highest point on the graph of the quadratic function.

The **axis of symmetry** or the line of symmetry of a parabola is the vertical line that passes through the vertex and divides the parabola into two mirror images. Because the axis of symmetry always divides the parabola into two mirror images, you can say that a parabola has reflectional symmetry.

1 Use patty paper to trace the graph representing the area of the dog enclosure. Then, fold the graph to show the symmetry of the parabola and trace the axis of symmetry.

(a) Place the patty paper over the original graph. What is the equation of the axis of symmetry?

(b) Draw and label the axis of symmetry on the graph from your patty paper.

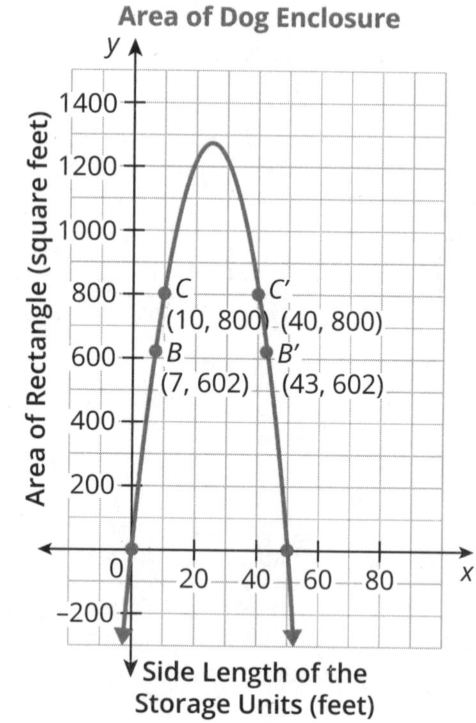

2 Analyze the symmetric points labeled on the graph.

(a) What do you notice about the y-coordinates of the points?

(b) What do you notice about each point's horizontal distance from the axis of symmetry?

(c) How does the x-coordinate of each symmetric point compare to the x-coordinate of the vertex?

© Carnegie Learning, Inc.

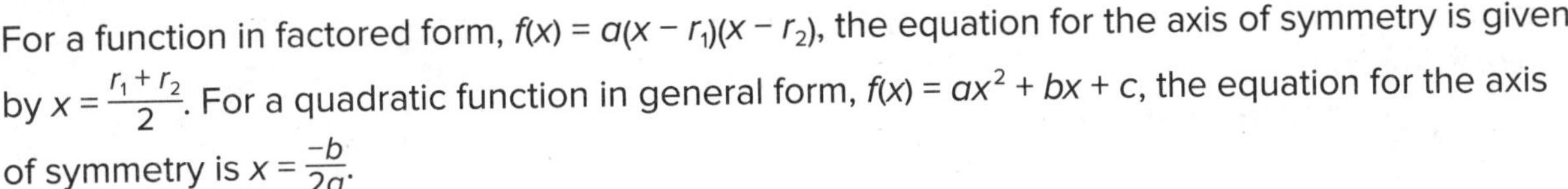

For a function in factored form, $f(x) = a(x - r_1)(x - r_2)$, the equation for the axis of symmetry is given by $x = \frac{r_1 + r_2}{2}$. For a quadratic function in general form, $f(x) = ax^2 + bx + c$, the equation for the axis of symmetry is $x = \frac{-b}{2a}$.

3 Identify the axis of symmetry of the graph of each situation from the Getting Started using the factored form of each equation.

4 Describe the meaning of the axis of symmetry in each situation, if possible.

5 Describe how you can use the axis of symmetry to determine the vertex of a quadratic function, given the equation for the function in factored form.

THINK ABOUT . . .
The y-value of the vertex is either the absolute minimum or absolute maximum point of the graph.

As you analyze a parabola from left to right, it will have either an interval of increase followed by an interval of decrease, or an interval of decrease followed by an interval of increase.

6 How does the absolute maximum or absolute minimum point help you determine each interval?

© Carnegie Learning, Inc.

> Consider the graph of the quadratic function representing the Punkin' Chunkin' problem situation.

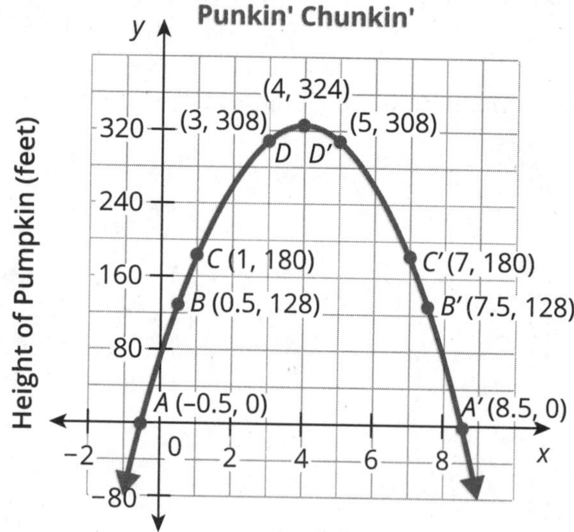

7 Determine the average rate of change between each pair. Then, summarize what you notice.

REMEMBER . . .
The formula for the average rate of change is $\frac{f(b) - f(a)}{b - a}$.

(a) Points A and B

(b) Points A' and B'

(c) Points B and C

(d) Points B' and C'

(e) What do you notice about the average rates of change between pairs of symmetric points?

© Carnegie Learning, Inc.

8 For each function, identify the domain, range, x-intercepts, y-intercept, axis of symmetry, vertex, and interval of increase and decrease.

ⓐ This graph represents the function $f(x) = -2x^2 + 4x$.

Domain: Range:

x-intercepts: y-intercept:

Axis of symmetry: Vertex:

Interval of increase: Interval of decrease:

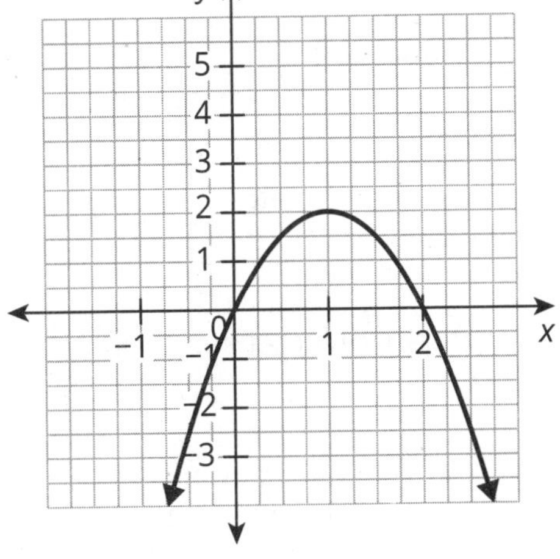

ⓑ This graph represents the function $f(x) = x^2 + 5x + 6$.

Domain: Range:

x-intercepts: y-intercept:

Axis of symmetry: Vertex:

Interval of increase: Interval of decrease:

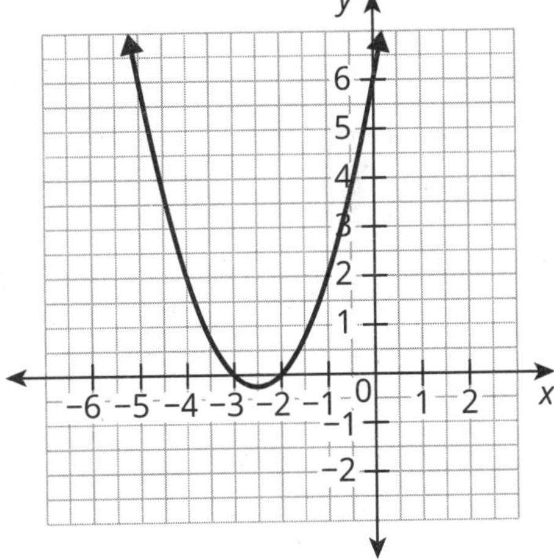

© Carnegie Learning, Inc.

ⓒ This graph represents the function $f(x) = x^2 - x - 2$.

Domain: Range:

x-intercepts: *y*-intercept:

Axis of symmetry: Vertex:

Interval of increase: Interval of decrease:

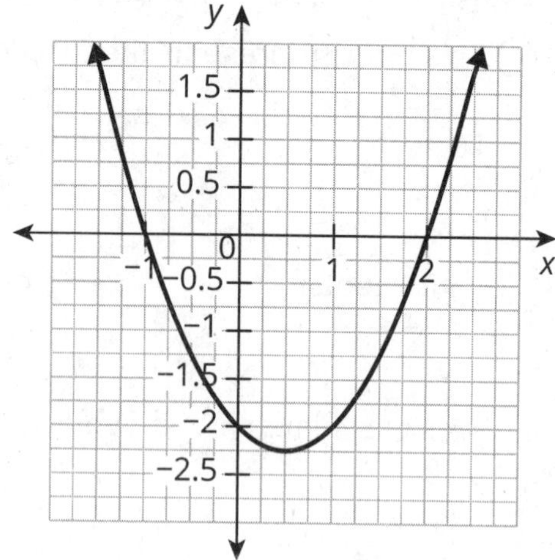

ⓓ This graph represents the function $f(x) = x^2 - 3x + 2$.

Domain: Range:

x-intercepts: *y*-intercept:

Axis of symmetry: Vertex:

Interval of increase: Interval of decrease:

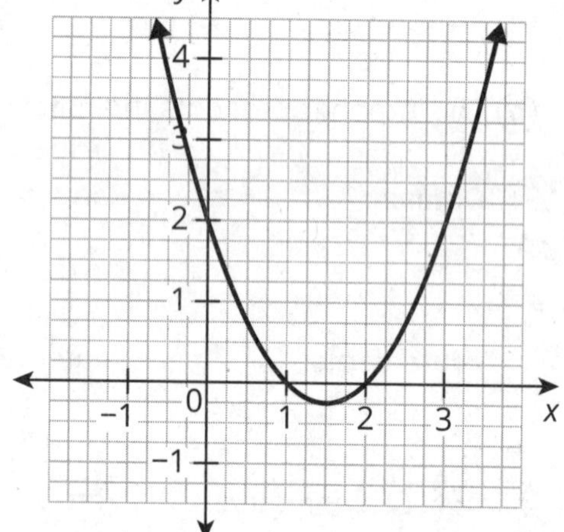

© Carnegie Learning, Inc.

Exploring Factored Form

HABIT OF MIND
- Attend to precision.

You have analyzed quadratic functions and their equations.
Let's look at the factored form of a quadratic function in more detail.

1. A group of students each write a quadratic function in factored form to represent a parabola that opens downward and has zeros at $x = 4$ and $x = -1$.

THINK ABOUT . . .
If given a function $g(x)$ with a zero at $x = 4$, then $g(4) = 0$. You can also interpret this as an x-intercept at (4, 0).

Maureen
My function is
$k(x) = -(x - 4)(x + 1)$.

Tom
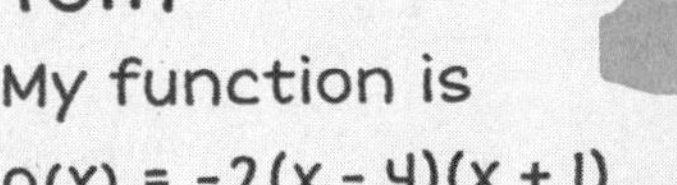
My function is
$g(x) = -2(x - 4)(x + 1)$.

Tim
My function is
$m(x) = 2(x - 4)(x + 1)$.

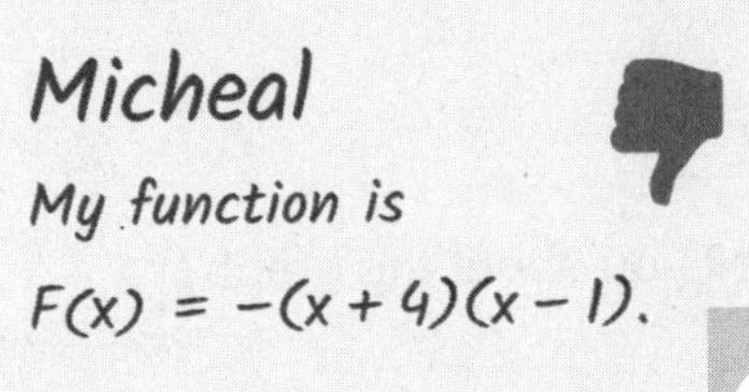
Micheal
My function is
$F(x) = -(x + 4)(x - 1)$.

a) Sketch a graph of each student's function and label key points. What are the similarities among all the graphs? What are the differences among the graphs?

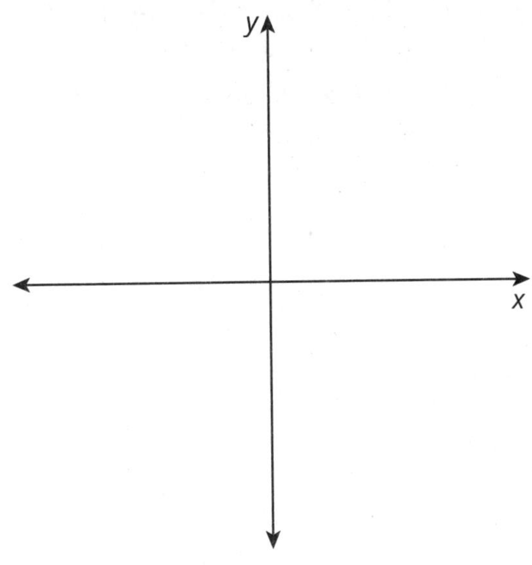

b) What would you tell Tim and Micheal to correct their functions?

© Carnegie Learning, Inc.

ⓒ How is it possible to have more than one correct function?

ⓓ How many possible functions can represent the given characteristics? **Explain your reasoning.**

2 Consider a quadratic function written in factored form, $f(x) = a(x - r_1)(x - r_2)$.

ⓐ What does the sign of the a-value tell you about the graph?

ⓑ What do r_1 and r_2 tell you about the graph?

3 Use the given information to write a function in factored form. Sketch a graph of each function and label key points, which include the vertex and the x- and y-intercepts.

ⓐ The parabola opens upward, and the zeros are at $x = 2$ and $x = 4$.

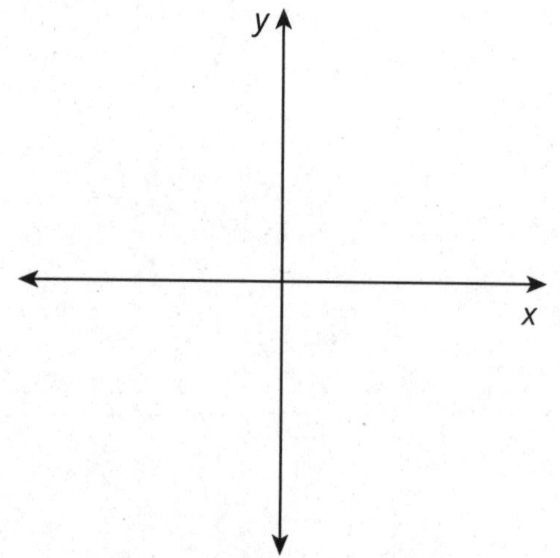

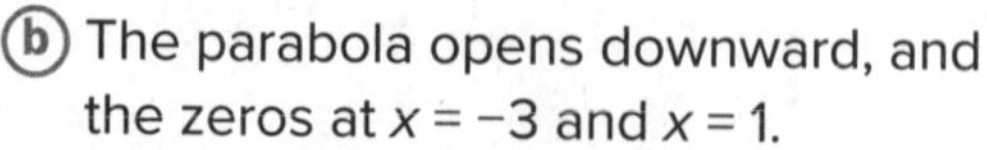

ⓑ The parabola opens downward, and the zeros at $x = -3$ and $x = 1$.

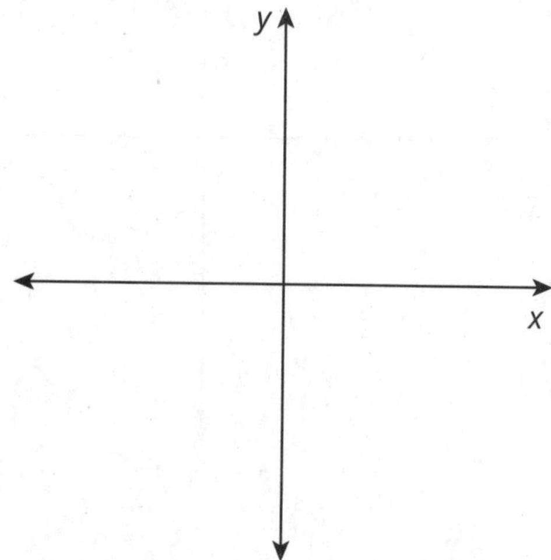

© Carnegie Learning, Inc.

ⓒ The parabola opens downward, and the zeros are at $x = 0$ and $x = 5$.

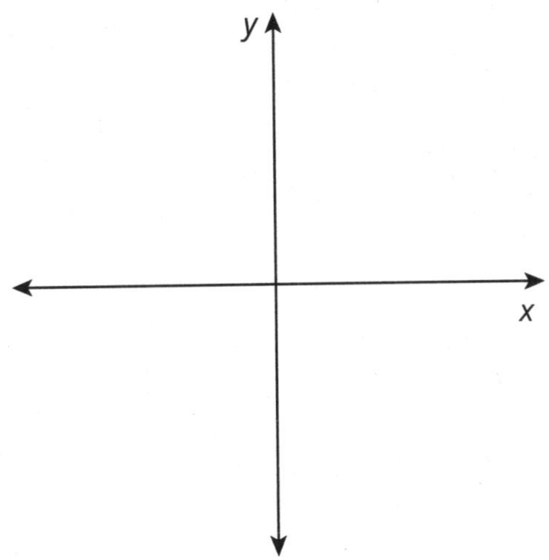

ⓓ The parabola opens upward, and the zeros are at $x = -2.5$ and $x = 4.3$.

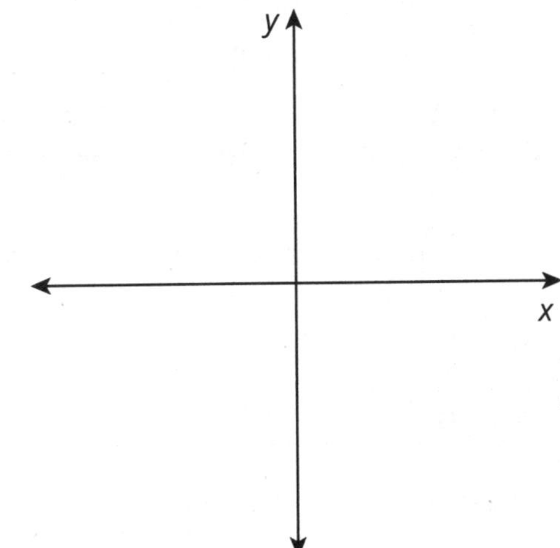

4 Compare your quadratic functions with your classmates' functions. **How does the *a*-value affect the shape of the graph?**

© Carnegie Learning, Inc.

5 For each quadratic function:

- Use the general form to determine the axis of symmetry, the vertex, and the y-intercept. Graph and label each characteristic.
- Use technology to identify the zeros. Label the zeros on the graph.
- Draw the parabola. Use the curve to write the function in factored form.
- Verify the function you wrote in factored form is equivalent to the given function in general form.

REMEMBER . . .
A function written in general form, $f(x) = ax^2 + bx + c$, has an axis of symmetry at $x = \frac{-b}{2a}$.

(a) $h(x) = x^2 - 8x + 12$

Zeros: ______________________

Factored form: ______________________

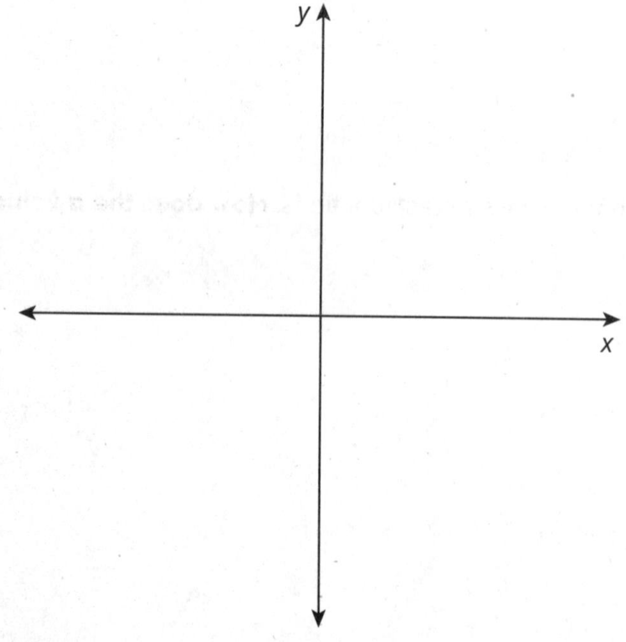

© Carnegie Learning, Inc.

(b) $r(x) = -2x^2 + 6x + 20$

Zeros: ______________________

Factored form: ______________________

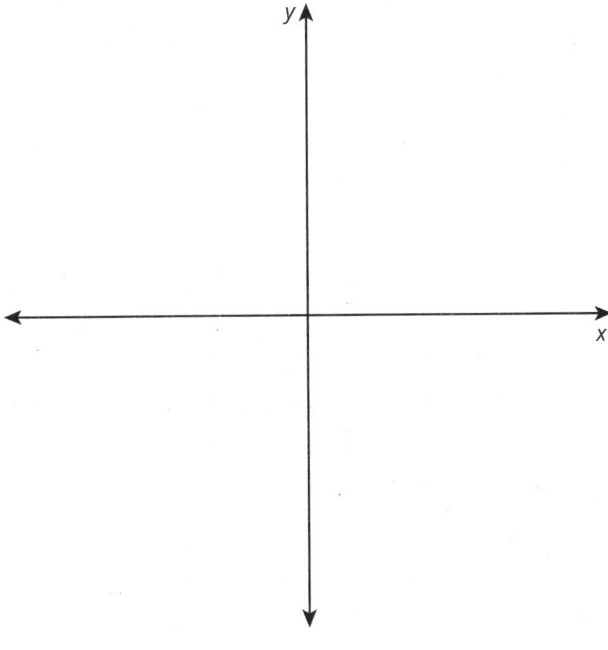

(c) $w(x) = -x^2 - 4x$

Zeros: ______________________

Factored form: ______________________

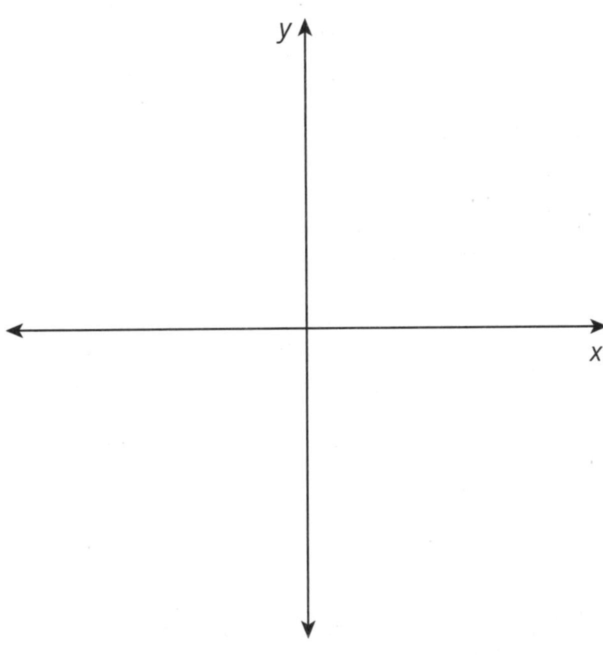

© Carnegie Learning, Inc.

(d) $c(x) = 3x^2 - 3$

Zeros: ____________________

Factored form: ____________________

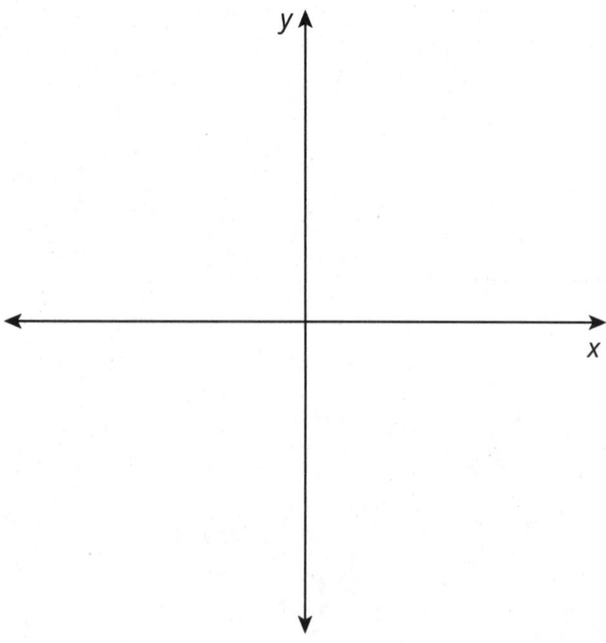

© Carnegie Learning, Inc.

Quadratic Sleuthing

> Use the given information to answer each question. Do not use technology. **Show your work.**

THINK ABOUT . . .
Sketch a graph by hand if you need a model.

1. Determine the axis of symmetry of each parabola.

   a) The x-intercepts of the parabola are (1, 0) and (5, 0).

   b) The x-intercepts of the parabola are (−3.5, 0) and (4.1, 0).

   c) Two symmetric points on the parabola are (−7, 2) and (0, 2).

2. Describe how to determine the axis of symmetry given the x-intercepts of a parabola.

3. Determine the location of the vertex of each parabola.

   a) The function $f(x) = x^2 + 4x + 3$ has the axis of symmetry $x = -2$.

   b) The equation of the parabola is $y = x^2 - 4$, and the x-intercepts are (−2, 0) and (2, 0).

   c) The function $f(x) = x^2 + 6x - 5$ has two symmetric points (−1, −10) and (−5, −10).

© Carnegie Learning, Inc.

4 Describe how to determine the vertex of a parabola given the equation and the axis of symmetry.

5 Determine another point on each parabola.

(a) The axis of symmetry is $x = 2$, and a point on the parabola is (0, 5).

(b) The vertex is (0.5, 9), and an x-intercept is (−2.5, 0).

(c) The vertex is (−2, −8), and a point on the parabola is (−1, −7).

6 Describe how to determine another point on a parabola when you are given one point and the axis of symmetry.

© Carnegie Learning, Inc.

LESSON 2 ASSIGNMENT

> Use a separate piece of paper for your Journal entry.

JOURNAL

1. Describe the characteristics of a quadratic function that you can determine from its equation in general form.
2. Describe the characteristics of a quadratic function that you can determine from its equation in factored form.

REMEMBER

The sign of the leading coefficient of a quadratic function in standard form or factored form describes whether the function has an absolute maximum or absolute minimum.

A parabola is a smooth curve with reflectional symmetry. The axis of symmetry contains the vertex of the graph of the function, which is located at the absolute minimum or maximum point of the function.

PRACTICE

1. Analyze each quadratic function.

   $g(x) = 4x^2 - 12x + 16$ $h(x) = -\frac{1}{4}(x - 3)(x + 2)$

   (a) Identify the quadratic function as general form or factored form.

   (b) Does the quadratic function have an absolute maximum or absolute minimum?

   (c) Does the graph open upward or downward?

   (d) Determine any intercepts from the given form of the function.

2. Analyze each quadratic function.

   $f(x) = -\frac{2}{3}x^2 - 3x + 15$ $g(x) = \frac{3}{4}x^2 + 12x - 27$

   (a) Identify the axis of symmetry.

   (b) Use the axis of symmetry to determine the ordered pair of the vertex.

© Carnegie Learning, Inc.

Go to LiveHint.com for help on the PRACTICE questions.

ⓒ Describe the intervals of increase and decrease.

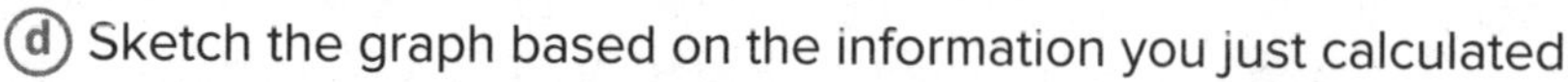

ⓓ Sketch the graph based on the information you just calculated.

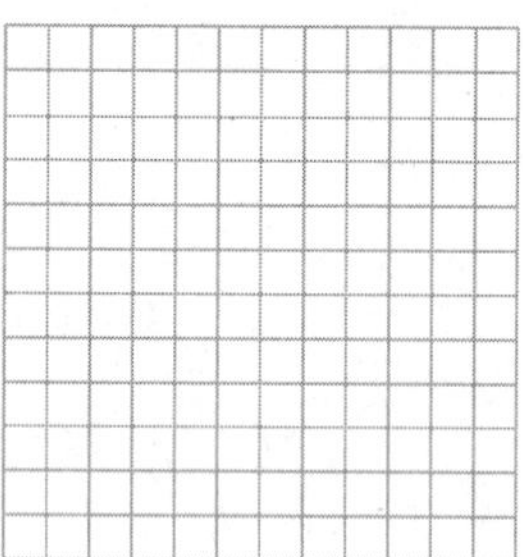

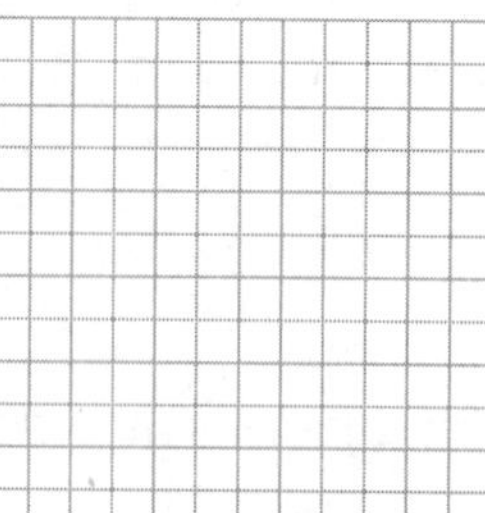

ⓔ Use technology to identify the zeros.

ⓕ Place two pairs of symmetric points on your graph. What is the average rate of change between these pairs of symmetric points?

ⓖ Write the function in factored form.

STRETCH Optional

> Sketch the graph $f(x) = -3x^2 - 4$.

1. How could you change the quadratic function to make the graph open upward? Show the change on the graph.
2. How could you change the quadratic function $f(x) = -3x^2 - 4$ to shift the graph up or down? Show on the graph.
3. How could you change the quadratic function $f(x) = -3x^2 - 4$ to shift the graph right or left? Show the change on the graph.

© Carnegie Learning, Inc.

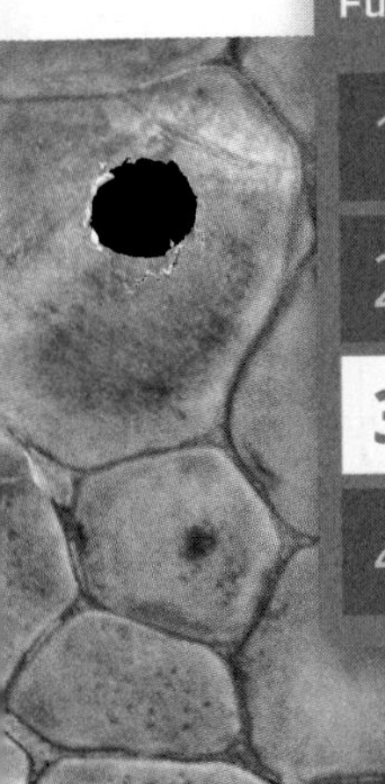

LESSON 3

More Than Meets the Eye

Transformations of Quadratic Functions

KEY TERM

vertex form

Learning Goals

- Translate, reflect, and dilate quadratic functions horizontally and vertically.
- Write equations of quadratic functions given multiple transformations.
- Graph quadratic functions given multiple transformations.
- Identify multiple transformations of quadratic functions given equations.
- Understand the form in which a quadratic function is written can reveal different key characteristics.
- Write quadratic equations in vertex and factored form.

REVIEW (1–2 minutes)

> Write the equation for the axis of symmetry given each quadratic function.

1. $f(x) = -3x^2 - 4x + 5$

2. $f(x) = \frac{1}{4}(x - 1)(x + 2)$

3. $f(x) = -x^2 + 3$

© Carnegie Learning, Inc.

You know how to transform linear, absolute value, and exponential functions.

How can you apply what you know about transformation functions to quadratic functions?

Quadratics and Absolutes

The coordinate plane shows the graph of the absolute value function $f(x) = |x - 4|$ and a quadratic function, $q(x)$.

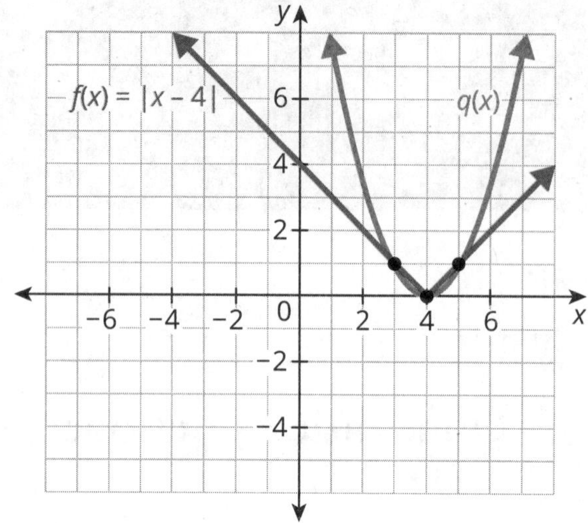

1 How was the basic absolute value function $f(x) = |x|$ transformed to produce this graph?

2 Write an equation that can represent the quadratic function, $q(x)$. **Test your equation with the graph to see whether it is correct.**

3 How does knowing that $1^2 = |1|$ and $(-1)^2 = |-1|$ explain the intersection points of the graph of the absolute value function and the graph of the quadratic function?

© Carnegie Learning, Inc.

ACTIVITY 1

MATHia CONNECTION

- Vertically Translating Quadratic Functions
- Horizontally Translating Quadratic Functions

Translations and Reflections of Quadratic Functions

HABITS OF MIND

- Model with mathematics.
- Use appropriate tools strategically.

Given $g(x) = f(x - C) + D$, consider how to transform the basic function, $f(x) = x^2$, to graph the transformed function.

1 Consider the four quadratic functions, where $f(x) = x^2$ is the basic function.

- $c(x) = x^2 + 3$
- $d(x) = x^2 - 3$
- $j(x) = (x + 3)^2$
- $k(x) = (x - 3)^2$

ASK YOURSELF . . .
How do you think translating quadratics is similar to translating other functions?

(a) Write the functions $c(x)$, $d(x)$, $j(x)$, and $k(x)$ in terms of the basic function. For each, determine whether an operation is performed on the function or on the argument of the function. **Describe the operation.**

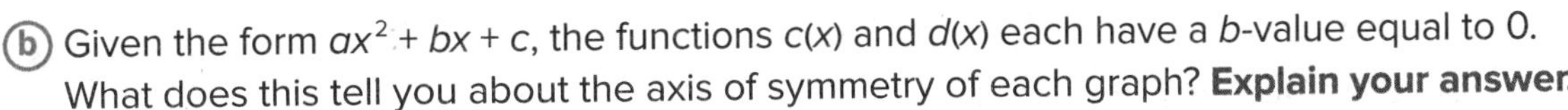

(b) Given the form $ax^2 + bx + c$, the functions $c(x)$ and $d(x)$ each have a b-value equal to 0. What does this tell you about the axis of symmetry of each graph? **Explain your answer.**

(c) Sketch a graph of each function. Label each graph and include key points.

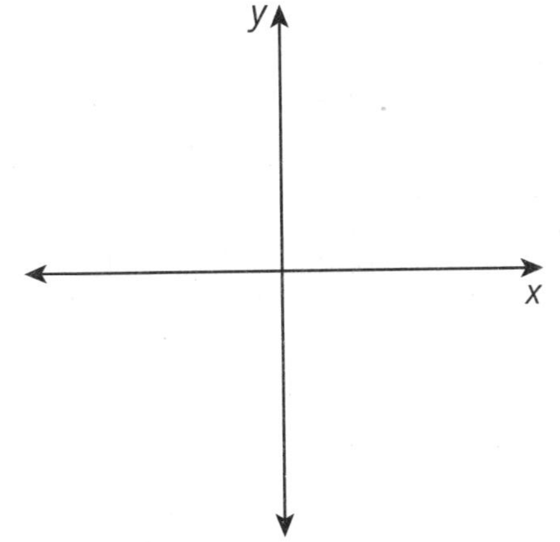

(d) Use coordinate notation to represent the vertical or horizontal translation of each function, c, d, j, and k. Each point (x, y) on the graph of $f(x)$:

- becomes the point __________ on the graph of $c(x)$.
- becomes the point __________ on the graph of $d(x)$.
- becomes the point __________ on the graph of $j(x)$.
- becomes the point __________ on the graph of $k(x)$.

© Carnegie Learning, Inc.

You know that for any basic function, the *C*- and *D*-values describe translations of the function. The *C*-value defines an operation performed on the argument, and it describes a horizontal translation that affects the input values. The *D*-value defines an operation performed on the function, and it describes a vertical translation that affects the output values.

Now, let's consider reflections of graphs. You know that when a negative is on the outside of a function, the graph reflects across a horizontal line of reflection. When a negative is on the inside of a function, the graph reflects across a vertical line of reflection.

> Given $f(x) = x^2$, consider $g(x) = -f(x)$ and $h(x) = f(-x)$.

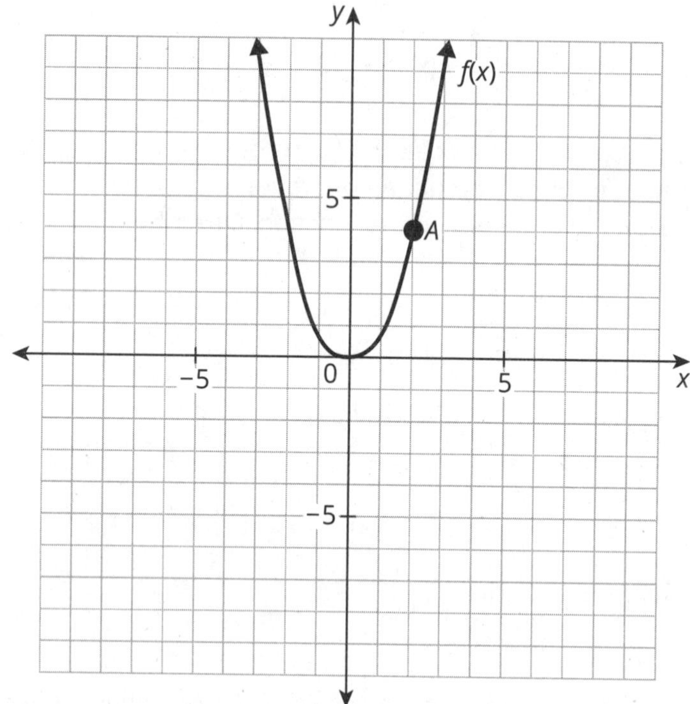

2 Consider the placement of the negative sign in each function, $g(x)$ and $h(x)$.

ⓐ Sketch the graph and describe the line of reflection for $g(x)$. Label A' on your graph.

ⓑ Sketch the graph and describe the line of reflection for $h(x)$. Label A'' on your graph.

ⓒ Use coordinate notation to represent the reflection of each function. Each point (x, y) on the graph of $f(x)$:

- becomes the point ____________ on the graph of $g(x)$.
- becomes the point ____________ on the graph of $h(x)$.

© Carnegie Learning, Inc.

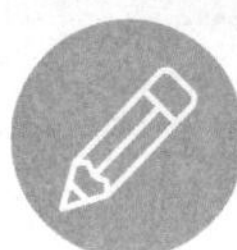

(d) Given the basic quadratic function, $f(x) = x^2$, why does the graph of $f(-x)$ map onto itself?

3 Consider the graph of each given function. Sketch the result of the transformed function. Label A' on your graph. Then describe the transformation you performed.

(a) Given the graph of $v(x)$, sketch $m(x) = v(-x)$.

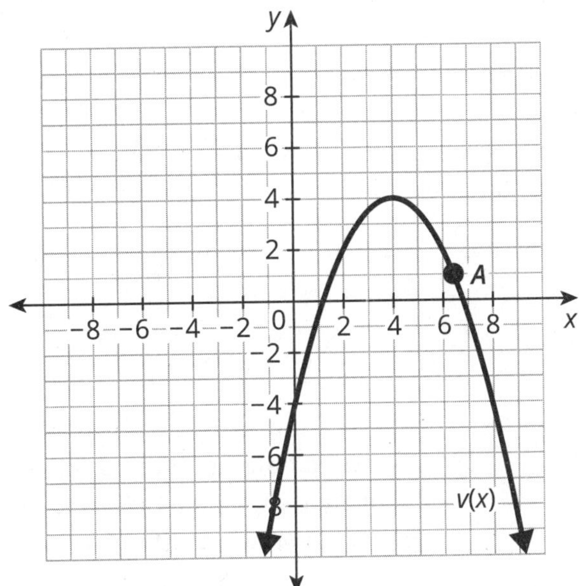

(b) Given the graph of $w(x)$, sketch $z(x) = -w(x)$.

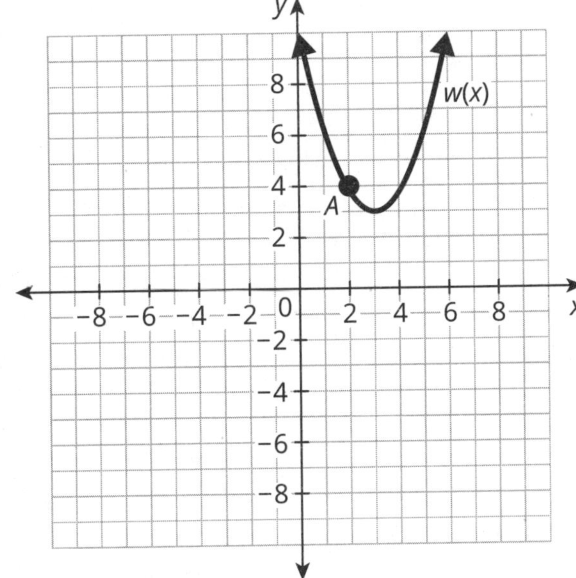

© Carnegie Learning, Inc.

MATHia CONNECTION

- Reflecting and Dilating Quadratic Functions Using Graphs

Vertical and Horizontal Dilations of Quadratic Functions

HABITS OF MIND

- Model with mathematics.
- Use appropriate tools strategically.

You can vertically and horizontally dilate quadratic functions just like other functions you have studied.

1 Consider the three quadratic functions, where $f(x) = x^2$ is the basic function.

- $f(x) = x^2$
- $n(x) = \frac{1}{2}x^2$
- $p(x) = 2x^2$

(a) Write the functions $n(x)$ and $p(x)$ in terms of the basic function $f(x)$. For each, determine whether an operation is performed on the function $f(x)$ or on the argument of the function $f(x)$. **Describe the operation.**

(b) Sketch the graph of each function. Label each graph and include key points.

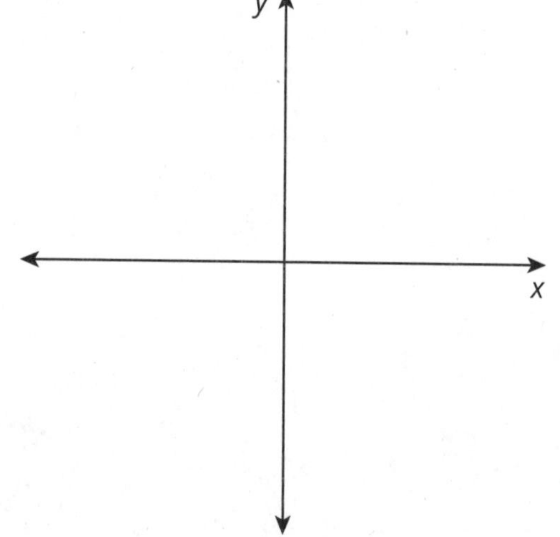

(c) Use coordinate notation to represent the dilation of each function. Each point (x, y) on the graph of $f(x)$:

- becomes the point ________ on the graph of $n(x)$.
- becomes the point ________ on the graph of $p(x)$.

© Carnegie Learning, Inc.

2 Consider the three quadratic functions, where $f(x) = x^2$ is the basic function.

- $f(x) = x^2$
- $t(x) = (3x)^2$
- $q(x) = \left(\frac{1}{3}x\right)^2$

ⓐ Write the functions $t(x)$ and $q(x)$ in terms of the basic function $f(x)$. For each, determine whether an operation is performed on the function $f(x)$ or on the argument of the function $f(x)$. **Describe the operation.**

ⓑ Sketch the graph of each function. Label each graph and include key points.

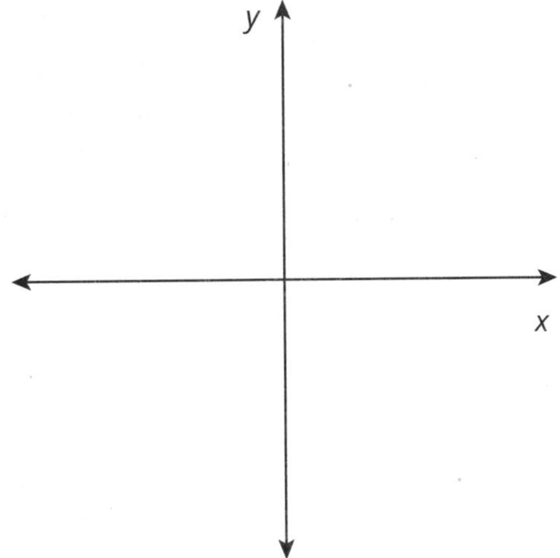

ⓒ Use coordinate notation to represent the dilation of each function. Each point (x, y) on the graph of $f(x)$:

- becomes the point __________ on the graph of $t(x)$.
- becomes the point __________ on the graph of $q(x)$.

© Carnegie Learning, Inc.

Remember, a horizontal dilation is a type of transformation that stretches or compresses the entire graph.

- Horizontal stretching is the stretching of a graph away from the y-axis.
- Horizontal compression is the squeezing of a graph towards the y-axis.

Now, let's compare the graph of $f(x) = x^2$ with $r(x) = f\left(\frac{1}{2}x\right)$.

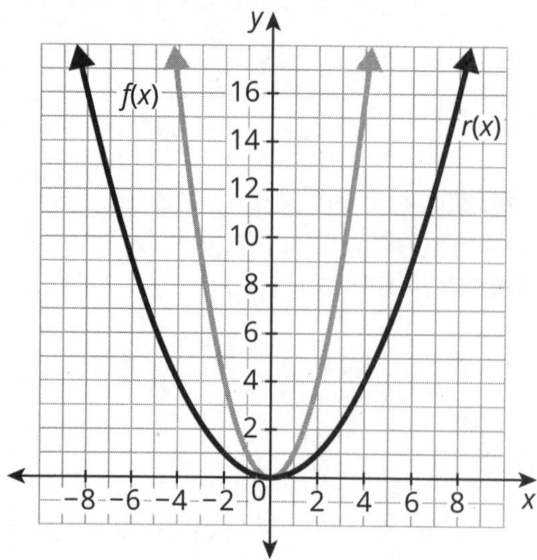

3 Consider the graphs of $f(x)$ and $r(x)$.

ⓐ Analyze the table of values that correspond to the graph. Circle instances where the y-values for each function are the same. Then, list all the points where $f(x)$ and $r(x)$ have the same y-value. The first instance has been circled for you.

x	$f(x) = x^2$	$r(x) = p(\frac{1}{2}x)$
0	0	0
1	1	0.25
2	4	1
3	9	2.25
4	16	4
5	25	6.25
6	36	9

ⓑ How do the x-values compare when the y-values are the same?

ⓒ Complete the statement.

The function $r(x)$ is a ______________ of $f(x)$ by a factor of ______________.

ⓓ How does the factor of stretching or compression compare to the B-value in $r(x)$?

© Carnegie Learning, Inc.

Compared with the graph of $f(x)$, the graph of $f(Bx)$ is:

- Horizontally compressed by a factor of $\frac{1}{|B|}$ when $|B| > 1$.
- Horizontally stretched by a factor of $\frac{1}{|B|}$ when $0 < |B| < 1$.

WORKED EXAMPLE

You can use reference points to graph the function $q(x) = f\left(\frac{1}{3}x\right)$ when $f(x) = x^2$.

From $q(x)$, you know that $C = 0$, $D = 0$, and $B = \frac{1}{3}$. The vertex for $q(x)$ is (0, 0).

Notice $0 < |B| < 1$, so the graph will horizontally stretch by a factor of $\frac{1}{\frac{1}{3}}$, or 3.

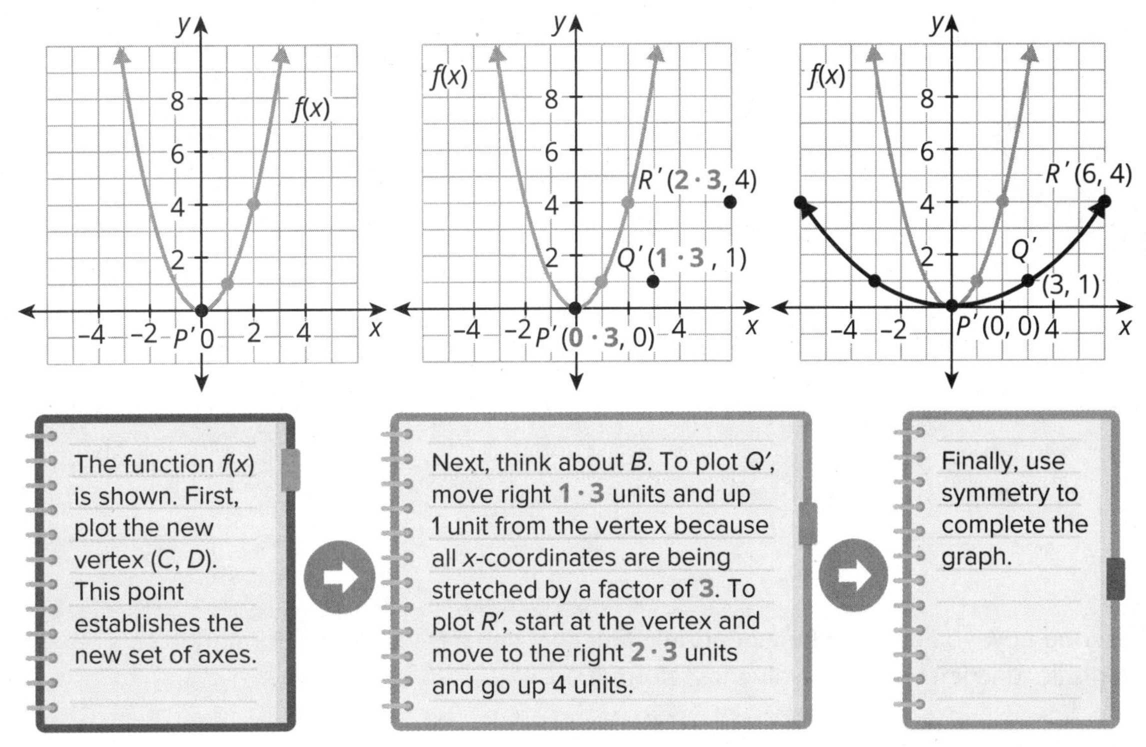

y
x
f(x)
8
6
4
2
−4
−2
P′
0
2
4
R′(2 · 3, 4)
Q′(1 · 3, 1)
P′(0 · 3, 0)
R′(6, 4)
Q′
(3, 1)
P′(0, 0)
The function f(x) is shown. First, plot the new vertex (C, D). This point establishes the new set of axes.
Next, think about B. To plot Q′, move right 1 · 3 units and up 1 unit from the vertex because all x-coordinates are being stretched by a factor of 3. To plot R′, start at the vertex and move to the right 2 · 3 units and go up 4 units.
Finally, use symmetry to complete the graph.

4. If you were asked to graph $p(x) = f(3x)$, describe how the graph would change. If (x, y) is any point on $f(x)$, describe any point on $p(x)$.

© Carnegie Learning, Inc.

5 Consider the graph showing the quadratic functions $k(x)$ and $m(x)$. Antoine and Xi Ling are writing the function $m(x)$ in terms of $k(x)$. Who's correct? **Justify your reasoning.**

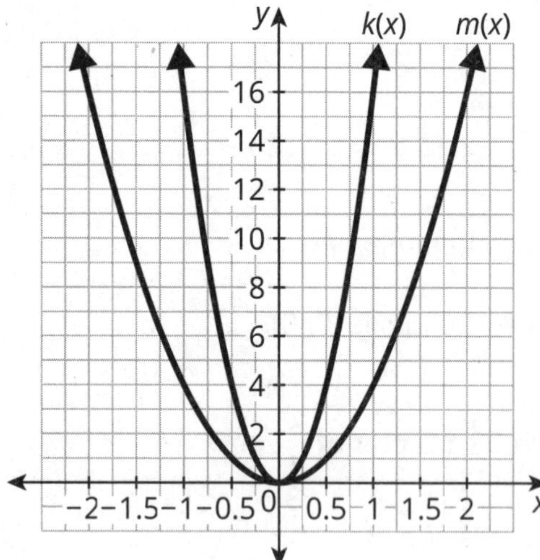

Antoine

m(x) is a transformation of the A-value.

$m(x) = \frac{1}{4}k(x)$

Xi Ling

m(x) is a transformation of the B-value.

$m(x) = k\left(\frac{1}{2}x\right)$

6 Describe how you can rewrite a quadratic function with a *B*-value transformation as a quadratic function with an *A*-value transformation.

7 Rewrite the function from the Worked Example, $q(x) = f\left(\frac{1}{3}x\right)$, without a *B*-value.

© Carnegie Learning, Inc.

> Consider the formula to calculate the area of a circle, $A = \pi r^2$. You can represent the area formula as the function $A(r) = \pi r^2$ and represent it on a coordinate plane.

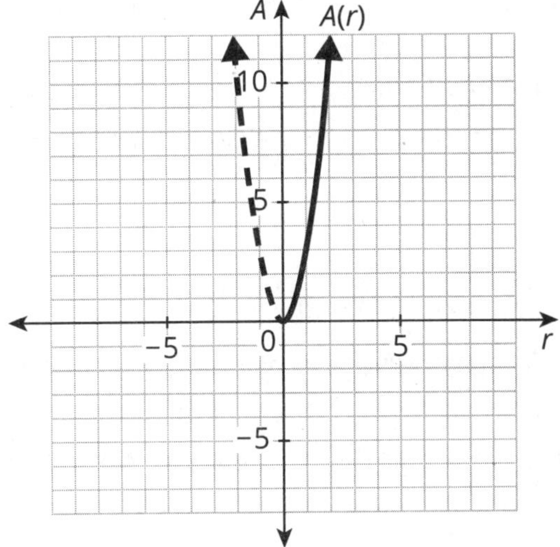

ASK YOURSELF . . .
Why is part of the graph represented with a dashed smooth curve?

8 How is the area affected when you double the radius? **Explain the change in area in terms of a transformation of the graph.**

© Carnegie Learning, Inc.

MATHia CONNECTION

- Transforming Quadratic Functions Using Tables
- Multiple Transformations of Quadratic Functions

Using Reference Points to Graph Quadratic Functions

HABIT OF MIND

- Attend to precision.

Given $y = f(x)$ is the basic quadratic function, you can use reference points to graph $y = Af(B(x - C)) + D$. Any point (x, y) on $f(x)$ maps to the point $\left(\frac{1}{B}x + C, Ay + D\right)$.

WORKED EXAMPLE

Given $f(x) = x^2$, graph the function $g(x) = 2f(x - 3) + 4$.

You can use reference points for $f(x)$ and your knowledge about transformations to graph the function $g(x)$.

From $g(x)$, you know that $A = 2$, $C = 3$, and $D = 4$. The vertex for $g(x)$ is at (3, 4).

Notice $A > 0$, so the graph of the function will vertically stretch by a factor of 2.

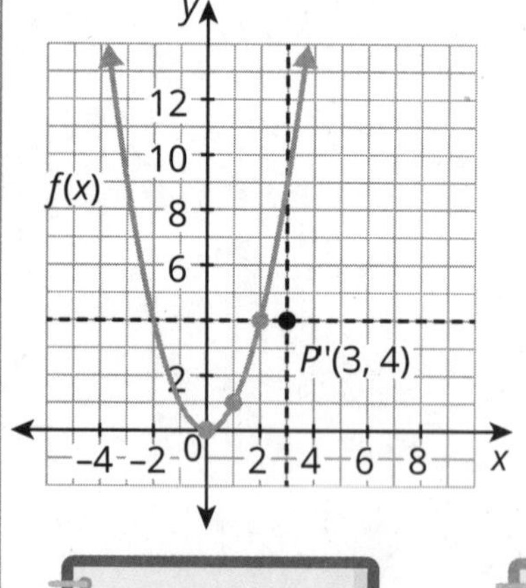

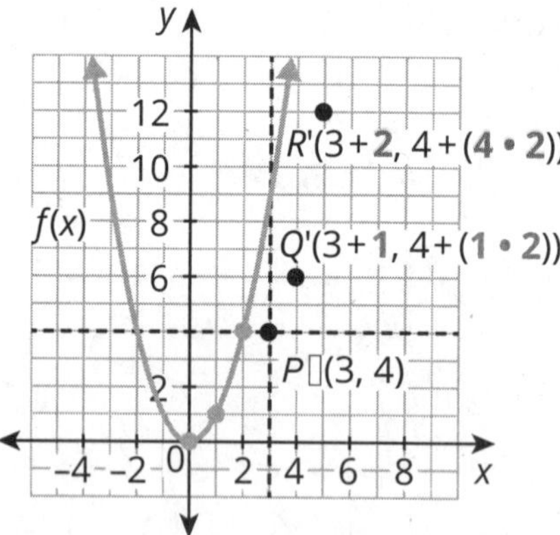

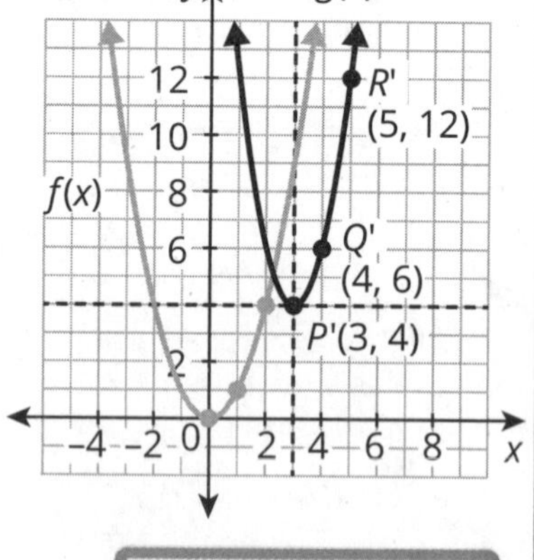

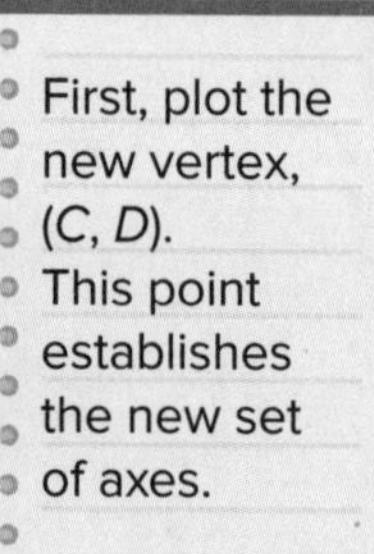

First, plot the new vertex, (C, D). This point establishes the new set of axes.

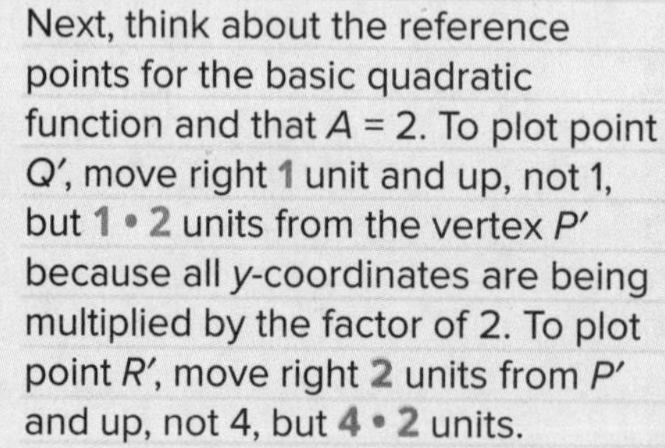

Next, think about the reference points for the basic quadratic function and that $A = 2$. To plot point Q', move right **1** unit and up, not 1, but **1 • 2** units from the vertex P' because all y-coordinates are being multiplied by the factor of 2. To plot point R', move right **2** units from P' and up, not 4, but **4 • 2** units.

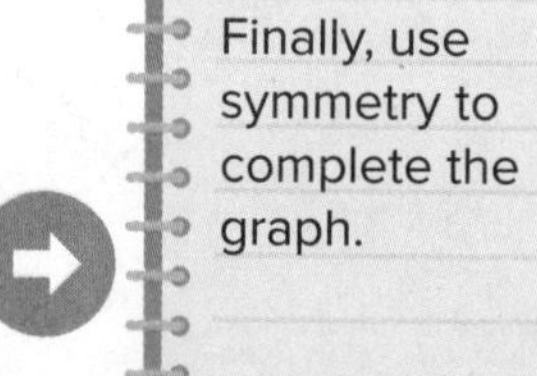

Finally, use symmetry to complete the graph.

THINK ABOUT . . .

What is the pattern of the A-value when transforming the basic quadratic function?

© Carnegie Learning, Inc.

1 Christian, Julia, and Emily each sketched a graph of the equation $y = -x^2 - 3$ using different strategies. **Provide the step-by-step reasoning used by each student.**

Christian

$A = -1$ and $D = -3$

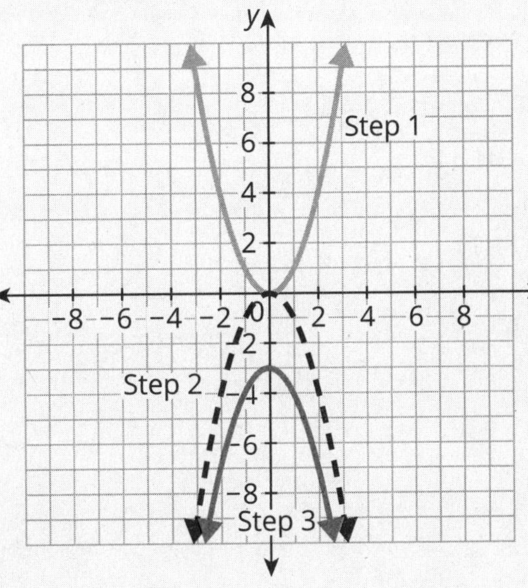

Step 1:

Step 2:

Step 3:

Julia

$D = -3$ and $A = -1$

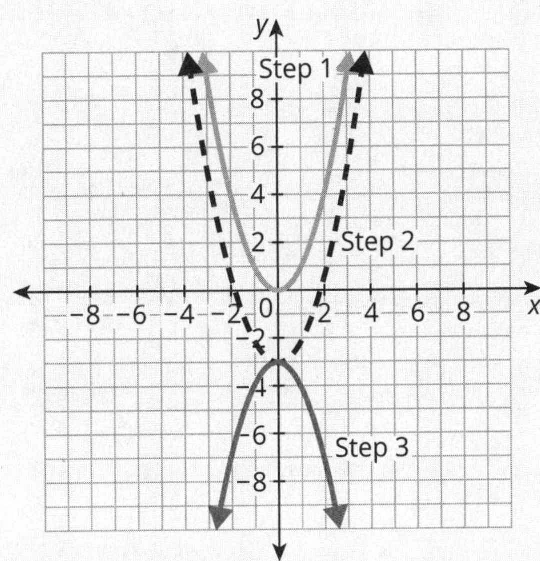

Step 1:

Step 2:

Step 3:

© Carnegie Learning, Inc.

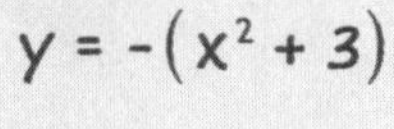

I rewrote the equation as
$y = -(x^2 + 3)$.

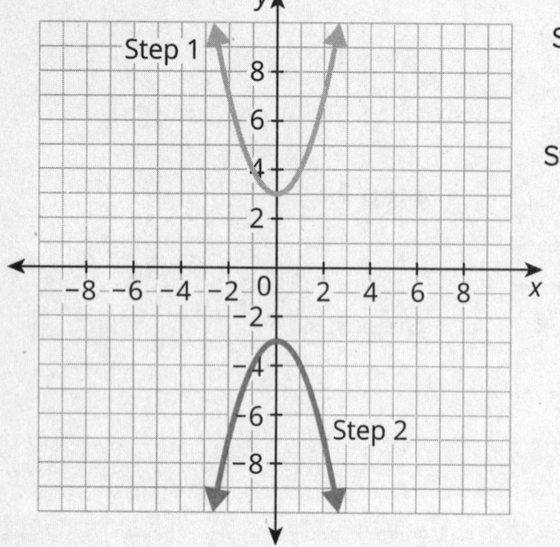

Step 1:

Step 2:

2 Given $y = p(x)$, sketch $m(x) = -p(x + 3)$. Describe the transformations you performed.

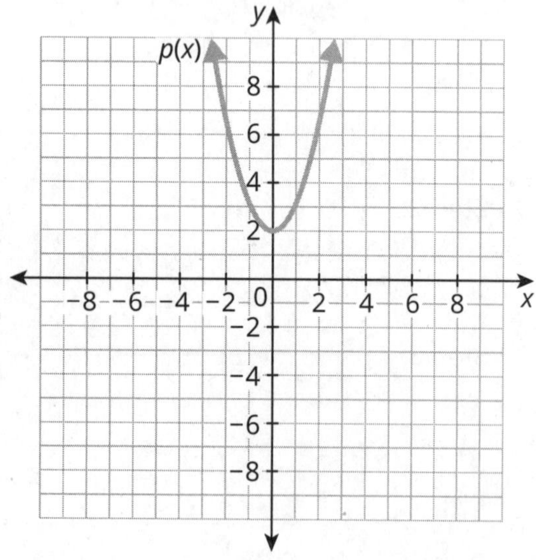

© Carnegie Learning, Inc.

3 Given $f(x) = x^2$, graph each function. Then, write each corresponding quadratic equation.

ⓐ $f'(x) = \frac{1}{2}f(x-2) + 3$

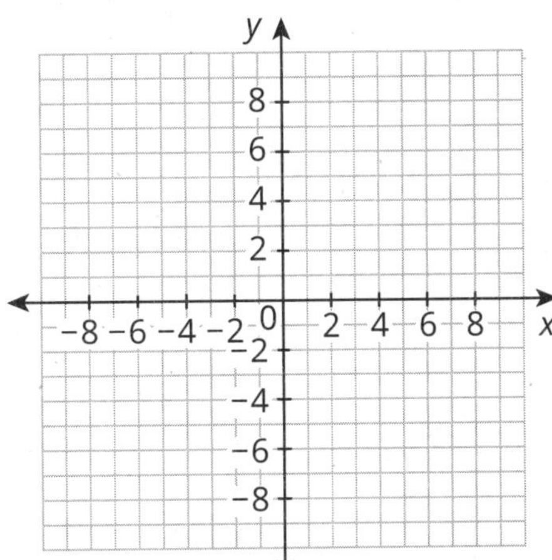

ⓑ $f'(x) = -3f(x+1) + 1$

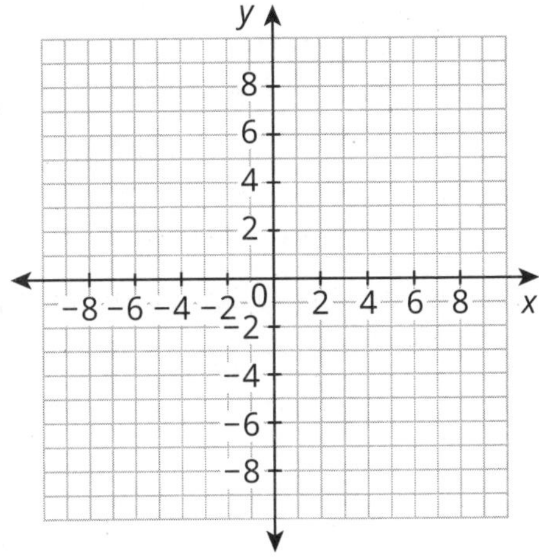

4 Write $n(x)$ in terms of $d(x)$. Then, write the quadratic equation for $n(x)$.

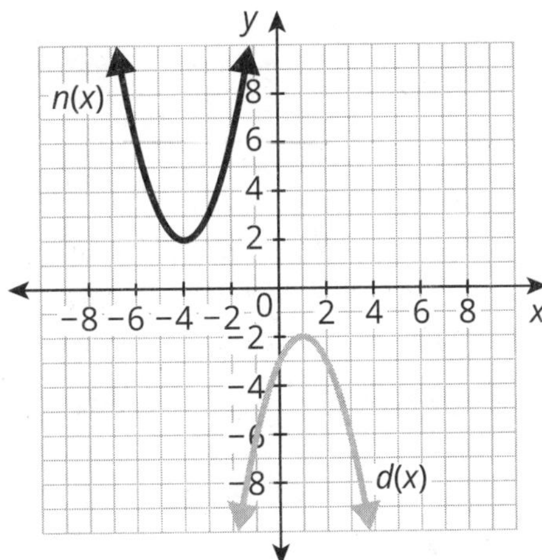

© Carnegie Learning, Inc.

Vertex Form of a Quadratic Function

HABITS OF MIND

- Model with mathematics.
- Use appropriate tools strategically.

Given a basic function $y = f(x)$, you have learned how to identify the effects and graph a function written in the transformation form $g(x) = Af(x - C) + D$. For quadratic functions written in transformation form, $A \neq 0$.

For quadratic functions specifically, you will also see them written in the form $f(x) = a(x - h)^2 + k$, where $a \neq 0$. This is **vertex form**.

TAKE NOTE . . .

In vertex form, the coefficient of x is always 1. Therefore, the B-value in the transformation form in this case is also 1 and is left out of the expression.

1. What does the variable h represent in the vertex form of a quadratic function?

THINK ABOUT . . .

Do you see how this form of the function tells you about the vertex?

2. What does the variable k represent in the vertex form of a quadratic function?

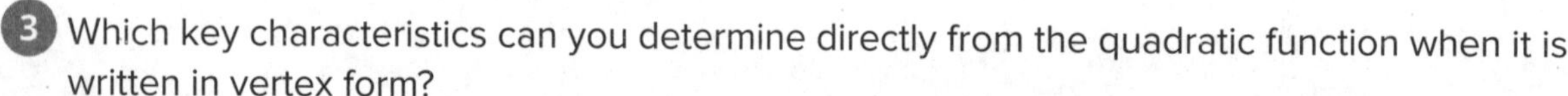

3. Which key characteristics can you determine directly from the quadratic function when it is written in vertex form?

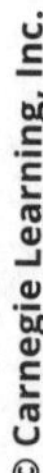

© Carnegie Learning, Inc.

4 Simone, Teresa, Jesse, Aricka, and Leon are working together to write a quadratic function to represent a parabola that opens upward and has a vertex at (−6, −4).

Simone

My function is

$s(x) = 3(x + 6)^2 - 4$.

Teresa

My function is

$t(x) = \frac{1}{4}(x + 6)^2 - 4$.

Jesse

My function is

$j(x) = -3(x + 6)^2 - 4$.

Aricka

My function is

$D(x) = (x + 6)^2 - 4$.

Leon

My function is

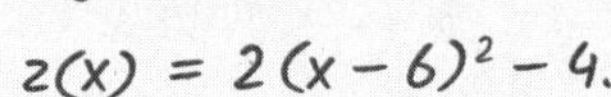

$z(x) = 2(x - 6)^2 - 4$.

(a) What are the similarities among all the graphs of the functions? What are the differences among the graphs?

(b) How is it possible to have more than one correct function?

(c) What would you tell Jesse and Leon to correct their functions?

(d) How many possible functions can you write for the parabola described in this problem? **Explain your reasoning.**

© Carnegie Learning, Inc.

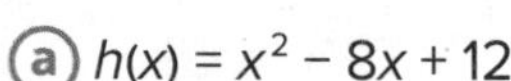

5 Use technology to graph each function. Use the graph to rewrite the function in vertex form and in factored form.

ⓐ $h(x) = x^2 - 8x + 12$

Vertex: ________________

Vertex form: ________________

Zero(s): ________________

Factored form: ________________

ⓑ $r(x) = -2x^2 + 6x + 20$

Vertex: ________________

Vertex form: ________________

Zero(s): ________________

Factored form: ________________

ⓒ $w(x) = -x^2 - 4x$

Vertex: ________________

Vertex form: ________________

Zero(s): ________________

Factored form: ________________

ⓓ $c(x) = 3x^2 - 3$

Vertex: ________________

Vertex form: ________________

Zero(s): ________________

Factored form: ________________

© Carnegie Learning, Inc.

6 Identify the form(s) of each quadratic function as either general form, factored form, or vertex form. Then, state all you know about each quadratic function's key characteristics, based only on the given equation of the function.

(a) $g(x) = -(x - 1)^2 + 9$

(b) $g(x) = x^2 + 4x$

(c) $g(x) = -\frac{1}{2}(x - 3)(x + 2)$

(d) $g(x) = x^2 - 5$

© Carnegie Learning, Inc.

Writing Equations in Vertex and Factored Forms

HABIT OF MIND

- Attend to precision.

You can write a quadratic function in vertex form when you know the coordinates of the vertex and another point on the graph.

WORKED EXAMPLE

Write an equation for a quadratic function with vertex (1, −2) that passes through the point (0, 1).

STEP 1 Substitute the coordinates of the vertex into vertex form of a quadratic function.

$y = a(x - h)^2 + k$

$y = a(x - 1)^2 - 2$

STEP 2 Substitute the coordinates of the other point on the graph for x and y.

$1 = a(0 - 1)^2 - 2$

STEP 3 Solve for the value of a.

$1 = a(-1)^2 - 2$

$1 = a(1) - 2$

$1 = a - 2$

$3 = a$

STEP 4 Rewrite the equation in vertex form, substituting the vertex and the value of a.

$f(x) = 3\,(x - 1)^2 - 2$

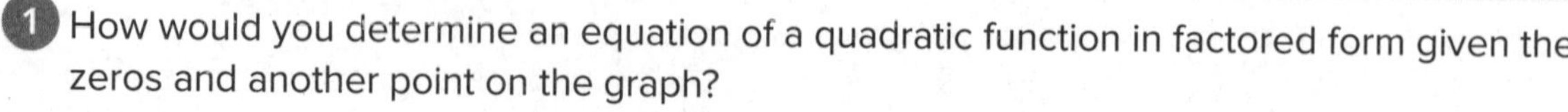

1 How would you determine an equation of a quadratic function in factored form given the zeros and another point on the graph?

© Carnegie Learning, Inc.

2 Dawson and Dave each wrote an equation for the function represented by this graph.

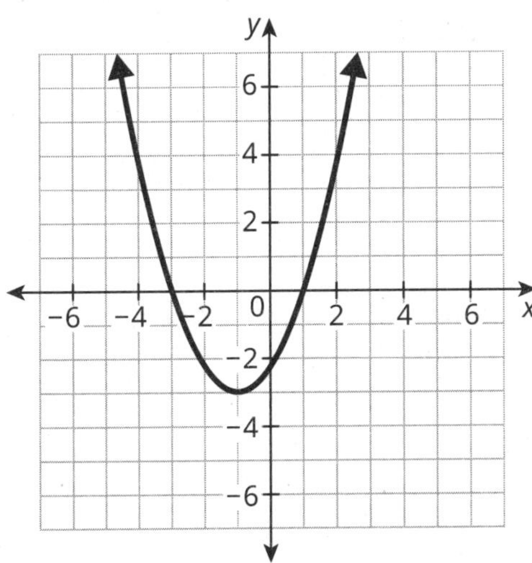

Dawson

$y = a(x + 1)^2 - 3$

$0 = a(1 + 1)^2 - 3$

$0 = 4a - 3$

$3 = 4a$

$a = \frac{3}{4}$

$y = \frac{3}{4}(x + 1)^2 - 3$

Dave

$y = a(x + 3)(x - 1)$

$-3 = a(-1 + 3)(-1 - 1)$

$-3 = a(2)(-2)$

$-3 = -4a$

$a = \frac{3}{4}$

$y = \frac{3}{4}(x + 3)(x - 1)$

(a) Explain Dawson's reasoning.

(b) Explain Dave's reasoning.

(c) Use technology to show that Dawson's equation and Dave's equation are equivalent.

© Carnegie Learning, Inc.

3 Write an equation for a quadratic function in vertex form with vertex (3, 1) that passes through the point (1, 9).

4 Write an equation for a quadratic function in factored form with zeros at $x = -4$ and $x = 0$ that passes through the point (−3, 6).

5 Write an equation for a quadratic function in vertex form with vertex (−1, 6) that passes through the point (−3, 4).

6 Write an equation for a quadratic function $g(x)$ in vertex form given the graph of $g(x)$.

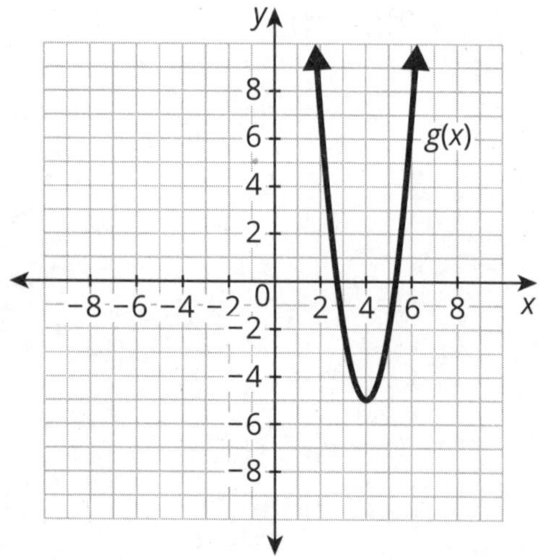

© Carnegie Learning, Inc.

Show What You Know

> Use what you know about the transformation function form to answer each question.

1. Based on the equation of each function, describe how the graph of each function compares to the graph of $f(x) = x^2$.

   a) $z(x) = -(x - 1)^2 - 10$

   b) $r(x) = \frac{1}{2}(x + 6)^2 + 7$

   c) $m(x) = (4x)^2 + 5$

© Carnegie Learning, Inc.

2 Describe each transformation in relation to the basic function $f(x) = x^2$.

(a) $h(x) = f(x) + D$ when $D > 0$

(b) $h(x) = f(x) + D$ when $D < 0$

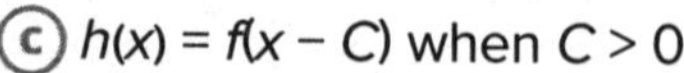

(c) $h(x) = f(x - C)$ when $C > 0$

(d) $h(x) = f(x - C)$ when $C < 0$

(e) $h(x) = Af(x)$ when $|A| > 1$

(f) $h(x) = Af(x)$ when $0 < |A| < 1$

(g) $h(x) = Af(x)$ when $A = -1$

© Carnegie Learning, Inc.

LESSON 3 ASSIGNMENT

> Use a separate piece of paper for your Journal entry.

JOURNAL

Describe the connections between the vertex form of a quadratic function, $f(x) = a(x - h)^2 + k$, and the transformation form, $g(x) = A \cdot f(x - C) + D$, of the basic quadratic function, $y = f(x)$.

REMEMBER

You can describe transformations performed on any function $f(x)$ using the transformation function $g(x) = Af(B(x + C)) + D$, where the C-value horizontally translates the function $f(x)$, the D-value vertically translates $f(x)$, the A-value vertically stretches or compresses $f(x)$, and the B-value horizontally stretches or compresses $f(x)$. When the A-value is negative, the function $f(x)$ reflects across a horizontal line of reflection. When the B-value is negative, the function $f(x)$ reflects across a vertical line of reflection.

PRACTICE

1. Given $f(x) = x^2$, graph each function and write the corresponding quadratic equation.

   a) $g(x) = 3f(x - 1)$

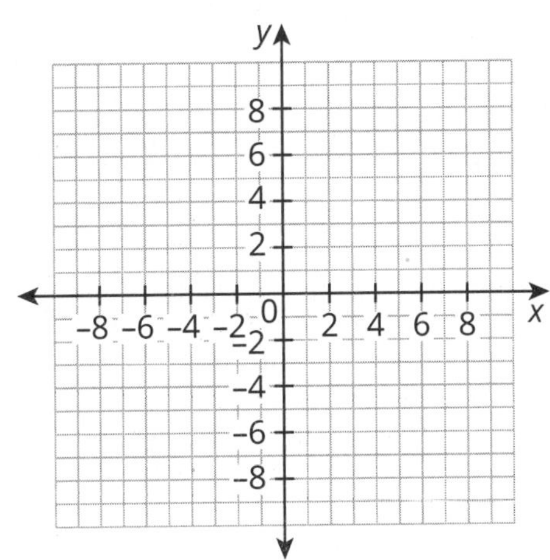

   b) $g(x) = f(3x) - 1$

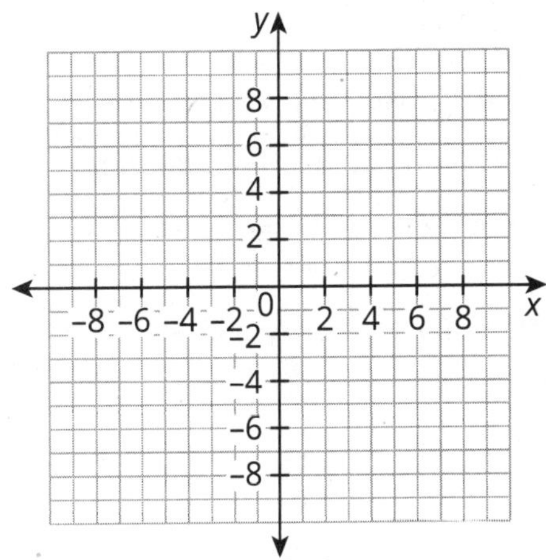

   c) $g(x) = \frac{1}{2}f(x) + 5$

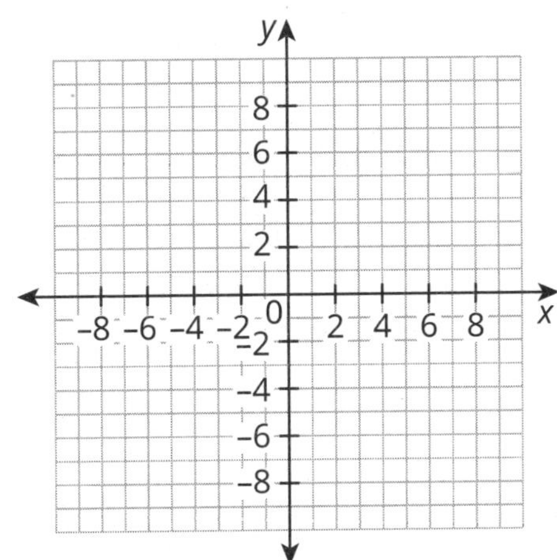

   d) $g(x) = 2f(x - 3) + 1$

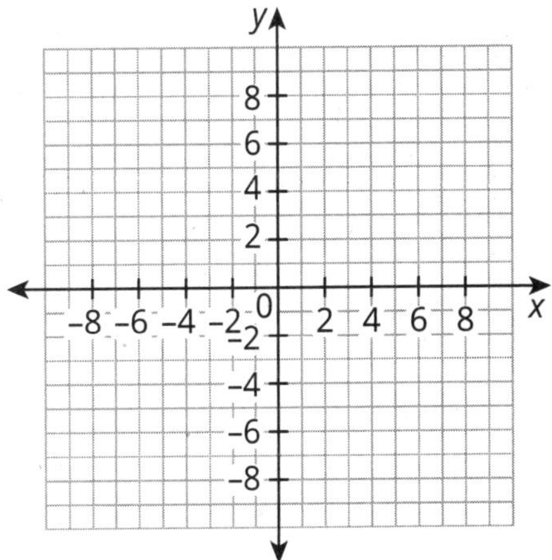

© Carnegie Learning, Inc.

Go to LiveHint.com for help on the PRACTICE questions.

2 The graph shows the basic function $f(x) = x^2$ the function $h(x)$.

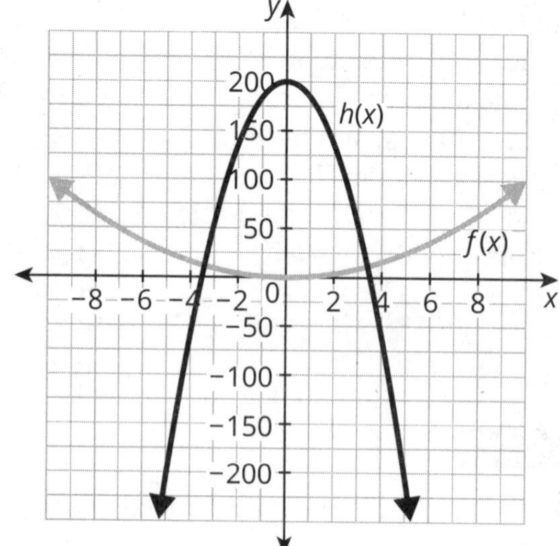

(a) Describe the types of transformations performed on $f(x)$ to result in $h(x)$.

(b) Write the function $h(x)$ when the dilation factor is 16.

3 Use the given characteristics to write a function $R(x)$ in vertex form. Then, sketch the graph of $R(x)$ and the basic function $f(x) = x^2$.

- The function has an absolute maximum.
- The function translates $f(x)$ 75 units up and 100 units to the right.
- The function vertically dilates $f(x)$ by a factor of $\frac{1}{5}$.

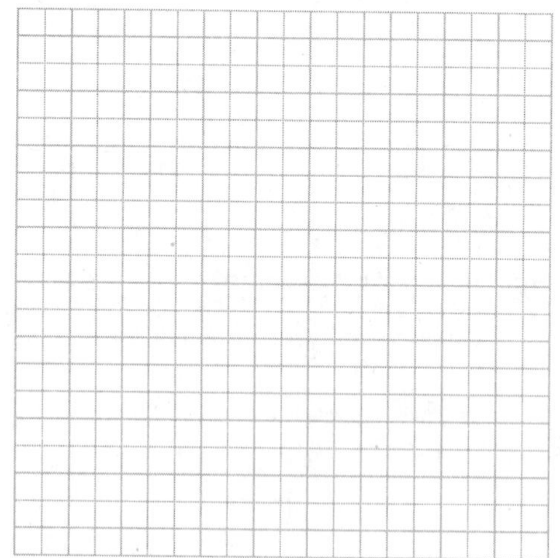

STRETCH Optional

> Given $f(x) = x^2$. Sketch each function. Label point A' for each transformation.

1. $m(x) = f(-x + 3)$
2. $n(x) = f(-(x + 3))$
3. $r(x) = f(-(x - 3))$
4. $t(x) = f(-x - 3)$

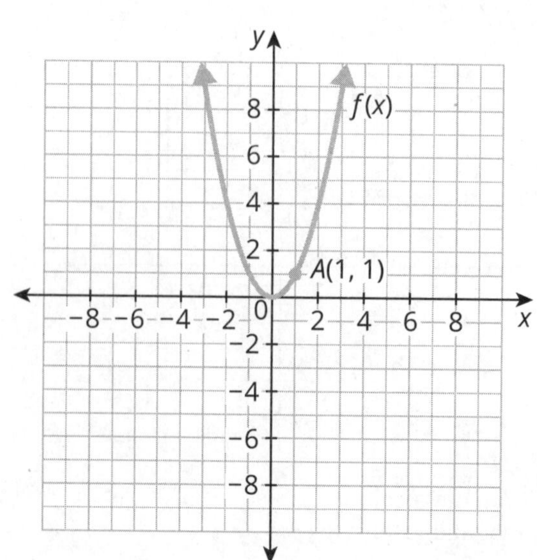

© Carnegie Learning, Inc.

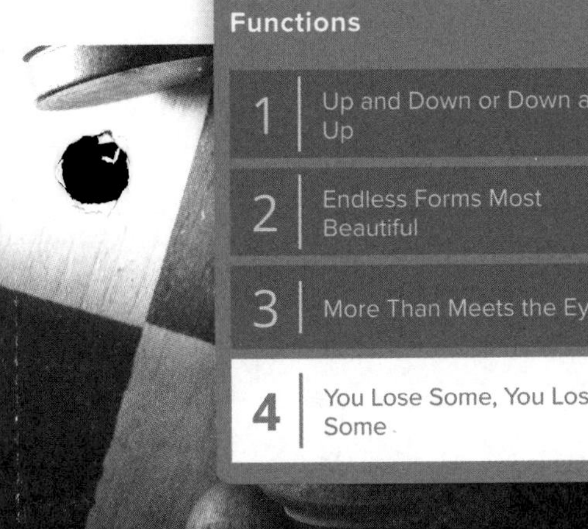

LESSON 4

You Lose Some, You Lose Some

Comparing Functions Using Key Characteristics and Average Rate of Change

Learning Goals

- Understand that the form in which a quadratic function is written can reveal different key characteristics.
- Show different rearrangements of quadratic functions in general form, factored form, and vertex form and analyze their properties.
- Compare properties of quadratic functions represented in different ways.
- Compare functions increasing linearly, quadratically, and exponentially by analyzing the average rate of change of the function.
- Use multiple representations of quadratic functions to identify key characteristics, such as the maximum, minimum, intercepts, and the axis of symmetry.

© Carnegie Learning, Inc.

REVIEW (1–2 minutes)

> Write the ordered pair for the y-intercept of each quadratic function.

1. $f(x) = 4(x - 2)(x - 3)$

2. $f(x) = -6x^2 + 9x - 5$

3. $f(x) = 5(x - 1)^2 + 14$

You have seen quadratic functions modeled using tables, equations, and graphs.

How can you use the different representations of quadratic functions to analyze their key characteristics?

Function Form File Cabinet

1. Complete each graphic organizer located on pages 735 and 736 using the general form of the function given. For each form of the equation, check the box of any characteristic that you can identify using that form of the equation. Then, sketch a graph of the equation and identify key points.

© Carnegie Learning, Inc.

MATHia CONNECTION
- Comparing Increasing Linear, Exponential, and Quadratic Functions

Comparing Functions Increasing Linearly, Quadratically, and Exponentially

HABITS OF MIND
- Look for and make use of structure.
- Look for and express regularity in repeated reasoning.

> Think about the two functions you studied in the previous activity.

$$f(x) = x^2 + 2x - 3$$
$$g(x) = 2x^2 - 4x - 30$$

1. Compare the two functions. **Show your work and explain your reasoning.**

   a. Which function has the lowest minimum point?

   b. Which function has a greater value at $x = 8$?

   c. Which function has a greater value at $x = 9$?

© Carnegie Learning, Inc.

Let's compare the average rate of change of the two functions over given intervals. You have previously used inequalities to represent intervals. You can also use interval notation to describe continuous sets of real numbers between two given numbers.

You use a rectangular bracket symbol, [ ], to describe sets with a "greater than or equal to" or a "less than or equal to" element, respectively. You use a parenthesis symbol, ( ), to describe sets with a "greater than" or "less than" element, respectively. When an interval has no lower or upper bound, then use the $-\infty$ or $+\infty$ symbols.

2 Complete the table. **Show your work.**

Interval	Average Rate of Change $f(x) = x^2 + 2x - 3$	Average Rate of Change $g(x) = 2x^2 - 4x - 30$
[0, 1]		
[0, 2]		
[0, 3]		
[4, 5]		

REMEMBER . . .
The average rate of change of any function over an interval is the slope of a linear function passing through the beginning and end points of the interval.

3 The two functions you compared increase or decrease quadratically, but they do not have the same average rates of change on the given intervals. **Explain why.**

Let's compare a quadratic function with other function types you have studied. You can say that a quadratic function increases or decreases quadratically, so a linear function increases or decreases linearly, and an exponential function increases or decreases exponentially.

4 Consider the linear, the exponential, and the quadratic functions.

$h(x) = 2x$

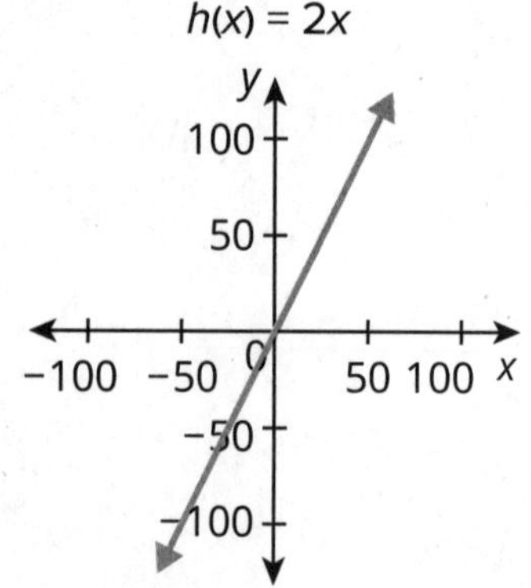

$j(x) = 2^x$

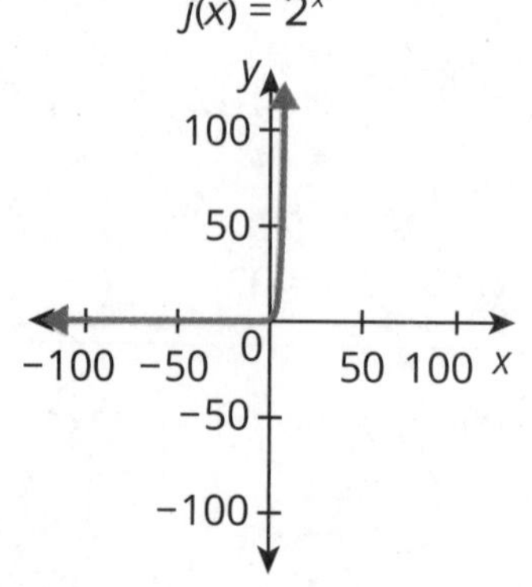

$k(x) = x^2$

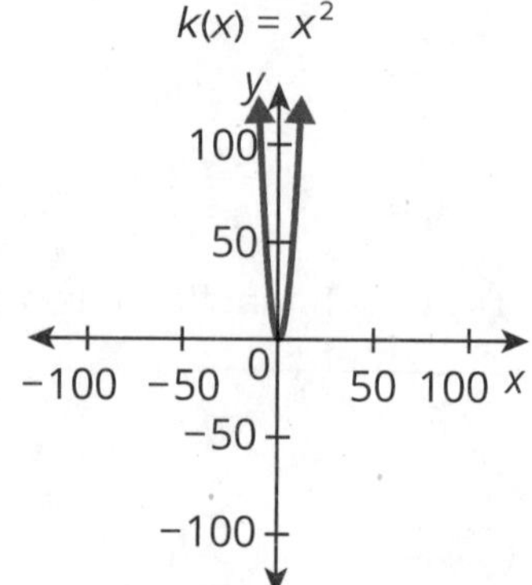

© Carnegie Learning, Inc.

(a) At what point do the three graphs intersect? **Explain how you know.**

(b) Which function do you think has the greatest average rate of change from negative infinity to positive infinity? **Explain your reasoning.**

This table organizes the average rates of change of the three functions across different intervals of their domains. Some of the rates have been provided.

	Domain Intervals		
	[−10, 10]	**[10, 100]**	**[100, 1000]**
$h(x) = 2x$			
$j(x) = 2^x$		6.34×10^{27}	1.07×10^{298}
$k(x) = x^2$	0		

5 Consider the quadratic function.

(a) Why is the average rate of change for the quadratic function 0 across the interval [−10, 10]? **Use a calculation to explain your reasoning.**

© Carnegie Learning, Inc.

(b) Enter the average rate of change for the quadratic function across the intervals [10, 100] and [100, 1000] in the table. **Explain why your answers are correct.**

6 Enter the average rate of change for the linear function across each of the three intervals in the table. **Justify your answers.**

7 Enter the average rate of change for the exponential function across the interval [−10, 10] in the table. **Show your work.**

8 Do the average rates of change for the exponential function in the table seem reasonable? **Explain why or why not.**

9 Compare the change in the average rates of change for the functions in the table across the different intervals. **What do you notice?**

10 Parker says that any function increasing exponentially will eventually have a greater value than any function increasing linearly or quadratically.

Is Parker correct? **Explain why or why not.**

© Carnegie Learning, Inc.

Comparing Equations, Tables, and Graphs

HABITS OF MIND
- Model with mathematics.
- Use appropriate tools strategically.

In this activity, you will analyze quadratic functions represented in different ways to compare them to a real-world situation.

Maya saved up some money and decided to take a risk and invest in some stocks. She invested her money in a tech company. Unfortunately, she lost it all in just 25 months. You can represent the change in her money during this time using the function $v(x) = 75 + 72x - 3x^2$, where v is the value of her investment and x is the time in months.

> Consider the three quadratic functions.

Model 1

$k(x) = -3(x + 1)(x - 25)$

Model 2

x	y
0	0
3	197
15	450
25	0

Model 3

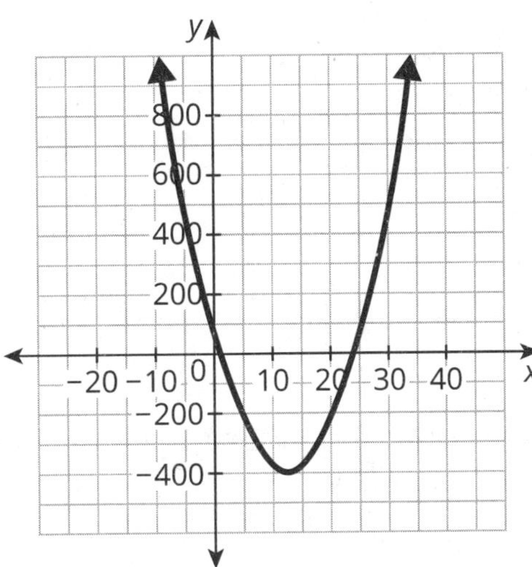

1 Which of these models represents Maya's investment money over time? **Explain your choice and why you eliminated the other model(s).**

© Carnegie Learning, Inc.

2 How much money did Maya initially invest? **Explain how you determined your answer.**

3 The function that models Maya's investment over time has a maximum value.

(a) What was the greatest value of Maya's investment account over the time of her investment? **Show your work.**

(b) How much time did it take for Maya's account to reach its maximum value?

(c) On average, how much did Maya's account gain in value each month from the time she opened the account to the time it reached its maximum value?

© Carnegie Learning, Inc.

ACTIVITY 3

MATHia CONNECTION

- Sketching Quadratic Functions

Representations of Transformations of Quadratic Functions

HABITS OF MIND

- Model with mathematics.
- Use appropriate tools strategically.

> Consider the quadratic function $h(t) = -5(t - 3)^2 + 60$.

1. Sketch a graph of the function and label the vertex and the *y*-intercept. **Explain your work.**

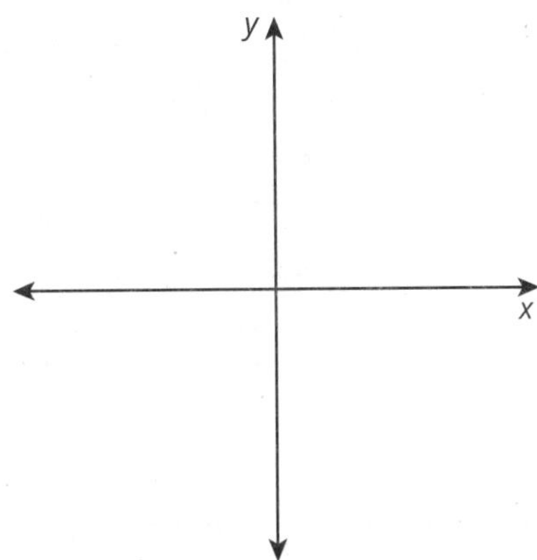

2. Identify the table that represents the function. **Explain why you eliminated the other tables.**

A

t	$h(t)$
−1	55
0	60
1	55
2	40

B

t	$h(t)$
0	45
1	20
4	5
5	20

C

t	$h(t)$
$-\sqrt{12} + 3$	0
0	15
3	60
$\sqrt{12} + 3$	0

D

t	$h(t)$
$-\sqrt{12} + 3$	−60
0	−45
3	0
$\sqrt{12} + 3$	−60

3. Describe how the function $h(t)$ has been transformed from the basic function $f(t) = t^2$.

© Carnegie Learning, Inc.

Comparing Quadratics in Different Forms

HABITS OF MIND
- Reason abstractly and quantitatively.
- Construct viable arguments and critique the reasoning of others.

In this activity, you will compare quadratic functions represented in different forms.

1 Josiah compared the table of values for $f(x)$ and the graph of $g(x)$ to determine which quadratic function has the greater maximum.

x	$f(x)$
−1	0
0	4.5
1	8
2	10.5
3	12

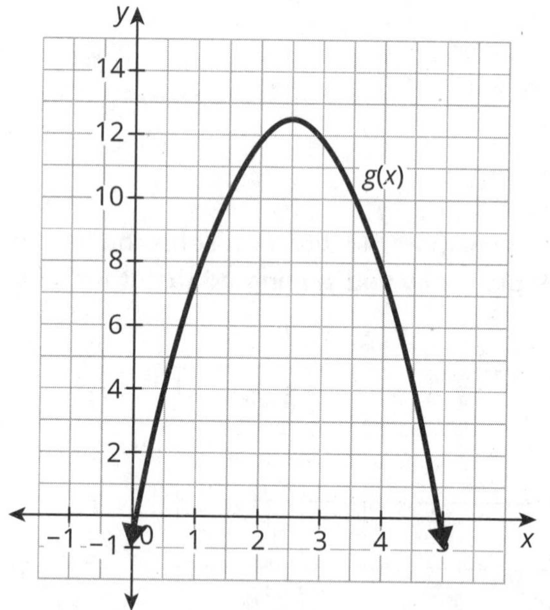

Josiah says that the function $g(x)$ has a greater maximum because it has an output value greater than 12 at its maximum, while the table for $f(x)$ shows a greatest output of 12. Is Josiah's reasoning correct? **Explain your answer.**

2 Approximate the absolute maximum for each function. **Show your work.**

© Carnegie Learning, Inc.

Ben and Corinne are trying out their new drones, but they're not very good at flying them yet. The drones keep very precise records of their elevations.

3 Compare these two drone flights, launched at the same time.

Drone 1

The function $c(x) = -3x^2 + 7x + 1$ models the height in feet of Corinne's drone flight over time in seconds.

Drone 2

The table of values shows the height in feet of Ben's drone at different times.

x	$b(x)$
0	4
0.25	4.25
0.5	4
1	2
1.281	0

(a) Which flight began at a higher elevation? **How do you know?**

(b) Which drone began descending first? **Show your work.**

(c) Which of the drones had a greater average increase in height over time up to its maximum height? **Explain your reasoning.**

© Carnegie Learning, Inc.

More Ups and Downs

> Analyze each pair of representations and answer each question. **Justify your reasoning.**

1. Which function has a greater average rate of change for the interval (2, 4)?

Function A

$f(x) = (x + 1)^2 + 20$

Function B

x	y
0	4
2	0
4	4

2. Which function has a greater absolute minimum?

Function A

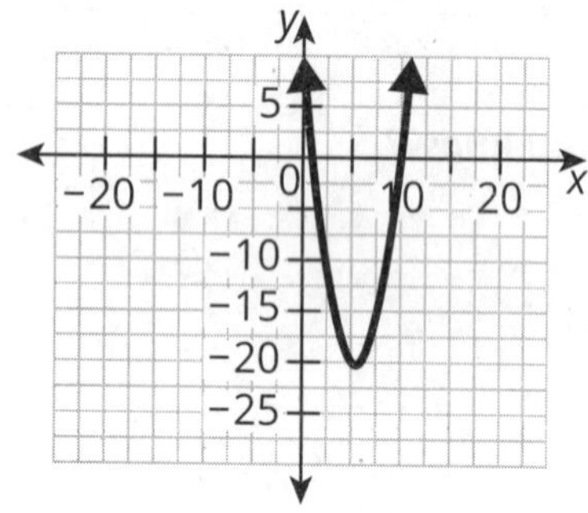

Function B

x	y
0	4
1	0
4	0

3. Which function's axis of symmetry has a greater x-value?

Function A

$f(x) = 2x^2 + 4$

Function B

x	y
−3	4
1	0
4	0

© Carnegie Learning, Inc.

Key Characteristics of a Quadratic Function

General Form

Equation: $f(x) = x^2 + 2x - 3$

Select which key features of the graph you can identify from the general form of the equation.

- ☐ parabola opens up/down
- ☐ location of vertex
- ☐ zeros
- ☐ *y*-intercept

Factored Form

Equation: ______________________

Select which key features of the graph you can identify from the factored form of the equation.

- ☐ parabola opens up/down
- ☐ location of vertex
- ☐ zeros
- ☐ *y*-intercept

Vertex Form

Equation: ______________________

Select which key features of the graph you can identify from the vertex form of the equation.

- ☐ parabola opens up/down
- ☐ location of vertex
- ☐ zeros
- ☐ *y*-intercept

Graph of the Quadratic Function

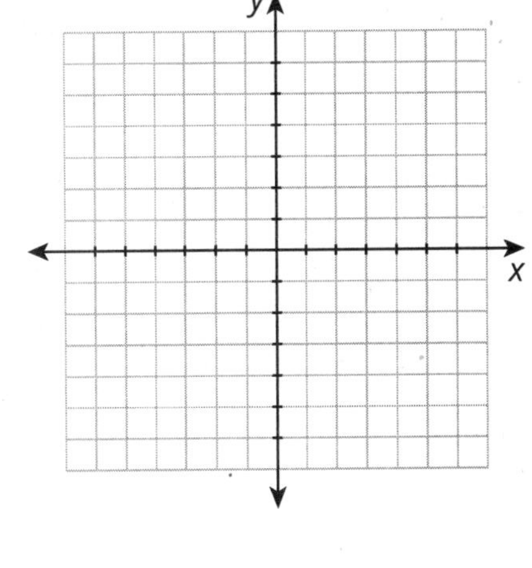

© Carnegie Learning, Inc.

Key Characteristics of a Quadratic Function

General Form

Equation: $g(x) = 2x^2 - 4x - 30$

Select which key features of the graph you can identify from the general form of the equation.

- ☐ parabola opens up/down
- ☐ location of vertex
- ☐ zeros
- ☐ y-intercept

Factored Form

Equation: ____________________

Select which key features of the graph you can identify from the factored form of the equation.

- ☐ parabola opens up/down
- ☐ location of vertex
- ☐ zeros
- ☐ y-intercept

Vertex Form

Equation: ____________________

Select which key features of the graph you can identify from the vertex form of the equation.

- ☐ parabola opens up/down
- ☐ location of vertex
- ☐ zeros
- ☐ y-intercept

Graph of the Quadratic Function

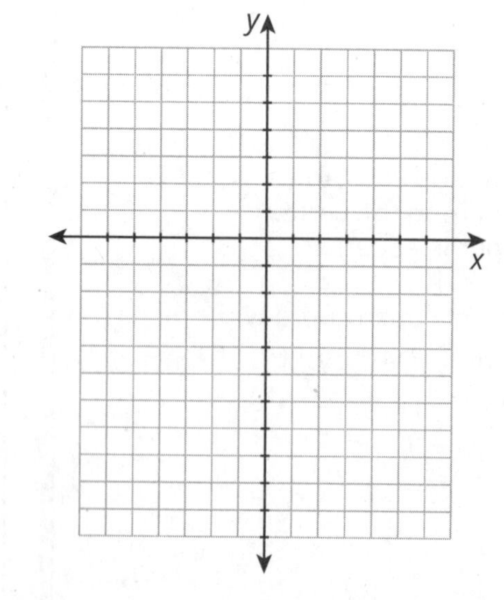

© Carnegie Learning, Inc.

> Use a separate piece of paper for your Journal entry.

JOURNAL

Describe the difference between quadratic equations in general form, factored form, and vertex form.

REMEMBER

You can use what you know about the structure of quadratic functions represented as tables, equations, graphs, and scenarios to compare the characteristics of two quadratic functions represented in different forms.

PRACTICE

Analyze each pair of representations. Then, answer each question and justify your reasoning.

1. Which function has a greater y-intercept?

Function A

$f(x) = \frac{1}{3}x^2 - 4x + 12$

Function B

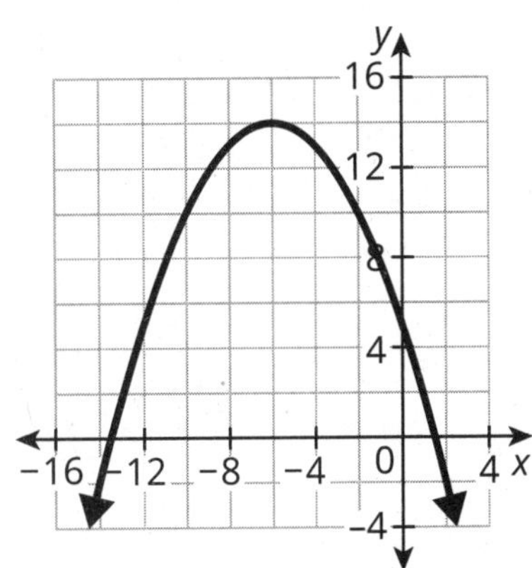

2. Which function has a greater average rate of change for the interval (1, 2)?

Function A

$f(x) = \frac{1}{2}x^2 - 4x + 12$

Function B

x	y
0	9
1	7
2	1

© Carnegie Learning, Inc.

Go to LiveHint.com for help on the PRACTICE questions.

3 Which function has an absolute maximum with a greater y-value?

Function A

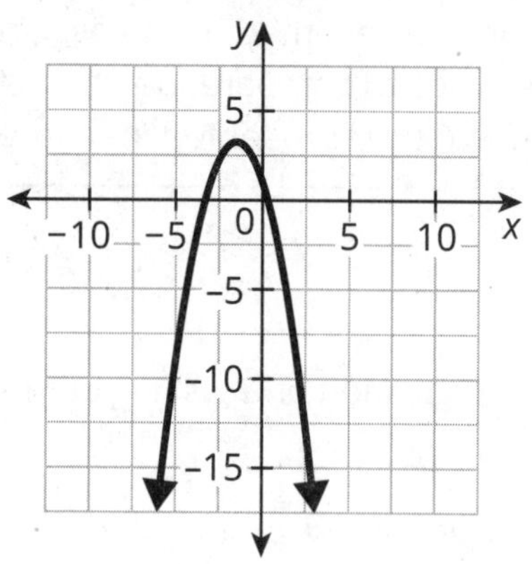

Function B

x	y
−1	0
0	0
0.5	−0.75

STRETCH Optional

> Analyze each pair of representations.

Function A

$f(x) = x^2 + 2x - 3$

Function B

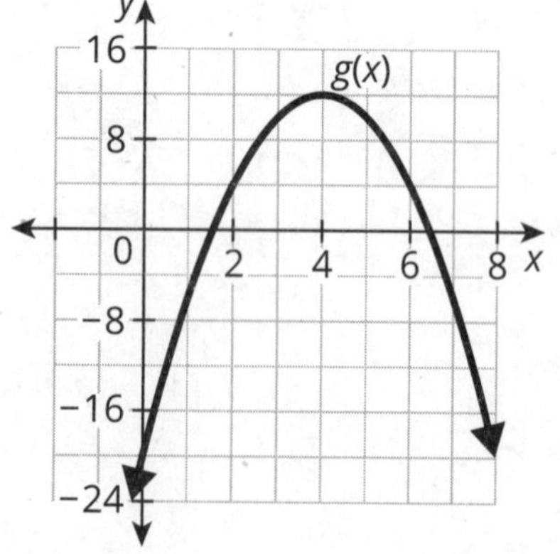

1 Write a function $m(x)$ that has an average rate of change for the interval (1, 2) that falls between the average rate of change for the same interval for $f(x)$ and $g(x)$.

© Carnegie Learning, Inc.

MIXED PRACTICE

> This Mixed Practice worksheet includes two sections: Spaced Review and End-of-Topic Review. **Use a separate piece of paper to show your work.**

Spaced Review

> Practice concepts from previous topics.

1 A realtor recorded the number of homes she sold each month for a year. Her numbers are shown in the dot plot.

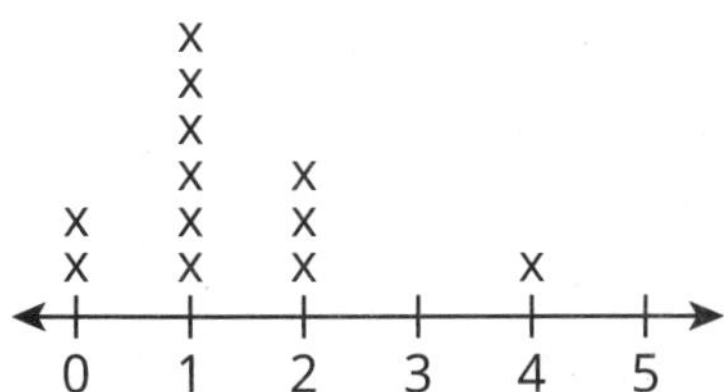

(a) Describe the distribution of the dot plot.

(b) Calculate the mean and median. Explain what they mean in terms of the problem situation.

(c) Which measure of center do you think best represents these data? Explain your reasoning.

2 The basic function $f(x) = |x|$ translates 3 units to the right and 4 units up. What is the equation of the transformed function?

3 The basic function $f(x) = 4^x$ vertically stretches by a factor of 2 and translates 5 units down. What is the equation of the transformed function?

4 For each function $f(x)$, sketch a graph of the given transformation, $g(x)$, and describe the transformation from the graph of $f(x)$ to $g(x)$.

(a) $g(x) = -f(x)$

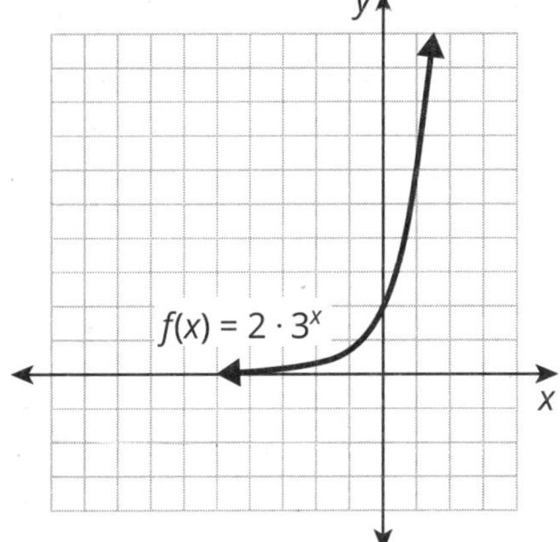

(b) $g(x) = f(-x)$

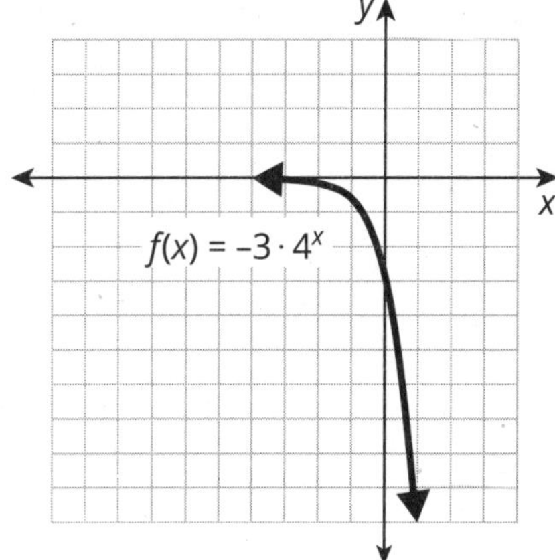

5 Solve each equation for x.

(a) $\frac{1}{5^{x-3}} = 25^{2x}$

(b) $16^{-2x} = \left(\frac{4}{64}\right)^{x+6}$

6 Graph each function.

(a) $y = -3|x + 4| - 2$

(b) $y = 2|x - 1| + 2$

© Carnegie Learning, Inc.

End-of-Topic Review

AVAILABLE ONLINE

1. A **Topic Summary** reviews the main concepts for the topic.
2. A video of the **Worked Example** is provided.

> Practice concepts you learned in **Introduction to Quadratic Functions**.

7 Use the equation $f(x) = \frac{1}{3}(x - 5)(x - 3)$ to determine each characteristic.

(a) Axis of symmetry

(b) x-intercepts

(c) Will the graph open upward or downward?

8 Use the equation $f(x) = 4x^2 + 3x - 10$ to determine each characteristic.

(a) Axis of symmetry

(b) y-intercept

9 Write an equation for a quadratic function in vertex form with vertex (4, 9) that has a y-intercept of (0, 12.2).

10 Write the equation of the function, $g(x)$, whose graph transforms the graph $f(x) = x^2$ by reflecting it across the x-axis, vertically stretching it by a factor of 2, and translating it up 5 units.

11 Write an equation for a quadratic function in factored form with zeros (−7, 0) and (10, 0) that passes through the point (−4, −10).

12 Alfonzo is building a deck on his house. He was originally going to make it a square with a side length of x feet. Alfonzo decides to make it a rectangular deck, with 1 foot added to one pair of opposite sides and 2 feet added to the other pair of opposite sides.

(a) Determine the expressions for the length and width of the new deck in terms of x, the length of the sides of the original deck.

(b) Write the function for the area of the new deck, $A(x)$, in terms of x, the length of the sides of the original deck. Does this function have a minimum or maximum? Explain your answer.

© Carnegie Learning, Inc.

LESSON 1

This Time, with Polynomials

Adding, Subtracting, and Multiplying Polynomials

KEY TERMS

monomial

binomial

trinomial

closed, closure

difference of two squares

perfect square trinomial

Learning Goals

- Name polynomials by number of terms or degree.
- Understand that you can perform operations on functions as well as numbers.
- Add, subtract, and multiply polynomials.
- Explain why polynomials are closed under addition, subtraction and multiplication.
- Recognize and use special products when multiplying binomials.

REVIEW (1–2 minutes)

> Rewrite each expression by combining like terms.

1. $-3x + 4y - 9x - 5y$

2. $2xy^2 + 5x^2y - 7xy + xy^2$

3. $6 - 2m^2 + 5m^2$

4. $-8 - (-4k) + 7 + 1 - 4k$

You know that a linear expression is one type of polynomial expression.

What are other polynomial expressions, and how do you add, subtract, and multiply them?

© Carnegie Learning, Inc.

Sorting It Out

You are familiar with many types of mathematical expressions.

> Cut out the 12 expressions located on page 761. Analyze and sort them into groups based upon common characteristics.

GETTING STARTED CUTOUTS

Expression Cards

$4x - 6x^2$	$125p$	$\frac{4}{5}r^2 + \frac{2}{5}r - 1$
$-\frac{2}{3}$	$y^2 - 4y + 10$	$5 - 7h$
$-3 + 7n + n^2$	-6	$-13s + 6$
$12.5t^3$	$78j^3 - 3j$	$25 - 18m^2$

Lesson 1 > This Time, With Polynomials 761

1. Summarize the groups you formed by listing the expressions that you grouped together and your description for each group. Use mathematical terms in your descriptions.

2. Compare your groups of expressions to your classmates' groups. **Describe any similarities and differences.**

3. Jimmy and Andrew agree that $4x - 6x^2$ and $25 - 18m^2$ belong in the same group. They each add these expressions to the group. Who is correct? **Explain your reasoning.**

Jimmy

$5 - 7h$

$78j^3 - 3$

$-13s + 6$

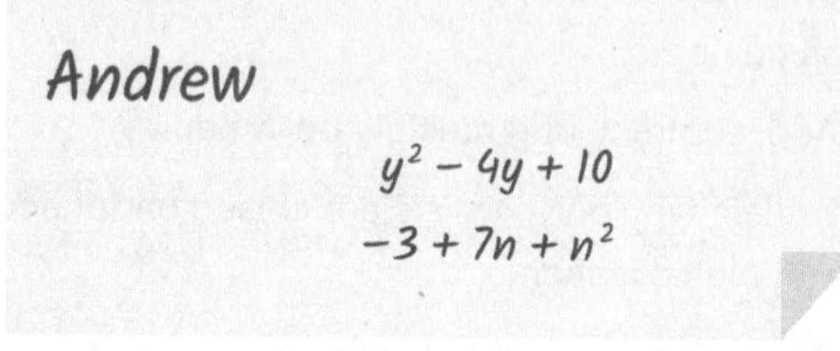

4. What characteristics do all 12 expressions share?

© Carnegie Learning, Inc.

MATHia CONNECTION
- Introduction to Polynomial Arithmetic
- Identifying Parts of Complex Algebraic Expressions

Categorizing Polynomials

HABITS OF MIND
- Look for and make use of structure.
- Look for and express regularity in repeated reasoning.

Previously, you worked with linear expressions in the form $ax + b$ and quadratic expressions in the form $ax^2 + bx + c$. Each is also part of a larger group of expressions known as *polynomials*.

Recall that a polynomial is a mathematical expression involving the sum of powers in one or more variables multiplied by coefficients. A polynomial in one variable is the sum of terms of the form ax^k, where a is any real number and k is a non-negative integer.

In general, a polynomial is of the form $a_1x^k + a_2x^{k-1} + \ldots + a_nx^0$. Within a polynomial, each product is a term, and the number being multiplied by a power is a coefficient.

WORKED EXAMPLE

The polynomial $m^3 + 8m^2 - 10m + 5$ has four terms. **Each term is written in the form ax^k.**

- The first term is m^3.
- The power is m^3, and its coefficient is 1.
- In this term, the variable is m and the exponent is 3.

1. Write each term from the Worked Example and identify the coefficient, power, and exponent. The first term has already been completed for you.

	1st	2nd	3rd	4th
Term	m^3			
Coefficient	1			
Variable	m			
Power	m^3			
Exponent	3			

© Carnegie Learning, Inc.

2 Identify the terms and coefficients in each polynomial.

ⓐ $-2x^2 + 100x$

ⓑ $4m^3 - 2m^2 - 5$

ⓒ $y^5 - y + 3$

You name polynomials according to the number of terms they have. Polynomials with only one term are **monomials**. Polynomials with exactly two terms are **binomials**. Polynomials with exactly three terms are **trinomials**.

The degree of a term in a polynomial is the exponent of the term. Recall that the greatest exponent in a polynomial determines the degree of the polynomial. In a previous topic, you determined that linear functions are polynomials with a degree of 1 because you can write them in the form $ax + b$.

3 Khalil says that $3x^{-2} + 4x - 1$ is a trinomial with a degree of 1 because 1 is the greatest exponent. Jazmin disagrees and says that this is not a polynomial at all because the power on the first term is not a whole number. Who is correct? **Explain your reasoning.**

4 Determine whether each expression is a polynomial. **Explain your reasoning.**

$x^2 + \sqrt{x}$

$5^x + 4^{x-1} + 3^{x-2}$

$x^4y + x^3y^2 + x^2y$

© Carnegie Learning, Inc.

A polynomial is in general form when the terms are in descending order, starting with the term with the greatest degree and ending with the term with the least degree.

5 Revisit the cards you sorted in the Getting Started.

(a) Identify any polynomial not written in general form and rewrite it in general form on the card.

(b) Identify the degree of each polynomial and write the degree on the card.

(c) Glue each card in the appropriate column based on the number of terms in each polynomial. Write your own polynomial to complete any empty boxes.

Monomial	Binomial	Trinomial

© Carnegie Learning, Inc.

Interpreting the Graphs of Polynomial Functions

HABITS OF MIND
- Model with mathematics.
- Use appropriate tools strategically.

Let's analyze the graphs of two different polynomial functions.

Consider the graphs of functions $V(x)$ and $A(x)$. The function $V(x)$ models people's reaction times to visual stimuli in milliseconds, based upon the age of a person in years. The function $A(x)$ models people's reaction times to audio stimuli in milliseconds based on the age of a person in years.

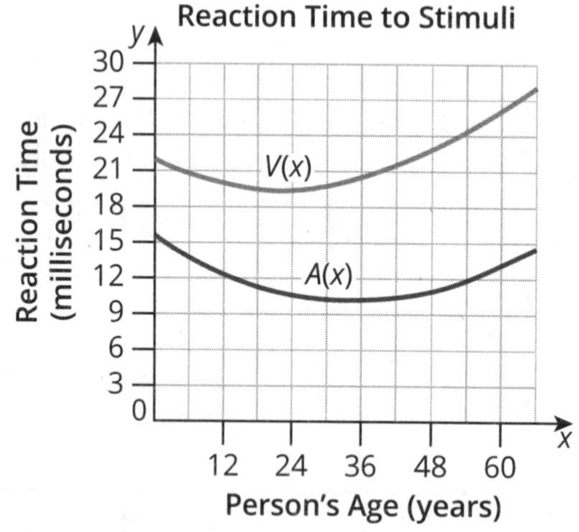

1 Interpret the graphs of the functions.

(a) Describe the functions $V(x)$ and $A(x)$.

(b) Write a summary to describe people's reaction times to visual stimuli and audio stimuli.

(c) Do you think a person would react faster to a car horn or a flashing light? **Explain your reasoning.**

© Carnegie Learning, Inc.

2 Estimate the age that a person has the quickest reaction time to each stimuli. **Explain how you determined each answer.**

(a) Visual stimuli

(b) Audio stimuli

Many times, auto insurance companies use test results similar to the ones shown to create insurance policies for different drivers.

3 How do you think an auto insurance company may use the information provided in the graphic representation?

4 Consider a new function $h(x)$, where $h(x) = V(x) - A(x)$. **What does $h(x)$ mean in terms of the problem situation?**

5 Write a report about drivers' reaction times to visual and audio stimuli. Discuss actions that may improve drivers' reaction times and distractions that may worsen drivers' reaction times. Discuss the importance of flashing lights and sirens on emergency vehicles.

THINK ABOUT . . .
How can you incorporate information about auto insurance rates and a driver's age in your report?

© Carnegie Learning, Inc.

Adding and Subtracting Polynomial Functions

You can perform operations on functions as well as numbers.

HABITS OF MIND
- Model with mathematics.
- Use appropriate tools strategically.

You are playing a new virtual reality game called "Species." You are an environmental scientist who is responsible for tracking two species of endangered parrots, the orange-bellied parrot and the yellow-headed parrot. Suppose you can model the orange-bellied parrots' population using the function $B(x)$, where x represents the number of years since the current year. Suppose that you can model the population of the yellow-headed parrot using the function $H(x)$.

$$B(x) = -18x + 120$$

$$H(x) = 4x^2 - 5x + 25$$

> Consider the graphs of $B(x)$ and $H(x)$.

Population of Two Species of Parrot

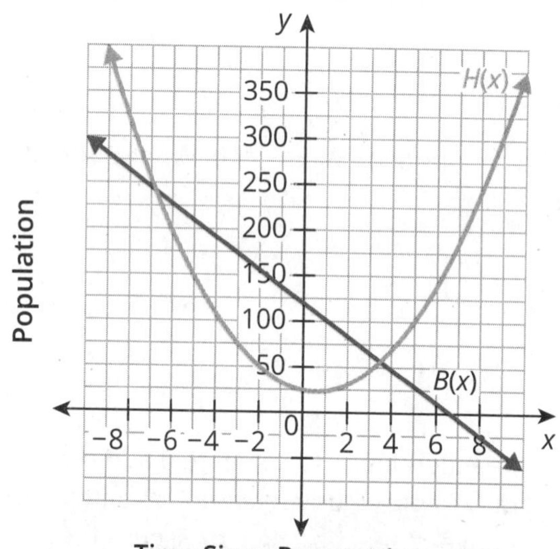

Your new task in this game is to determine the total number of these endangered parrots each year over a six-year span. You can calculate the total population of parrots using the two graphed functions.

1 Use the graphs of $B(x)$ and $H(x)$ to determine the function, $T(x)$, to represent the total population of parrots.

(a) Write $T(x)$ in terms of $B(x)$ and $H(x)$.

(b) Predict the shape of the graph of $T(x)$.

THINK ABOUT . . .
One place to start the sketch of $T(x)$ would be to consider the y-intercept for each function. What would the new y-intercept be for $T(x)$?

© Carnegie Learning, Inc.

ⓒ Sketch a graph of $T(x)$ on the same coordinate plane as $B(x)$ and $H(x)$. First, choose any five x-values and add their corresponding y-values to create a new point on the graph of $T(x)$. Then, connect the points with a smooth curve. Record the values in the table.

x	$B(x)$	$H(x)$	$T(x)$

ⓓ Did the graph of $T(x)$ match your prediction in part (b)? Identify the function family to which $T(x)$ belongs.

You can write a function, $T(x)$, in terms of x to calculate the total number of parrots at any time.

WORKED EXAMPLE

$T(x) = B(x) + H(x)$	**Write $T(x)$ in terms of two known functions.**
$T(x) = (-18x + 120) + (4x^2 - 5x + 25)$	Substitute the functions in terms of x.
$T(x) = 4x^2 + (-18x + (-5x)) + (120 + 25)$	Use the Commutative Property to reorder and the Associative Property to group like terms.
$T(x) = 4x^2 - 23x + 145$	Combine like terms.

2 Choose any two x-values in your table. Use the new polynomial function, $T(x)$, to confirm that your solution in the table for those times is correct. **Show your work.**

© Carnegie Learning, Inc.

3 Use technology to confirm that your graph and the remaining solutions in the table are correct. **Explain any discrepancies and how you corrected them.**

REMEMBER . . .
The table feature on graphing technology is an efficient tool to determine y-values.

4 Zoe says that using $T(x)$ will not work for any time after 6 years from now because by that point the orange-bellied parrot will be extinct. Is Zoe's statement correct? **Why or why not?**

Throughout the game "Species," you must always keep track of the difference between the population of each type of species. When the difference gets to be too great, you lose the game. Consider the graphs of $B(x) = -18x + 120$ and $H(x) = 4x^2 - 5x + 25$.

5 Use the graphs of $B(x)$ and $H(x)$ to determine the function, $D(x)$, to represent the difference between the populations of each type of species.

ⓐ Write $D(x)$ in terms of $B(x)$ and $H(x)$.

ⓑ Predict the shape of the graph of $D(x)$.

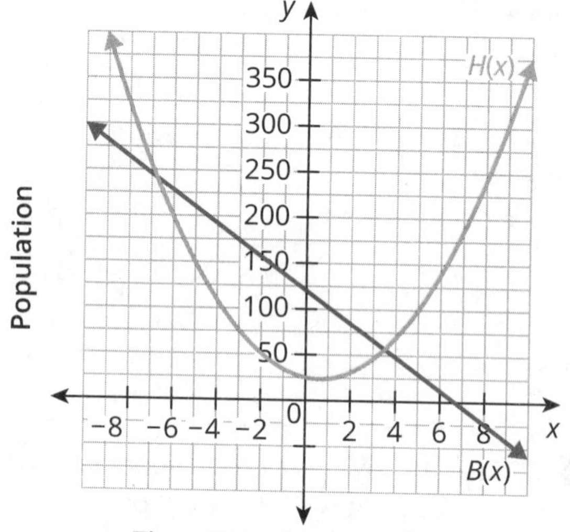

ⓒ Sketch a graph of $D(x)$ on the same coordinate plane as $B(x)$ and $H(x)$. First, choose any five x-values and subtract their corresponding y-values to create a new point on the graph of $D(x)$. Then, connect the points with a smooth curve. Record the values in the table.

x	$B(x)$	$H(x)$	$D(x)$

ⓓ Did the graph of $D(x)$ match your prediction in part (b)? Identify the function family to which $D(x)$ belongs.

© Carnegie Learning, Inc.

6 Write a function, $D(x)$, in terms of x to calculate the difference between the population of the orange-bellied parrots and the yellow-headed parrots. Write $D(x)$ as a polynomial in general form.

TAKE NOTE . . .
Refer to the Worked Example for adding polynomials as a guide.

7 Choose any two x-values in your table. Use your new polynomial function to confirm that your solution in the table for those times is correct. **Show your work.**

8 Use technology to confirm that your graph and the remaining solutions in the table are correct. **Explain any discrepancies and how you corrected them.**

9 Eric uses his function $D(x) = -4x^2 - 13x + 95$ to determine that the difference between the number of orange-bellied parrots and the number of yellow-headed parrots 7 years from now will be (−192). Is Eric correct or incorrect? **If he is correct, explain to him what his answer means in terms of the problem situation. If he is incorrect, explain where he made his error and how to correct it.**

© Carnegie Learning, Inc.

10 The next round of the Species game included the red-winged parrot, whose population you can model using the function $W(x) = -9x + 80$ and the rainbow lorikeet parrot, whose population you can model using the function $L(x) = 2x^2 - 4x + 10$. In both cases, x represents the number of years since the current year.

(a) Write a function, $S(x)$, in terms of x to calculate the total number of red-winged parrots and rainbow lorikeet parrots at any time.

(b) Write a function, $M(x)$, in terms of x to calculate the difference in the number of red-winged parrots and rainbow lorikeet parrots at any time.

(c) Calculate $S(4)$ and $M(4)$. Interpret the meaning of your results.

(d) In 4 years, how many red-winged parrots will there be? How many rainbow lorikeet parrots will there be?

© Carnegie Learning, Inc.

Combining Functions and Addressing Closure

HABIT OF MIND
- Attend to precision.

In this activity, you will practice adding and subtracting polynomials.

1 Analyze each student's work. **Determine the error and make the necessary corrections.**

Marco

$3x^2 + 5x^2 = 8x^4$

Kamiah

$2x - (4x + 5)$

$2x - 4x + 5$

$-2x + 5$

Alexis

$(4x^2 - 2x - 5) + (3x^2 + 7)$

$(4x^2 + 3x^2) - (2x) - (5 + 7)$

$7x^2 - 2x - 12$

© Carnegie Learning, Inc.

Consider each polynomial function.

$A(x) = x^3 + 5x^2 - 9$ $B(x) = -3x^2 - x + 1$ $C(x) = 2x^2 + 7x$ $D(x) = -2x^2 - 8x$

2 Determine each function. Write your answers in general form.

(a) $J(x) = A(x) + C(x)$

(b) $K(x) = D(x) - B(x)$

(c) $L(x) = C(x) + D(x)$

(d) $M(x) = B(x) - A(x)$

(e) $N(x) = A(x) - C(x) - D(x)$

3 Are the functions $J(x)$, $K(x)$, $L(x)$, $M(x)$ and $N(x)$ polynomial functions? **Explain why or why not.**

When an operation is performed on any of the numbers in a set and the result is a number that is also in the same set, the set is **closed**, or has **closure**, under that operation.

For example, the set of integers is closed under addition and subtraction. That means whenever you add or subtract two integers, the result is also an integer.

You can also apply the definition of closure to polynomials.

4 Based on the definition of closure, determine whether polynomials are closed under addition and subtraction. **Justify your answer.**

© Carnegie Learning, Inc.

MATHia CONNECTION

- Using a Factor Table to Multiply Binomials
- Multiplying Binomials

Multiplying Polynomial Functions

HABITS OF MIND

- Model with mathematics.
- Use appropriate tools strategically.

Consider the dog enclosure scenario from the previous topic.

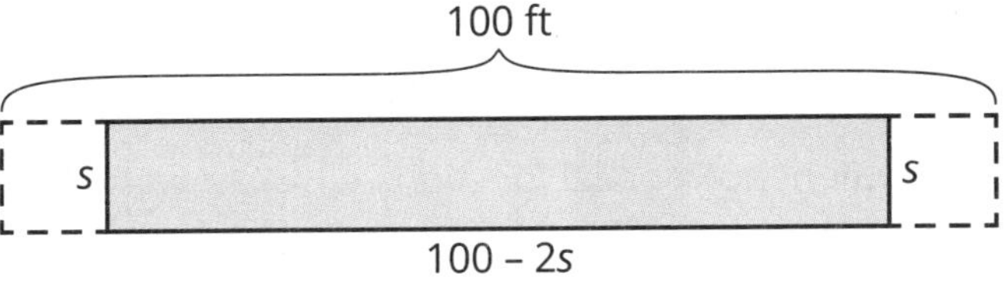

You expressed the area of the enclosure as $A(s) = s(100 - 2s)$, or the product of a monomial and a binomial.

1 Consider how Jason and Julie wrote an equivalent polynomial function in general form by calculating the product.

Jason

·	100	$-2s$
s	$100s$	$-2s$

$A(s) = -2s^2 + 100s$

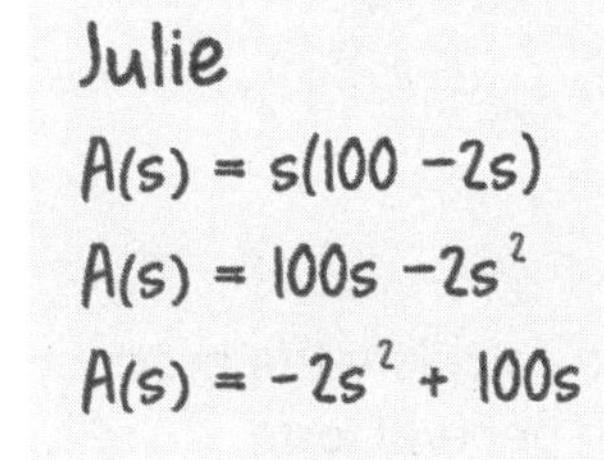

Julie

$A(s) = s(100 - 2s)$

$A(s) = 100s - 2s^2$

$A(s) = -2s^2 + 100s$

(a) Describe the strategy Jason used to calculate the product.

REMEMBER . . .
Develop a habit of writing answers in general form. It makes them easier to compare with others' answers.

(b) How is Jason's strategy similar to Julie's strategy?

© Carnegie Learning, Inc.

> Consider the ghost tour scenario from the previous topic. You expressed the revenue for the business as the product of a binomial times a binomial.

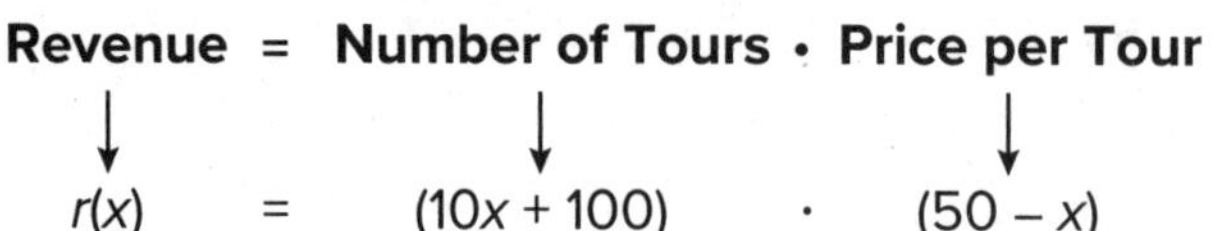

Revenue = Number of Tours • Price per Tour
r(x) = (10x + 100) · (50 – x)

2 Finish Jason's process to write an equivalent polynomial function for revenue in general form.

·	50	$-x$
$10x$	$500x$	$-10x^2$
100		

ASK YOURSELF . . .
How is the process of using a multiplication table to multiply polynomials the same as an area model?

3 Use an area model to calculate the product of each polynomial. Write each product in general form.

THINK ABOUT . . .
Does it matter where you place the polynomials in the multiplication table?

(a) $(3x + 2)(x - 4)$

(b) $(x - 5)(x + 5)$

(c) $(2x + 3)^2$

(d) $(4x^2 + x - 1)(3x - 7)$

© Carnegie Learning, Inc.

In Question 1, Julie used the Distributive Property to multiply a monomial and a binomial. She wants to use the Distributive Property to multiply any polynomials.

WORKED EXAMPLE

Consider the polynomials $x + 5$ and $x - 2$.
You can use the Distributive Property to multiply these polynomials.

Distribute x to each term of $(x - 2)$ and then distribute 5 to each term of $(x - 2)$.

$$(x + 5)(x - 2) = (x)(x - 2) + (5)(x - 2)$$
$$= x^2 - 2x + 5x - 10$$
$$= x^2 + 3x - 10$$

ASK YOURSELF . . .
How can you use technology to check your answers?

4 Use the Distributive Property to determine each product. Write the polynomial in general form.

(a) $(5x - 1)(2x + 1)$

(b) $(x - 7)(x + 7)$

(c) $(x + 2)(x - 9)$

(d) $(2x^2 + 1)(3x^2 + x - 1)$

5 Explain the mistake in Cheyanne's thinking. Then, determine the correct product.

Cheyanne 

$(x + 4)^2 = x^2 + 16$

I can just square each term to determine the product.

© Carnegie Learning, Inc.

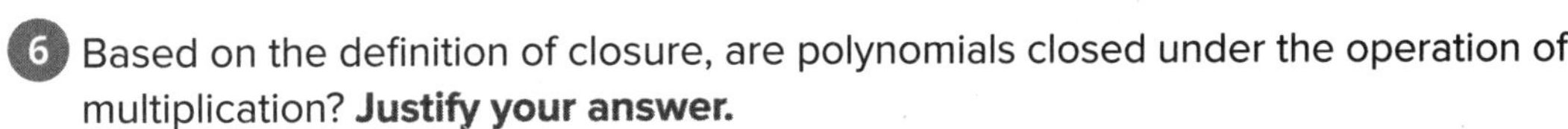

6 Based on the definition of closure, are polynomials closed under the operation of multiplication? **Justify your answer.**

Some binomials have special products when you multiply them.

Let's consider the product of two linear factors when one is the sum of the two terms and the other is the difference of the same two terms and when the two linear factors are the same.

7 Determine each product.

ⓐ $(x - 4)(x + 4) =$ ______

$(x + 4)(x + 4) =$ ______

$(x - 4)(x - 4) =$

ⓑ $(x - 3)(x + 3) =$ ______

$(x + 3)(x + 3) =$ ______

$(x - 3)(x - 3) =$ ______

ⓒ $(3x - 1)(3x + 1) =$ ______

$(3x + 1)(3x + 1) =$ ______

$(3x - 1)(3x - 1) =$ ______

ⓓ $(2x - 1)(2x + 1) =$ ______

$(2x + 1)(2x + 1) =$ ______

$(2x - 1)(2x - 1) =$

8 What patterns do you notice between the factors and the products?

9 Multiply each pair of binomials.

$(ax - b)(ax + b) =$ ______

$(ax + b)(ax + b) =$ ______

$(ax - b)(ax - b) =$ ______

© Carnegie Learning, Inc.

In Questions 7 and 9, you should have observed a few special products. The first type of special product is the *difference of two squares*. The **difference of two squares** is an expression in the form $a^2 - b^2$ that has factors $(a - b)(a + b)$.

10 Label the expressions in Questions 7 and 9 that are examples of the difference of two squares.

The second type of special product is a *perfect square trinomial*. A **perfect square trinomial** is an expression in the form $a^2 + 2ab + b^2$ or the form $a^2 - 2ab + b^2$. You can write a perfect square trinomial as the square of a binomial.

$$a^2 + 2ab + b^2 = (a + b)^2$$
$$a^2 - 2ab + b^2 = (a - b)^2$$

11 Label the expressions in Questions 7 and 9 that are examples of perfect square trinomials.

12 Use special products to determine each product.

(a) $(x - 8)(x - 8)$

(b) $(x + 8)(x - 8)$

(c) $(x + 8)^2$

(d) $(3x + 2)^2$

(e) $(3x - 2)(3x - 2)$

(f) $(3x - 2)(3x + 2)$

© Carnegie Learning, Inc.

Putting It Into Practice

> Match each expression with the equivalent polynomial.

Expressions	Polynomials
1 $(x^2 - 3) + (x^2 + 2)$	A. -1
2 $(x^2 - 3) - (x^2 + 2)$	B. $-2x^2 + 5$
3 $(x^2 - 3) - (x^2 - 2)$	C. $-2x^2 - 5$
4 $(x^2 - 3) + (x^2 - 2)$	D. $2x^2 - 1$
5 $(-x^2 + 3) - (x^2 - 2)$	E. $2x^2 - 5$
6 $-(x^2 + 3) - (x^2 + 2)$	F. -5
7 $(x - 3)(x + 2)$	G. $x^2 + 5x + 6$
8 $(x + 3)(x - 2)$	H. $x^2 - 5x + 6$
9 $(x + 3)(x + 2)$	I. $x^2 - x - 6$
10 $(x - 3)(x - 2)$	J. $x^2 + x - 6$

© Carnegie Learning, Inc.

Expression Cards

$4x - 6x^2$	$125p$	$\frac{4}{5}r^3 + \frac{2}{5}r - 1$
$-\frac{2}{3}$	$y^2 - 4y + 10$	$5 - 7h$
$-3 + 7n + n^2$	-6	$-13s + 6$
$12.5t^3$	$78j^3 - 3j$	$25 - 18m^2$

© Carnegie Learning, Inc.

Why is this page blank?

So you can cut out the expressions on the other side

© Carnegie Learning, Inc.

LESSON 1 ASSIGNMENT

Use a separate piece of paper for your Journal entry.

JOURNAL

Give an example of a monomial, binomial, and trinomial. Then, use two of your polynomials to write an addition expression, a subtraction expression, and a multiplication expression and perform the operation.

REMEMBER

A polynomial is a mathematical expression involving the sum of powers in one or more variables multiplied by coefficients. You can operate with polynomial expressions just as you would with numeric expressions.

PRACTICE

1. Ramona and James each build a rocket launcher. They launch a model rocket using Ramona's launcher and on its way back down it lands on the roof of a building that is 320 feet tall. You can represent the height of the rocket using the equation $H_1(x) = -16x^2 + 200x$, where x represents the time in seconds and $H_1(x)$ represents the height. Ramona and James re-launch the rocket from the roof using James's rocket launcher. You can represent the height of the rocket after this launch using the equation $H_2(x) = -16x^2 + 192x + 320$.

   a. Compare and contrast the polynomial functions.

   b. Use technology to sketch a graph of the functions.

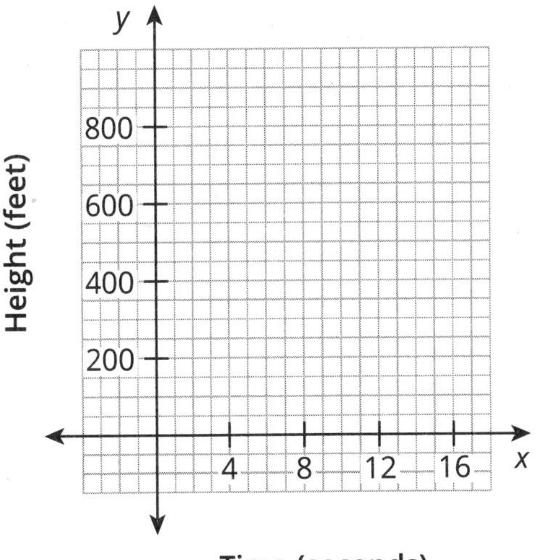

   c. Ramona believes that she can add the two functions to determine the total height of the rocket at any given time. Write a function $S(x)$ that represents the sum of $H_1(x)$ and $H_2(x)$. Show your work.

   d. Is Ramona correct? Explain your reasoning.

   e. Subtract $H_1(x)$ from $H_2(x)$ and write a new function, $D(x)$, that represents the difference. Then, explain what this function means in terms of the problem situation.

© Carnegie Learning, Inc.

Go to LiveHint.com for help on the PRACTICE questions.

2 Determine whether each expression is a polynomial. If so, identify the terms, coefficients, constants, and degree of the polynomial. If not, explain your reasoning.

a) $-2b^4 + 4b - 1$

b) $6 - g^{-2}$

c) $x^{\frac{1}{2}} + 2$

d) $\frac{4}{5}y + \frac{2}{3}y^2$

3 Given $A(x) = x^3 - 5x + 4$, $B(x) = 2x^2 + 5x - 6$, and $C(x) = -x^2 + 3$, determine each function. Write your answer in general form.

a) $D(x) = B(x) + C(x)$

b) $E(x) = A(x) + B(x)$

c) $F(x) = A(x) - C(x)$

d) $G(x) = C(x) - B(x)$

4 Determine each product.

a) $(x - 7)(x - 7)$

b) $(x + 10)(x - 10)$

c) $(x + 6)^2$

d) $(2x + 5)^2$

STRETCH Optional

> Consider the binomials $(x + 3)$, $(2x + 1)$, and $(x - 4)$.

1 Without multiplying, make a conjecture about the degree of the product of these binomials. Explain how you determined your answer.

2 Without multiplying, make a conjecture about the number of terms in the product of these binomials. Explain your reasoning.

3 Determine the product of the three binomials.

© Carnegie Learning, Inc.

LESSON 2

Solutions, More or Less

Representing Solutions to Quadratic Equations

KEY TERMS

principal square root

double root

Zero Product Property

Learning Goals

- Identify the zeros of a quadratic function, the roots of a quadratic equation, and the *x*-intercepts of a parabola using the equation of a quadratic function.
- Identify the double root of a quadratic equation as the two solutions of a quadratic equation at the minimum or maximum of the function.
- Write solutions of quadratic equations at specific output values using the axis of symmetry and the positive and negative square roots of the output value.
- Identify quadratic equations written as the difference of two perfect squares and rewrite these equations in factored form with a leading coefficient of 1.

REVIEW (1–2 minutes)

> Write each expression as the product of two whole number factors. Then, evaluate the expression.

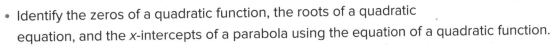

1. 4^2
2. 5^2
3. 7^2
4. 8^2

You have studied the graphs and equations for quadratic functions.

How can you use the structure of a parabola to understand the solutions of a quadratic equation?

© Carnegie Learning, Inc.

Plus or Minus

> Consider the absolute value function graphed.

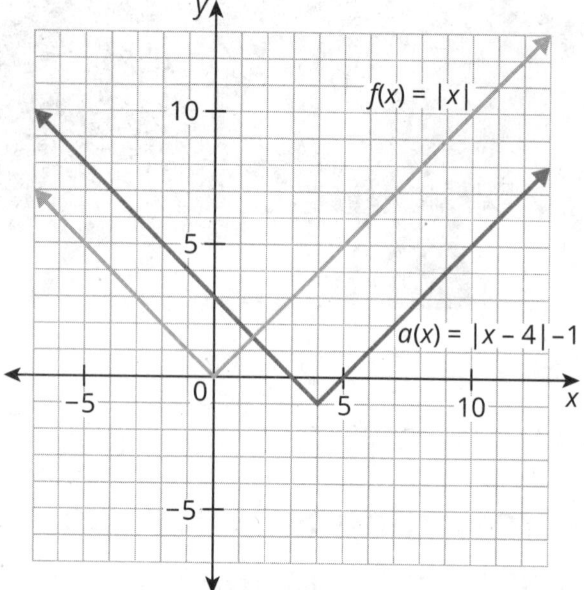

1 Describe how the function, $a(x)$, is transformed from the basic function $f(x) = |x|$.

2 For each $y > -1$, how many solutions does the equation $y = |x - 4| - 1$ have? **Use the graph to explain your answer.**

3 Determine the solutions to $|x - 4| - 1 = 0$ and identify the solutions on the graph.

4 Use the graph and the function equation to explain why Escher's equation is correct.

> **Escher**
>
> This absolute value function is symmetric about the line $x = 4$. So, for every y-value greater than -1, the solutions to the absolute value function are $x = 4 \pm (y + 1)$.

REMEMBER . . .
Solutions for a function at $y = 0$ are the zeros of the function.
The symbol ± means "plus or minus."

© Carnegie Learning, Inc.

Solutions of a Quadratic Function

HABITS OF MIND

- Look for and make use of structure.
- Look for and express regularity in repeated reasoning.

Recall that a quadratic function is a function of degree 2 because the greatest power for any of its terms is 2. This means that it has 2 zeros, or 2 solutions at $y = 0$.

You can represent the two solutions of a basic quadratic function as square roots of numbers. Every positive number has two square roots, a positive square root (or **principal square root**) and a negative square root.

WORKED EXAMPLE

To solve the equation $x^2 = 9$, you can take the square root of both sides of the equation.

$$x^2 = 9$$

$$x = \pm\sqrt{9}$$

$$x = \pm 3$$

Solving $x^2 = 9$ on a graph means that you are looking for the points of intersection between $y = x^2$ and $y = 9$.

1 Consider the graph of $q(x) = x^2$.

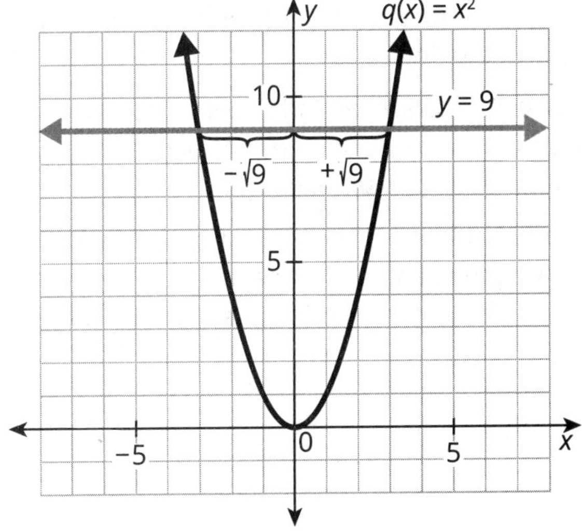

ⓐ What is the equation for the axis of symmetry? **Explain how you can use the function equation to determine your answer.**

ⓑ Explain how the graph shows the two solutions for the function at $y = 9$ and their relationship to the axis of symmetry. **Use the graph and the function equation to explain your answer.**

© Carnegie Learning, Inc.

(c) Describe how you can determine the two solutions for the function at $y = 2$. Indicate the solutions on the graph.

(d) Describe how you can determine the two solutions for the function at each y-value for $y \geq 0$.

The quadratic function $q(x) = x^2$ has two solutions at $y = 0$. Therefore, it has two zeros: $x = +\sqrt{0}$ and $x = -\sqrt{0}$. These two zeros of the function, or roots of the equation, are the same number, 0, so $y = x^2$ has a **double root**, or one unique root.

The root of an equation indicates where the graph of the equation crosses the x-axis. A double root occurs when the graph just touches the x-axis but does not cross it.

TAKE NOTE . . .
The x-coordinates of the x-intercepts of a graph of a quadratic function are the zeros of the quadratic function. The zeros are the roots of the quadratic equation.

2 Look back at Escher's equation in the Getting Started. How can you write the solutions for the function $q(x) = x^2$ in the same way, using the axis of symmetry? **Explain your reasoning.**

© Carnegie Learning, Inc.

Consider the graphs of three quadratic functions, $f(x)$, $h(x)$, and $g(x)$.

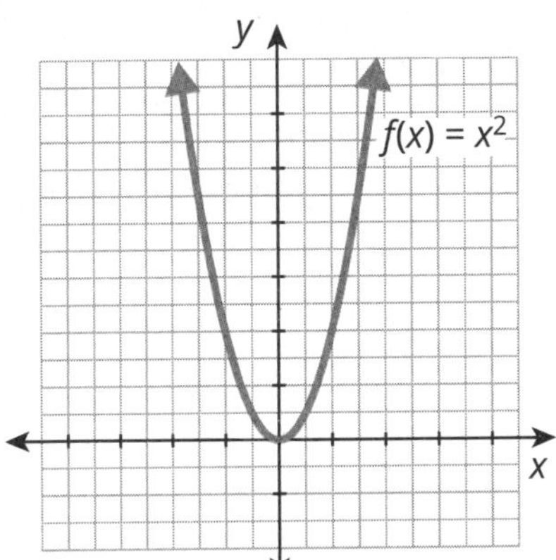

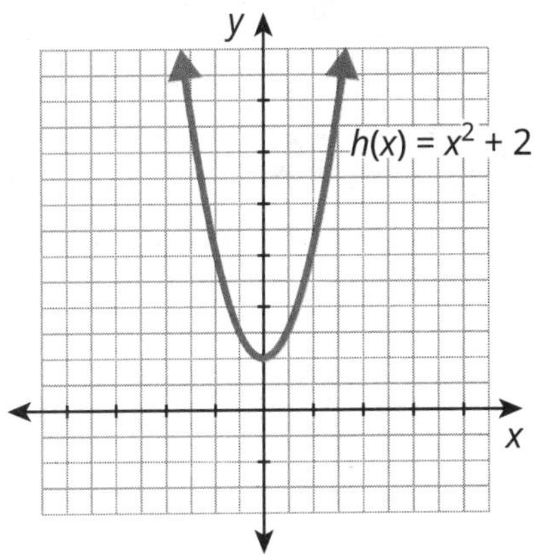

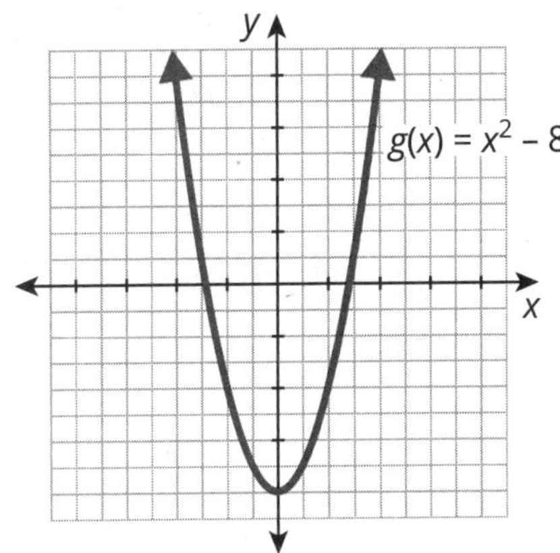

3 Use the graphs to identify the solutions to each equation. Then, determine the solutions algebraically and write the solutions in terms of their respective distances from the axis of symmetry.

a) $14 = x^2 + 2$

b) $x^2 = 10$

c) $-5 = x^2 - 8$

d) $19 = x^2 + 4$

e) $x^2 - 8 = 1$

f) $6 = x^2$

4 Consider the graphs of $f(x)$, $h(x)$, and $g(x)$, which function has a double zero? **Explain your answer.**

© Carnegie Learning, Inc.

When you are solving quadratic equations you may encounter solutions that are not perfect squares. You can either determine the approximate value of the radical or rewrite it in an equivalent radical form.

WORKED EXAMPLE

You can determine the approximate value of $\sqrt{75}$.

Determine the perfect square that is closest to but less than 75.

Then, determine the perfect square that is closest to but greater than 75.

$$64 \leq 75 \leq 81$$

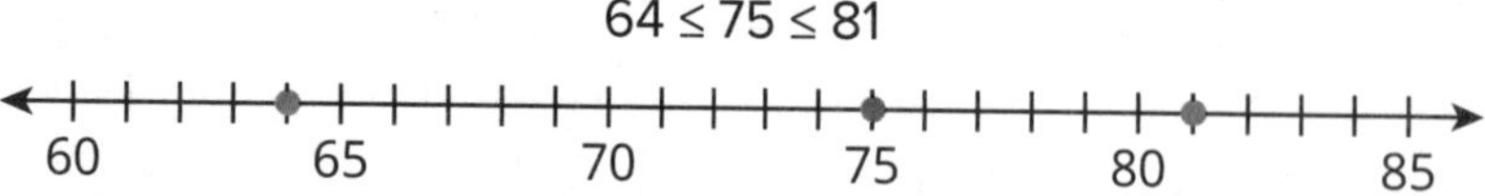

Determine the square roots of the perfect squares.

$\sqrt{64} = 8$ $\sqrt{75} = ?$ $\sqrt{81} = 9$

Now that you know that $\sqrt{75}$ is between 8 and 9, you can test the squares of numbers between 8 and 9.

$8.6^2 = 73.9$ $8.7^2 = 75.69$

Since 75 is closer to 75.69 than 73.96, 8.7 is the approximate square root of $\sqrt{75}$.

ASK YOURSELF . . .

Can you name all the perfect squares from 1^2 through 15^2?

WORKED EXAMPLE

You can use prime factors to rewrite $\sqrt{75}$ in an equivalent radical form.

First, rewrite the product of 75 to include any perfect square factors, and then extract the square roots of those perfect squares.

$$\begin{aligned}\sqrt{75} &= \sqrt{3 \cdot 5 \cdot 5}\\ &= \sqrt{3 \cdot 5^2}\\ &= \sqrt{3} \cdot \sqrt{5^2}\\ &= 5\sqrt{3}\end{aligned}$$

THINK ABOUT . . .

How can listing the prime factors of a radical expression help you extract square roots of perfect squares?

© Carnegie Learning, Inc.

5 Estimate the value of each radical expression. Then, rewrite each radical by extracting all perfect squares, if possible.

(a) $\sqrt{20}$

(b) $\sqrt{26}$

(c) $\sqrt{18}$

(d) $\sqrt{116}$

6 Rewrite your answers from Question 3 by extracting perfect squares, if possible. **Verify your rewritten answers using the graphs in Question 3.**

© Carnegie Learning, Inc.

Solutions from Standard Form to Factored Form

HABITS OF MIND

- Reason abstractly and quantitatively.
- Construct viable arguments and critique the reasoning of others.

Recall that a quadratic function written in factored form is in the form $f(x) = a(x - r_1)(x - r_2)$, where $a \neq 0$. In factored form, r_1 and r_2 represent the x-intercepts of the graph of the function.

1 Determine the zeros of the function $z(x) = x^2 - 16$. Then, write the function in factored form.

THINK ABOUT . . .

Do you recognize the form of this quadratic function?

The function $z(x)$ in factored form is a quadratic function made up of two linear factors. Let's analyze the linear factors as separate linear functions, $g(x)$ and $h(x)$. Therefore, $z(x) = g(x) \cdot h(x)$.

2 Complete the table by writing the algebraic expressions to represent $g(x)$ and $h(x)$ and then determine the output values for the two linear factors and the quadratic product. Finally, sketch a graph of $z(x)$.

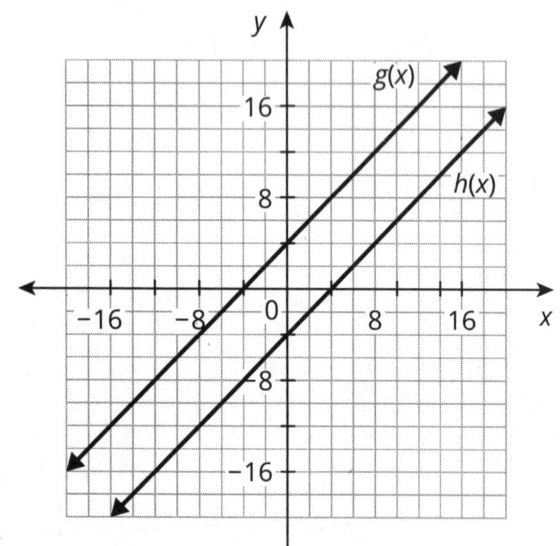

	$g(x)$	$h(x)$	$z(x)$
x			$x^2 - 16$
−4			
−2			
0			
2			
4			

© Carnegie Learning, Inc.

The **Zero Product Property** states that if the product of two or more factors is equal to zero, then at least one factor must be equal to zero.

WORKED EXAMPLE

You can use the Zero Product Property to identify the zeros of a function when the function is written in factored form.

$0 = x^2 - 16$

$0 = (x + 4)(x - 4)$	Rewrite the quadratic as linear factors.
$x - 4 = 0$ and $x + 4 = 0$	Apply the Zero Product Property.
$x = 4$ $\quad$ $x = -4$	Solve each equation for x.

3 Explain how the zeros of the linear function factors relate to the zeros of the quadratic function product.

Notice that the function $z(x) = x^2 - 16$ has an a-value of 1 and a b-value of 0. You can use a similar strategy to determine the zeros of a function when the leading coefficient is not 1, but the b-value is still 0.

WORKED EXAMPLE

You can determine the zeros of the function $f(x) = 9x^2 - 1$ by setting $f(x) = 0$ and using the Properties of Equality to solve for x.

$$9x^2 - 1 = 0$$

$$9x^2 = 1$$

$$x^2 = \frac{1}{9}$$

$$x = \pm\frac{1}{3}$$

You can use the leading coefficient of 9 and the zeros at $\frac{1}{3}$ and $(-\frac{1}{3})$ to rewrite the quadratic function in factored form.

$$f(x) = 9\left(x - \frac{1}{3}\right)\left(x + \frac{1}{3}\right)$$

4 Consider the Worked Example.

(a) Explain why $\sqrt{\frac{1}{9}} = \pm\frac{1}{3}$.

(b) Use graphing technology to verify that $9x^2 = 1 = 9\left(x - \frac{1}{3}\right)\left(x + \frac{1}{3}\right)$. **How can you tell from the graph that the two equations are equivalent?**

© Carnegie Learning, Inc.

Three students tried to rewrite the quadratic function $f(x) = 9\left(x - \frac{1}{3}\right)\left(x + \frac{1}{3}\right)$ as two linear factors using what they know about the difference of two squares.

Terrell

$9\left(x - \frac{1}{3}\right)\left(x + \frac{1}{3}\right) =$

$(9x - 3)\left(x + \frac{1}{3}\right)$

Jackson

$9\left(x - \frac{1}{3}\right)\left(x + \frac{1}{3}\right) =$

$(4.5x - 1.5)(4.5x + 1.5)$

Raychelle

$9\left(x - \frac{1}{3}\right)\left(x + \frac{1}{3}\right) =$

$(3x - 1)(3x + 1)$

5 Explain why Terrell and Jackson are incorrect and why Raychelle is correct.

ASK YOURSELF . . .
Are these expressions still in factored form?

6 Consider the graph of $f(x) = 9x^2 - 1$.

ⓐ Use Raychelle's function, $f(x) = (3x - 1)(3x + 1)$, to sketch a graph of the linear factors.

Then, use graphing technology to verify that $9x^2 - 1 = (3x - 1)(3x + 1)$.

ⓑ How do the zeros of the function relate to its two linear factors?

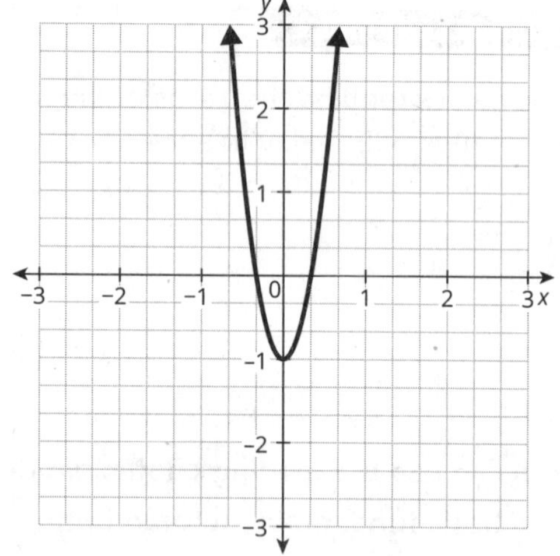

© Carnegie Learning, Inc.

7 For each function:

- Sketch a graph. Label the axis of symmetry and the vertex.
- Use the Properties of Equality to identify the zeros and then write the zeros in terms of their respective distances from the line of symmetry.
- Use what you know about the difference of two squares to rewrite each quadratic, as the product of two linear factors. Then, use the Zero Product Property to verify the values of x , when $f(x) = 0$.
- Use graphing technology to verify that the product of the two linear factors is equivalent to the given function.

(a) $f(x) = 4x^2 - 9$

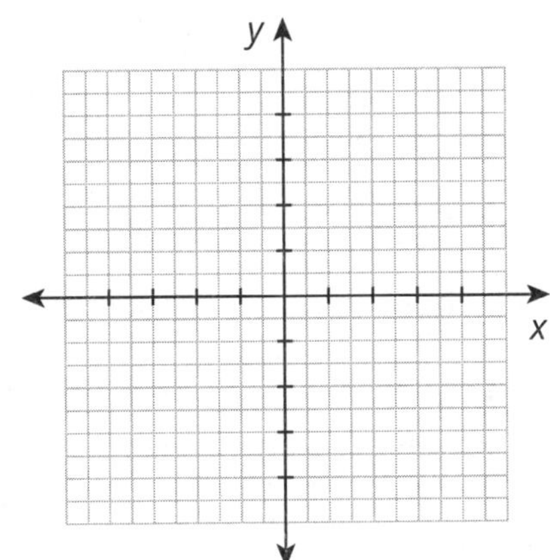

(b) $f(x) = x^2 - 2$

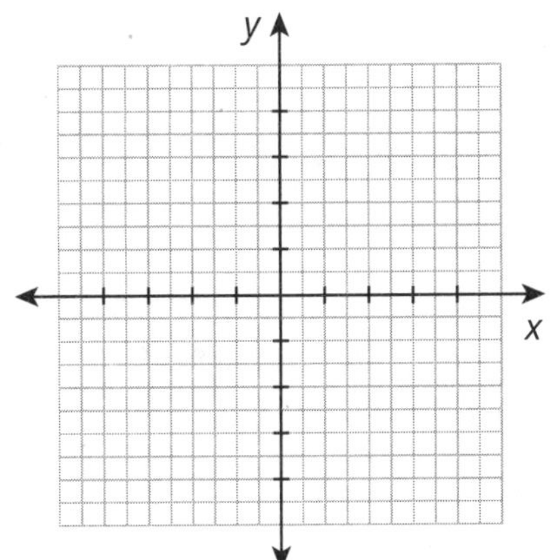

(c) $f(x) = 25x^2 - 1$

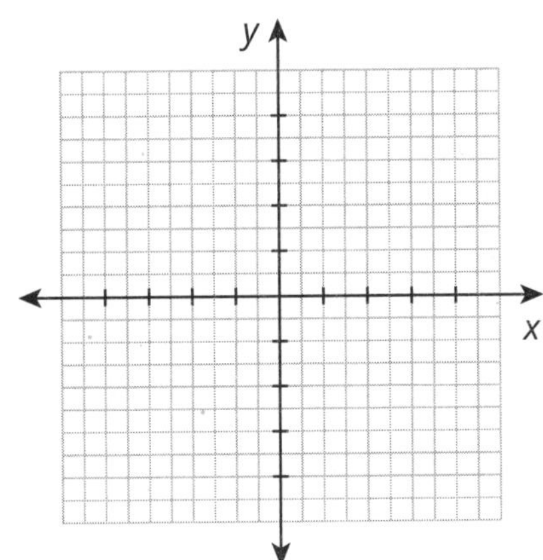

© Carnegie Learning, Inc.

The Difference of Squares

In this lesson, you determined the zeros of quadratics written in the form $f(x) = ax^2 - c$.

1. Solve each equation.

   (a) $x^2 - 25 = 0$

   (b) $4x^2 - 1 = 0$

   (c) $9x^2 - 2 = 0$

   (d) $x^2 - 80 = 0$

2. Rewrite each quadratic function as two linear factors using what you know about the difference of two squares.

   (a) $f(x) = x^2 - 49$

   (b) $f(x) = \frac{4}{9}x^2 - 1$

   (c) $f(x) = 16x^2 - 10$

   (d) $f(x) = x^2 + 9$

3. Explain how to write any function of the form $f(x) = ax^2 - c$, where a and c are any real numbers, as two linear factors using what you know about the difference of two squares.

© Carnegie Learning, Inc.

LESSON 2 ASSIGNMENT

> Use a separate piece of paper for your Journal entry.

JOURNAL

Complete each definition.

1. The Zero Product Property states that if the product of two or more factors is equal to ___________ , then at least one factor must be equal to ___________ .

REMEMBER

You can represent solutions to a quadratic equation in terms of their respective distances from the axis of symmetry.

2. Every positive number has both a ___________ square root and a ___________ square root.
3. The function $f(x) = x^2$ has a ___________ at (0, 0).

PRACTICE

1. Determine the solutions for each equation. Identify the solutions on one of the graphs. Then, write the solutions in terms of their respective differences from the axis of symmetry.

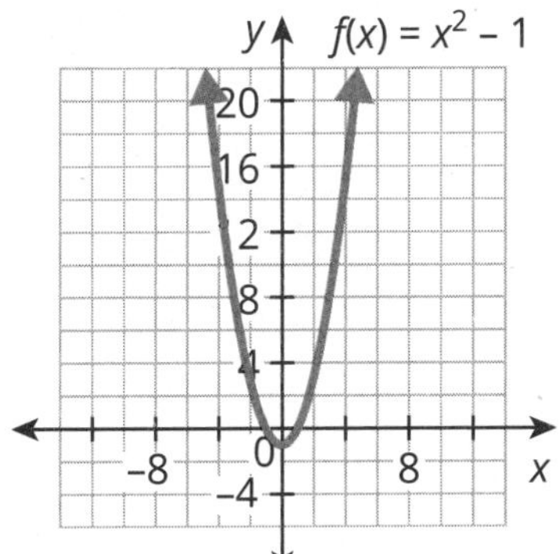

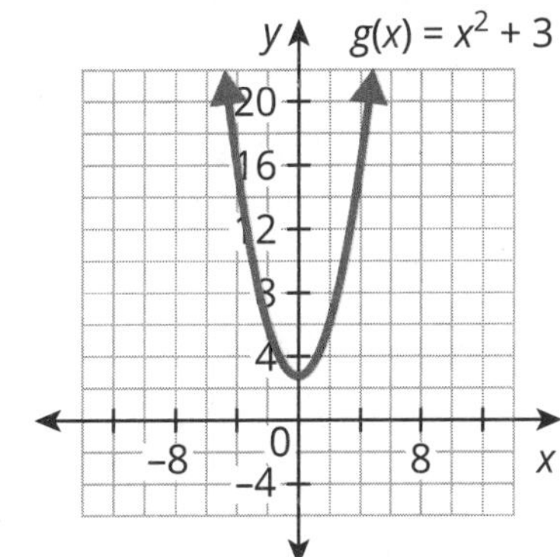

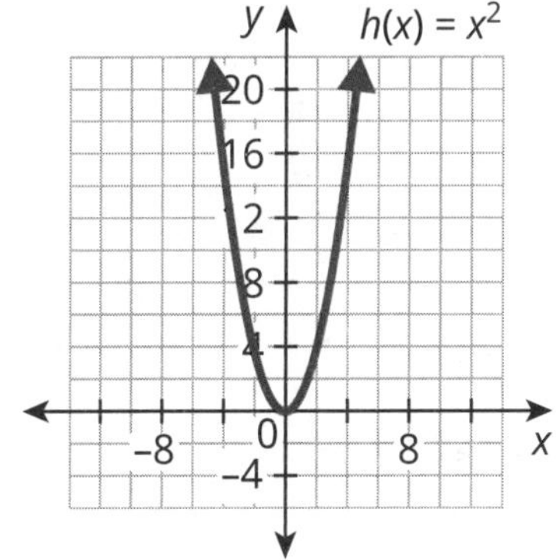

(a) $8 = x^2 + 3$

(b) $7 = x^2$

(c) $2 = x^2 - 1$

(d) $x^2 = 11$

(e) $x^2 + 9 = 13$

(f) $14 = x^2 - 1$

© Carnegie Learning, Inc.

Go to LiveHint.com for help on the PRACTICE questions.

2 Estimate the value of each radical expression. Then, rewrite each radical by extracting all perfect squares, if possible.

(a) $\sqrt{21}$

(b) $\sqrt{80}$

(c) $\sqrt{63}$

(d) $\sqrt{32}$

(e) $\sqrt{98}$

(f) $\sqrt{192}$

3 Rewrite each quadratic function as two linear factors using what you know about the difference of two squares.

(a) $f(x) = 9x^2 - 16$

(b) $f(x) = x^2 - 8$

(c) $f(x) = 36x^2 - 1$

(d) $f(x) = 25x^2 - 12$

STRETCH Optional

> Consider the graph of the function $f(x) = x^2 + 3x - 5$.

1 Determine the solutions for the equation $x^2 + 3x - 5 = 5$. Identify the solutions on the graph.

2 Rewrite the equation from Question 1 so that the right side of the equation is 0. What do the solutions from Question 1 represent in this new equation?

3 Use your solutions from Question 1 to write a product of two binomials, $(x - a)(x - b)$, where a and b are the solutions from Question 1. How does this relate to the left side of the equation in Question 2?

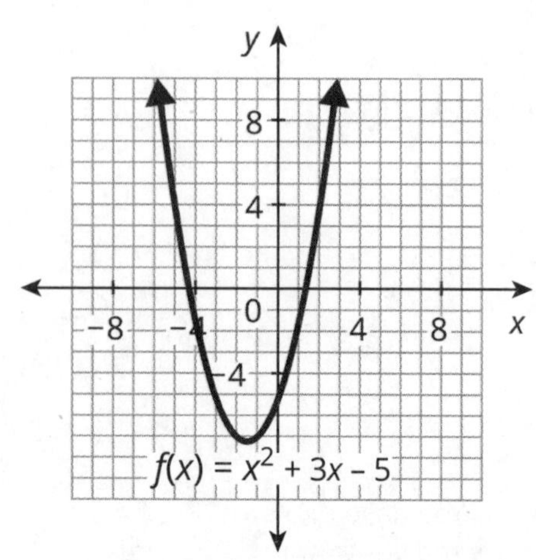

© Carnegie Learning, Inc.

LESSON 3

Transforming Solutions

Solutions to Quadratic Equations in Vertex Form

Learning Goals

- Identify solutions to and roots of quadratic equations given in the forms $f(x) = (x - c)^2$, $f(x) = a(x - c)^2$, and $f(x) = a(x - c)^2 + d$.
- Identify zeros of quadratic functions written in vertex form.

REVIEW (1–2 minutes)

> Describe the transformations to the graph of the basic function $f(x) = x^2$ given each equation.

1. $y = (x - 4)^2$

2. $y = \frac{1}{2}(x + 1)^2$

3. $y = -(10 + x)^2 - 3$

4. $y = (8 + x)^2 + 1$

© Carnegie Learning, Inc.

You have explored transformations of quadratic functions and vertex form.

How can you use vertex form and transformations to determine solutions to quadratic equations?

Slide, Slide, Slippity Slide

> Consider the graph of the function $g(x) = (x - 1)^2$.

1 Describe the transformation applied to the basic function $f(x) = x^2$ that produces the graph of this function.

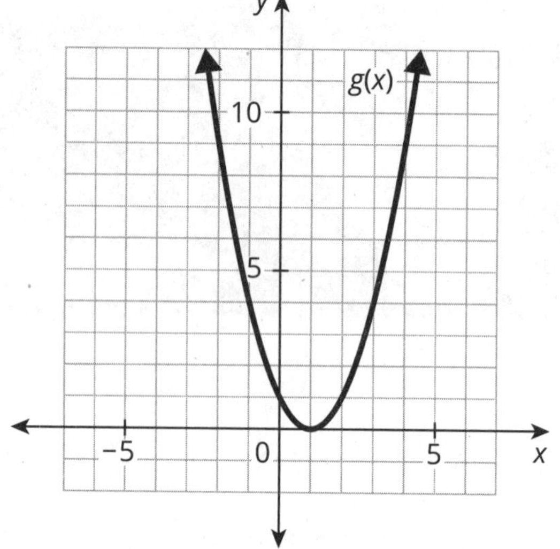

Lindsay and Casey determined the zeros of the function $g(x) = (x - 1)^2$ algebraically in different ways.

Lindsay

$0 = (x - 1)^2$

$0 = (x - 1)(x - 1)$

The Zero Product Property says that one or both of the factors is equal to 0. So, $x = 1$.

The equation has a double root at $x = 1$.

Casey

$(x - 1)^2 = 0$

$x - 1 = \pm\sqrt{0}$

$x = 1 \pm \sqrt{0}$

$x = 1 + 0$ $x = 1 - 0$

$x = 1$ $x = 1$

The only unique solution for $y = 0$ is $x = 1$.

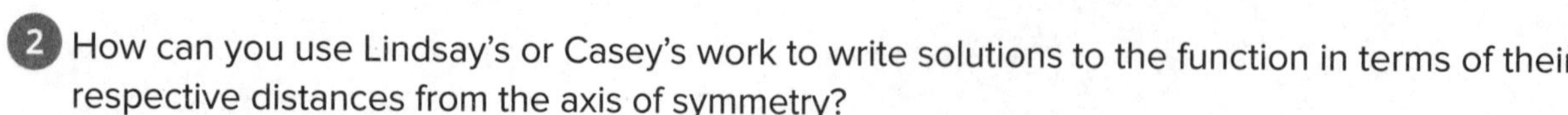

2 How can you use Lindsay's or Casey's work to write solutions to the function in terms of their respective distances from the axis of symmetry?

© Carnegie Learning, Inc.

Solutions for Horizontal Translations

HABITS OF MIND

- Look for and make use of structure.
- Look for and express regularity in repeated reasoning.

You have used graphs to solve equations. In this activity, you will use the graph of a quadratic equation to determine its solutions.

WORKED EXAMPLE

Consider the equation $(x - 1)^2 = 9$.

You can use the Properties of Equality to determine the solutions to an equation in this form.

First, take the square root of both sides of the equation and then isolate x.

$$(x - 1)^2 = 9$$
$$x - 1 = \pm\sqrt{9}$$
$$x - 1 = \pm 3$$
$$x = 1 \pm 3$$

1 Consider the graph of $y = (x - 1)^2$ in the Getting Started.

REMEMBER . . .
Solving $(x - 1)^2 = 9$ on a graph means locating where $y = (x - 1)^2$ intersects with $y = 9$.

(a) Graph the equation $y = 9$ on the same graph.

(b) Show the solutions on the graph. Interpret the solutions 1 ± 3 in terms of the axis of symmetry and the points on the parabola $y = (x - 1)^2$.

(c) What are the solutions to the equation $(x - 1)^2 = 9$?

© Carnegie Learning, Inc.

2 For each equation, show the solutions on the graph and interpret the solutions in terms of the axis of symmetry and the points on the parabola. Then, write the solutions.

ⓐ $(x - 1)^2 = 4$

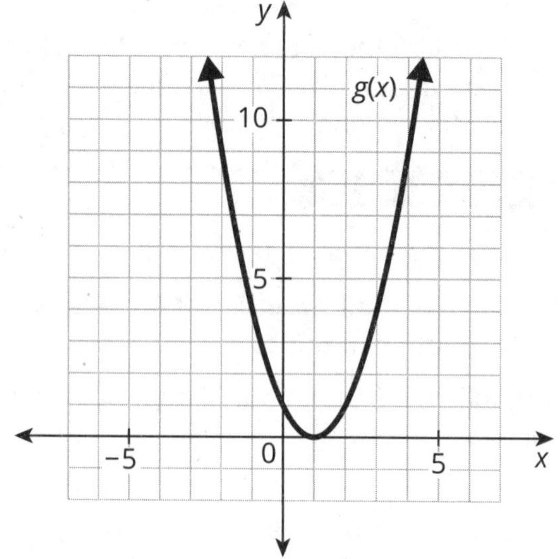

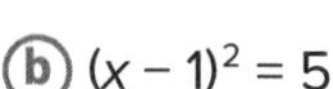
ⓑ $(x - 1)^2 = 5$

3 Determine the exact and approximate solutions for each of the given equations.

ⓐ $(r + 8)^2 = 83$

ⓑ $(17 - d)^2 = 55$

© Carnegie Learning, Inc.

Solutions for Vertical Dilations

You have seen how to solve an equation for a quadratic function in the form $f(x) = (x - c)^2$, which represents a horizontal translation of the function. In this activity, you will consider quadratic equations with an additional vertical dilation. First, let's start with just a horizontal translation.

HABITS OF MIND
- Look for and make use of structure.
- Look for and express regularity in repeated reasoning.

1. Consider the function $f(x) = (x - 5)^2$.

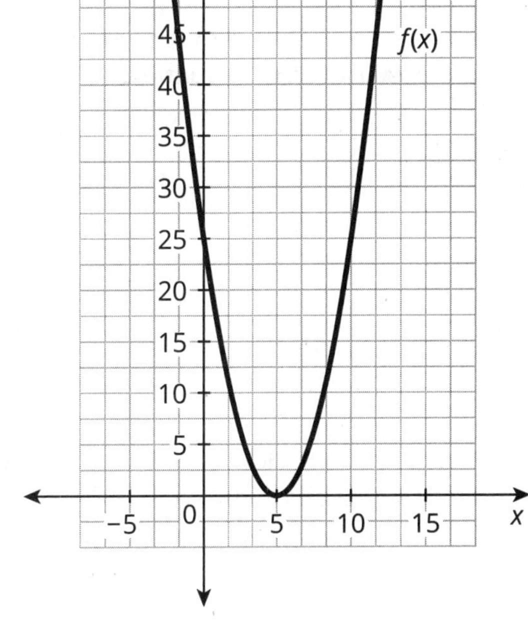

   a. Determine the solutions to $0 = (x - 5)^2$. Solve algebraically and label the solution on the graph.

   b. Interpret your solutions in terms of the axis of symmetry and the parabola $y = (x - 5)^2$.

   c. Describe the zeros of this function.

Now, let's add a dilation factor.

2. Consider the function $g(x) = 2(x - 5)^2$.

   a. Write $g(x)$ in terms of $f(x)$ and describe the transformation.

   b. Sketch a graph on the same coordinate plane as $f(x)$.

   c. How have the zeros changed from $f(x)$ to $g(x)$?

© Carnegie Learning, Inc.

TOPIC 2

3 Parker formulated a conjecture about how the solutions of the transformed quadratic equation change from the original equation.

Parker

The solutions of the original function are $x = 5 \pm \sqrt{y}$, so the solutions to the transformed equation are $x = 5 \pm 2\sqrt{y}$.

Is Parker correct? **If so, explain why. If not, describe the correct solutions for the transformed quadratic equation.**

4 Make a conjecture. How does changing the sign of the *a*-value affect the solutions to the quadratic equations in this form?

5 Solve each quadratic equation. Give both exact and approximate solutions.

ⓐ $(x - 4)^2 = 2$

ⓑ $2(x - 1)^2 = 18$

ⓒ $-2(x - 1)^2 = -18$

ⓓ $4(x + 5)^2 = 21$

ⓔ $-\frac{1}{2}(x + 8)^2 = -32$

ⓕ $\frac{2}{3}(12 - x)^2 = 1$

© Carnegie Learning, Inc.

ACTIVITY 3

MATHia CONNECTION

- Using Properties of Equality to Solve Quadratic Equations

Solutions for Vertical Translations

HABITS OF MIND

- Look for and make use of structure.
- Look for and express regularity in repeated reasoning.

You have determined solutions to quadratic equations, given an equation in the form $f(x) = a(x - c)^2$.

How can you solve a quadratic equation that also includes a vertical translation in the form $f(x) = a(x - c)^2 + d$?

Consider the graph of $g(x) = 2(x - 5)^2$. You know that the solution to the equation $0 = 2(x - 5)^2$ is $x = 5$.

REMEMBER . . .
A quadratic function in vertex form is written $f(x) = a(x - k)^2 + h$.

1 Consider the function $h(x) = 2(x - 5)^2 - 1$.

(a) Write $h(x)$ in terms of $g(x)$ and describe the transformation.

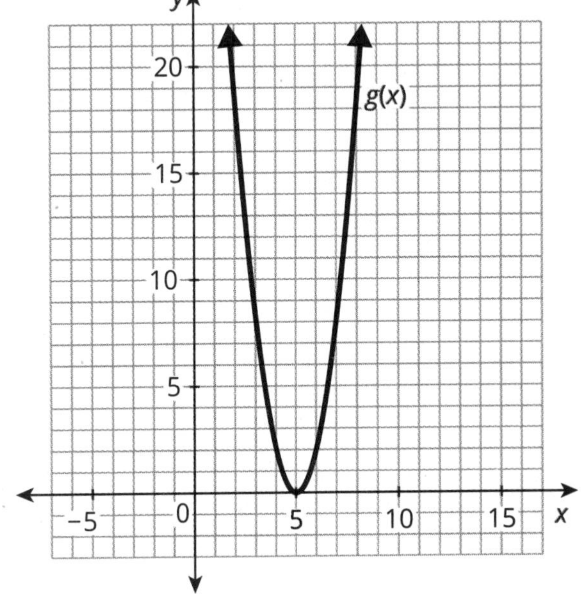

(b) Sketch a graph of $h(x)$ on the same coordinate plane as $g(x)$.

2 Consider the equation $0 = 2(x - 5)^2 - 1$.

(a) Determine the solution algebraically and label the solution on the graph.

(b) Interpret the solutions in terms of the axis of symmetry and the parabola $y = 2(x - 5)^2 - 1$.

(c) Describe the zeros of this function.

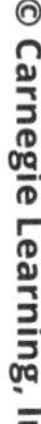
© Carnegie Learning, Inc.

Now, let's investigate the effect of an equation in the form $f(x) = a(x - c)^2 + d$, where $a > 0$ and $d > 0$.

> Consider the graph of the function $j(x) = 2(x - 5)^2 + 1$.

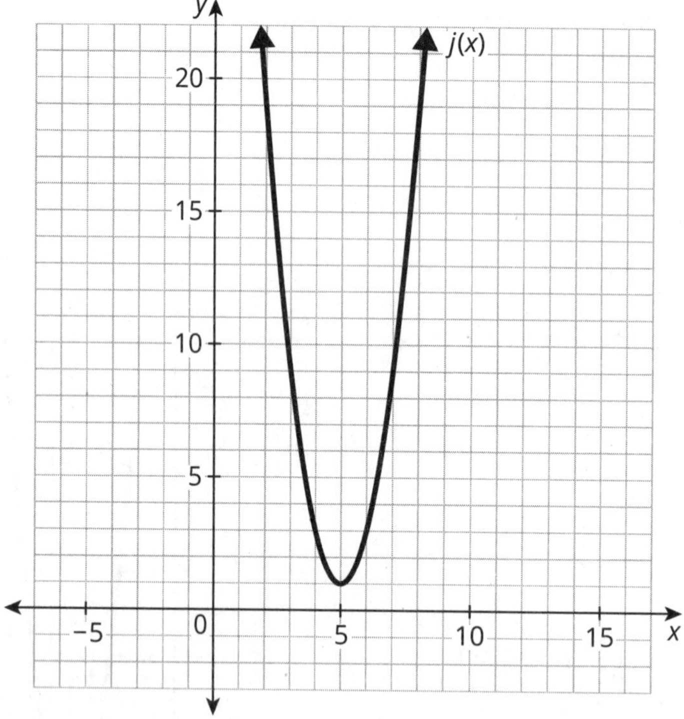

Notice the graph of $j(x)$ does not cross the x-axis, which means there are no real zeros for this function.

3 Solve $0 = 2(x - 5)^2 + 1$ algebraically to show that x is not a real number.

While there are no real zeros in this function, there is another type of zero you will learn about later in this topic.

© Carnegie Learning, Inc.

4 Sketch a graph of each quadratic function. Determine the types of zeros of each function. Solve algebraically and interpret on the graph in terms of the axis of symmetry and the points on the parabola.

TAKE NOTE . . .
A quadratic function can have one unique real zero, two real zeros, or no real zeros.

ⓐ $f(x) = -3(x - 2)^2 + 4$

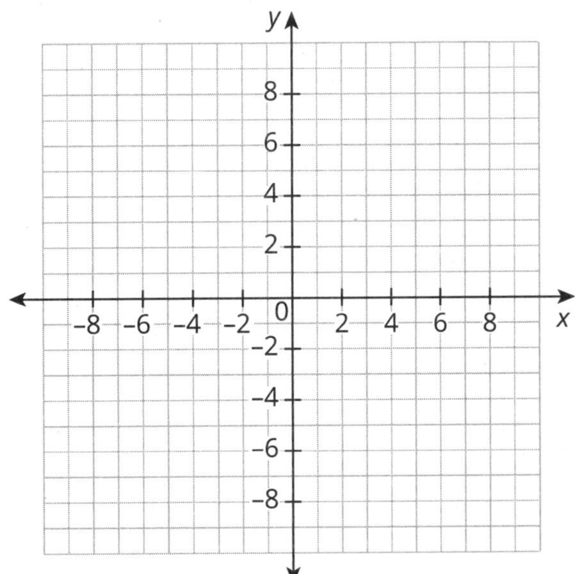

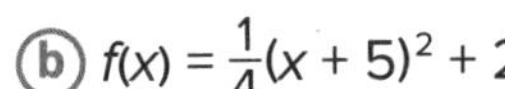

ⓑ $f(x) = \frac{1}{4}(x + 5)^2 + 2$

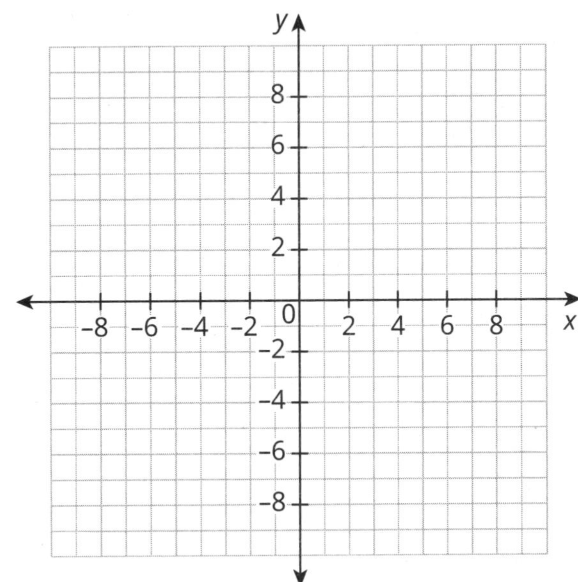

TOPIC 2

© Carnegie Learning, Inc.

Spell It Out

> Use what you know about the solutions to quadratic equations to answer each question.

1. Describe the solution of any quadratic equation in each form.

   a. $(x - c)^2 = 0$

   b. $(x - c)^2 + d = 0$

   c. $a(x - c)^2 + d = 0$

2. Write an equation and sketch a graph that shows each number of roots.

   a. One unique real root

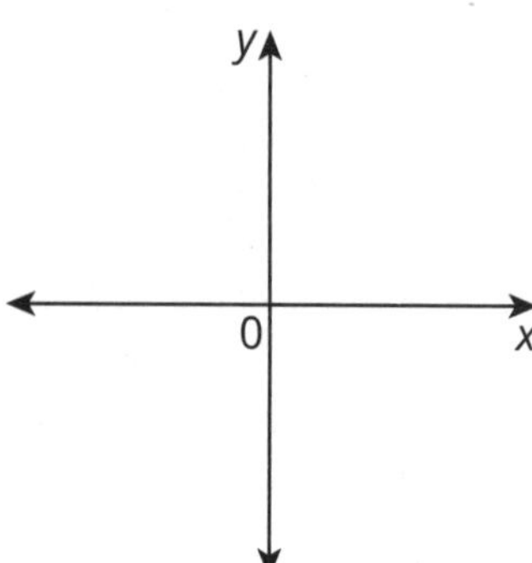

   b. Two real roots

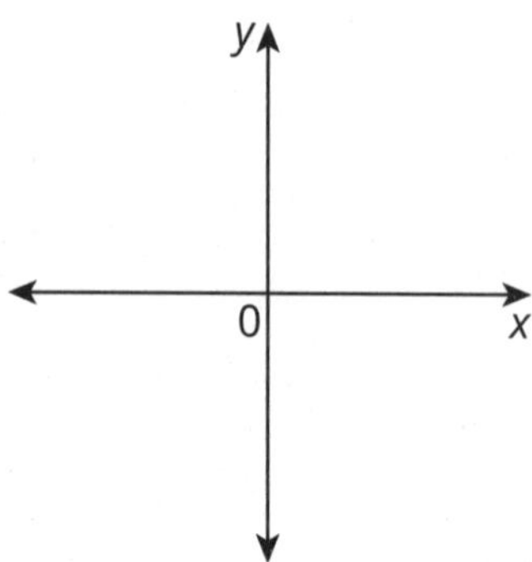

   c. No real roots

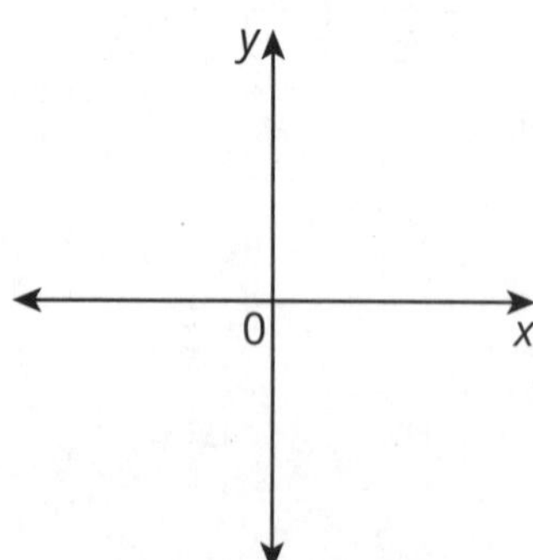

© Carnegie Learning, Inc.

LESSON 3 ASSIGNMENT

> Use a separate piece of paper for your Journal entry.

JOURNAL

Describe the number of possible real zeros for any quadratic function.

REMEMBER

The solutions to a quadratic equation of the form $y = a(x - c)^2 + d$ are $x = c \pm \sqrt{\frac{y - d}{a}}$.

PRACTICE

1. Sketch a graph of each quadratic function. Determine the zeros of each function and write each in terms of the axis of symmetry and its distance to the parabola.

(a) $f(x) = (x - 3)^2$

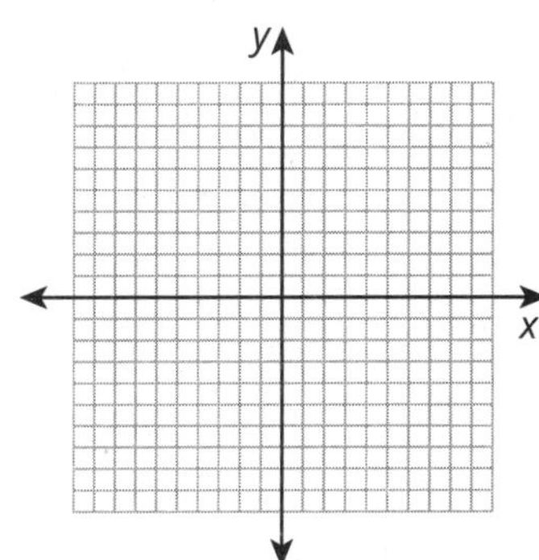

(b) $f(x) = (x + 5)^2$

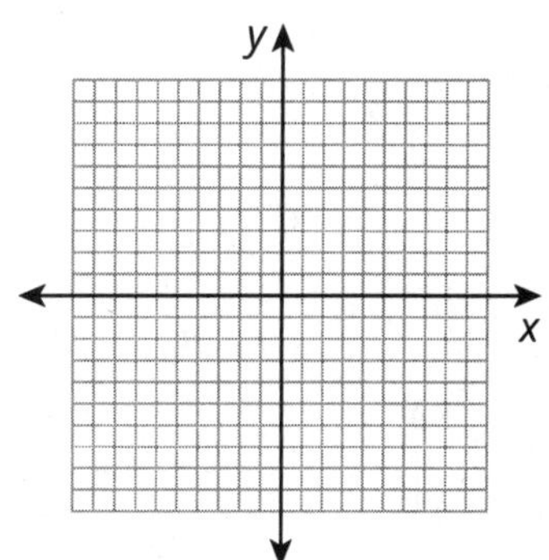

(c) $f(x) = \left(x - \frac{1}{2}\right)^2$

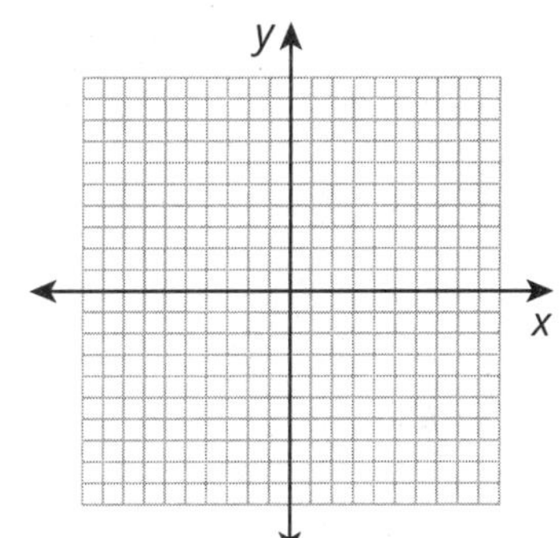

(d) $f(x) = (x - 6)^2$

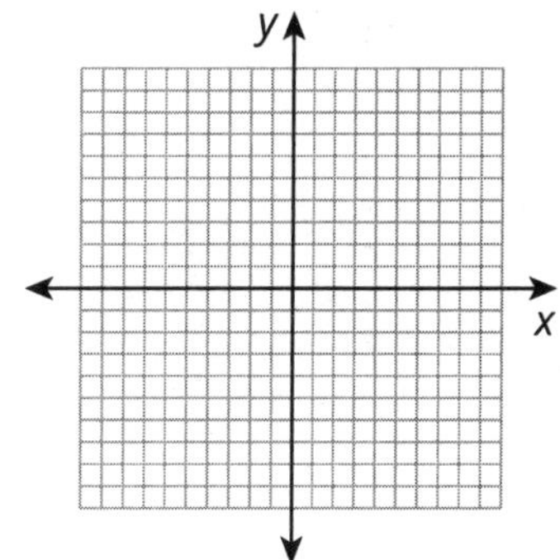

(e) $f(x) = \left(x + \frac{15}{7}\right)^2$

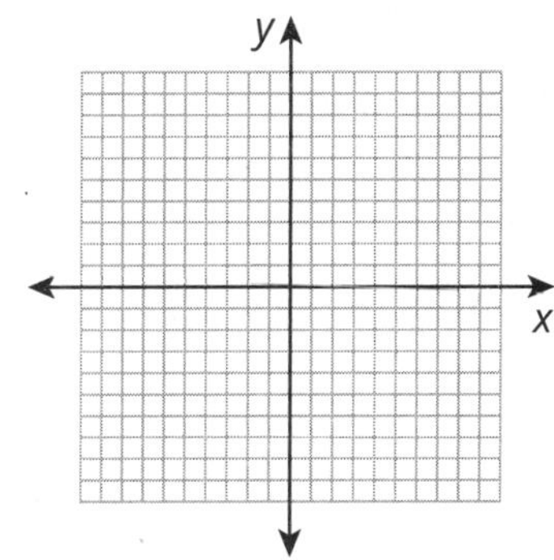

(f) $f(x) = (x + 7)^2$

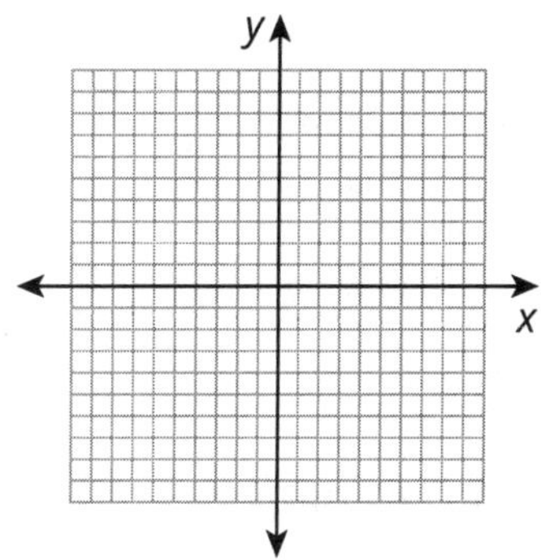

© Carnegie Learning, Inc.

Go to LiveHint.com for help on the PRACTICE questions.

2 Sketch a graph of each quadratic function. Determine the zeros of each function and write in terms of the axis of symmetry and its distance to the parabola.

(a) $f(x) = 2(x - 1)^2 - 1$

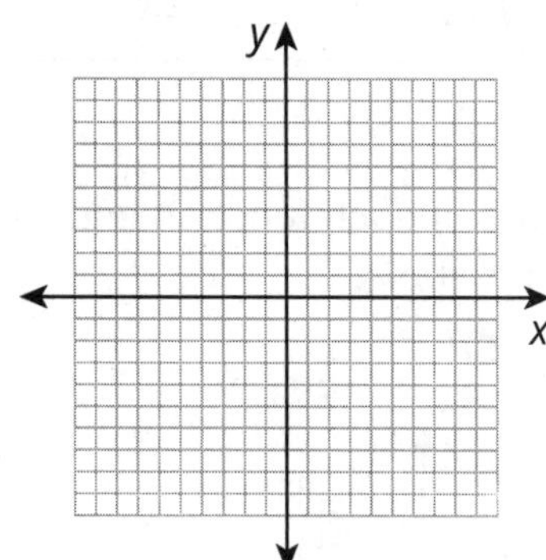

(b) $f(x) = \frac{1}{2}(x + 2)^2 - 5$

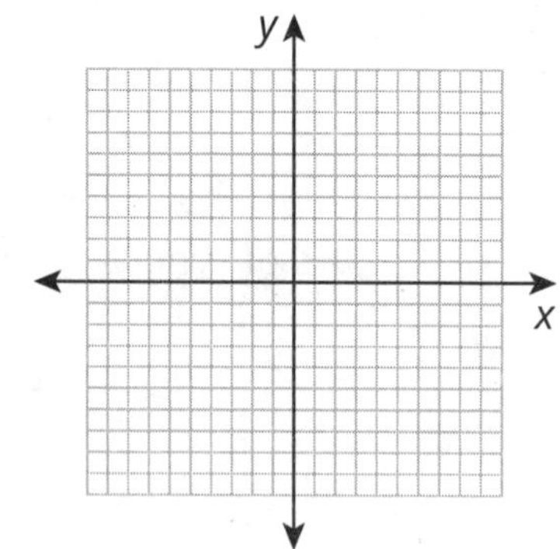

(c) $f(x) = 4\left(x + \frac{1}{3}\right)^2 - 1$

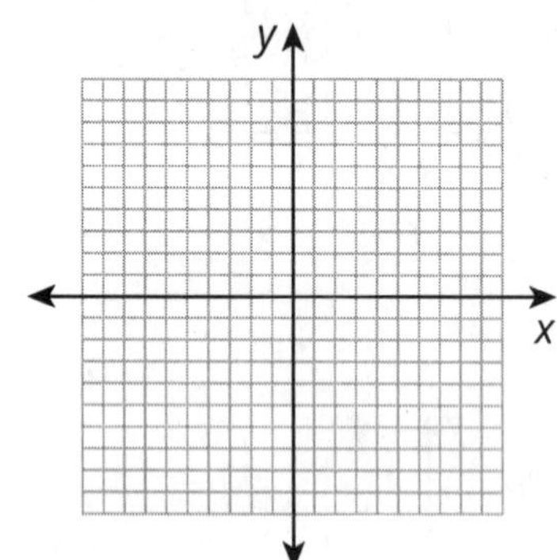

(d) $f(x) = -3(x - 6)^2$

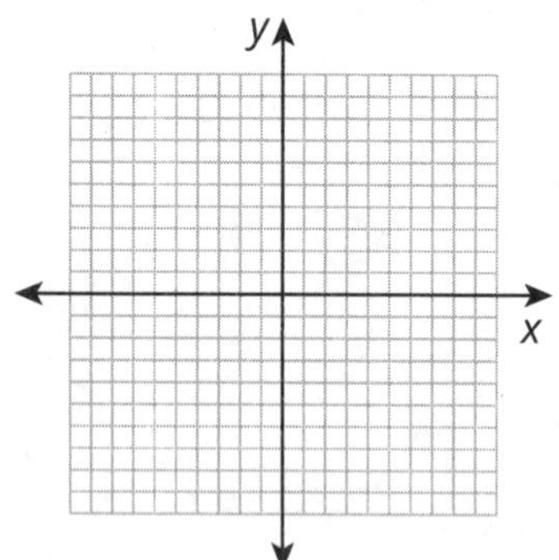

(e) $f(x) = \frac{3}{4}(x + 5)^2 - \frac{2}{3}$

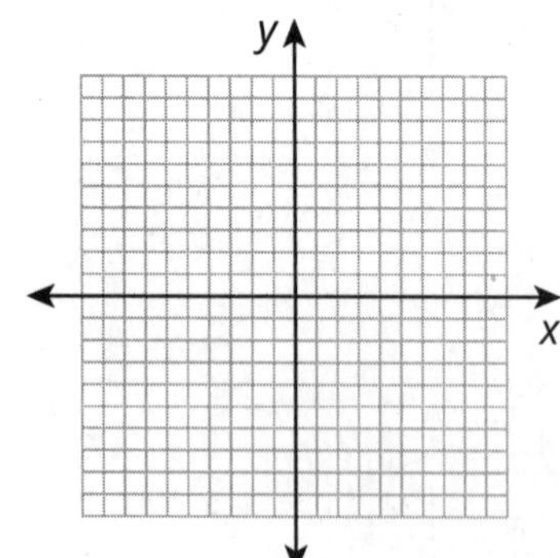

(f) $f(x) = (x - 4)^2 - 2$

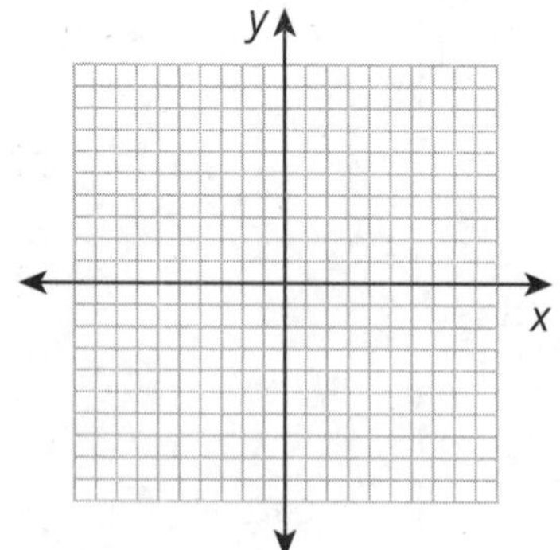

© Carnegie Learning, Inc.

STRETCH Optional

A quadratic function has zeros at $x = -2 \pm \sqrt{15}$.

1 Write the function in general form. Show your work.

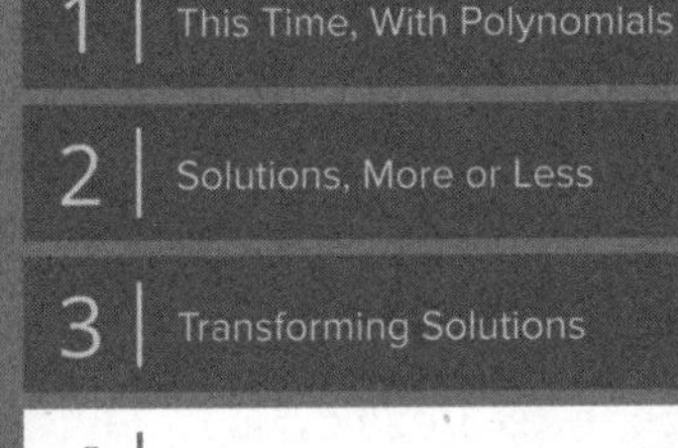

LESSON 4

The Missing Link

Factoring and Completing the Square

KEY TERM

completing the square

Learning Goals

- Factor out the greatest common factor (GCF) of polynomials.
- Rewrite quadratic equations of the form $x^2 + bx$ in vertex form by completing the square.
- Factor quadratic trinomials to determine the roots of quadratic equations and to rewrite quadratic functions in forms that reveal different key characteristics.
- Demonstrate the reasoning behind the method of completing the square and use the method to determine the roots of quadratic equations of the form $ax^2 + bx + c$.

REVIEW (1–2 minutes)

> Use the Distribute Property to determine each product.

1 $(x + 1)(x + 2)$

2 $(x + 4)(x - 5)$

3 $(2x - 3)(x - 4)$

4 $(x + 2)^2$

© Carnegie Learning, Inc.

You have solved many different quadratic equations written as binomials.

How can you solve trinomial quadratic equations?

LOL the GCF Again

In previous lessons, you multiplied two linear expressions to determine a quadratic expression. You have also rewritten quadratics in factored form.

You may remember that one way to factor an expression is to factor out the greatest common factor.

WORKED EXAMPLE

Consider the polynomial $3x + 15$.

You can factor out the greatest common factor of the two terms, 3.

$$3x + 15 = 3x + 3(5)$$
$$= 3(x + 5)$$
$$3x + 15 = 3(x + 5)$$

1 Factor out the greatest common factor for each polynomial, if possible.

ⓐ $4x + 12$

ⓑ $x^2 - 5x$

ⓒ $3x^2 - 9x - 3$

ⓓ $-x - 7$

ⓔ $2x - 11$

ⓕ $5x^2 - 10x + 5$

© Carnegie Learning, Inc.

MATHia CONNECTION

- Introduction to Factoring
- Factoring Trinomials with Coefficients of One
- Factoring Trinomials with Coefficients Other than One
- Factoring Quadratic Expressions

Factoring Trinomials

HABITS OF MIND

- Look for and make use of structure.
- Look for and express regularity in repeated reasoning.

You have used special products—the difference of two squares and perfect square trinomials—to rewrite trinomials in factored form. In this activity, you will rewrite trinomials that are not special products in factored form.

1 Consider the equation $y = x^2 + 10x + 16$.

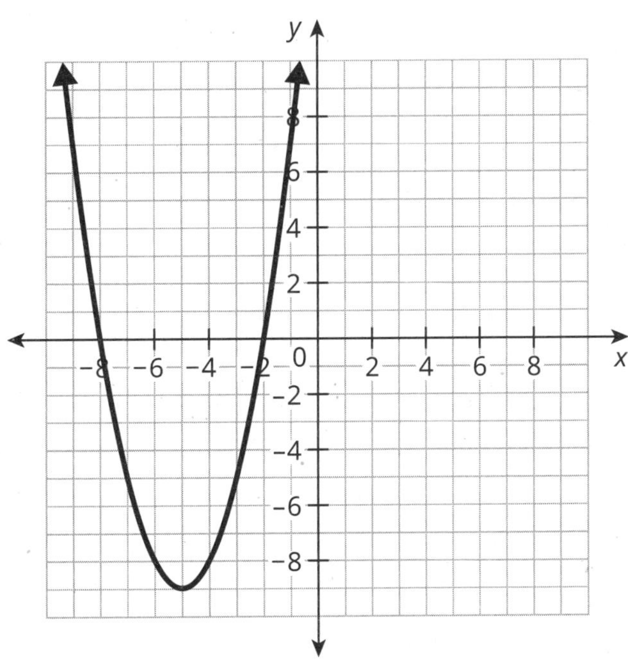

ⓐ Use the graph to identify the roots of the equation.

ⓑ Rewrite the original equation in factored form.

© Carnegie Learning, Inc.

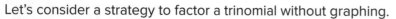

Let's consider a strategy to factor a trinomial without graphing.

WORKED EXAMPLE

You can use a multiplication table to factor trinomials.

Factor the trinomial $x^2 + 10x + 16$.

Start by writing the leading term (x^2) and the constant term (16) in the table.

·		
	x^2	
		16

Determine the two factors of the leading term and write them in the table.

·	x	
x	x^2	
		16

Determine the factor pairs of the constant term. The factors of 16 are (1)(16), (2)(8), and (4)(4). Experiment with factors of the constant term to determine the pair whose sum is the coefficient of the middle term, 10.

·	x	8
x	x^2	$8x$
2	$2x$	16

The sum of $2x$ and $8x$ is $10x$.

So, $x^2 + 10x + 16 = (x + 2)(x + 8)$.

2 Explain why the other factor pairs for $c = 16$ do not work.

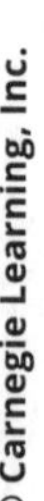

© Carnegie Learning, Inc.

3 Use the Worked Example to factor each trinomial.

ⓐ $x^2 + 17x + 16$

·		
	x^2	
		16

ⓑ $x^2 + 6x - 16$

·		
	x^2	
		−16

ⓒ $x^2 - 6x - 16$

·		
	x^2	
		−16

4 Factor each trinomial.

ⓐ $x^2 + 5x - 24$

ⓐ $x^2 - 3x - 28$

5 Consider these two examples.

Xavier

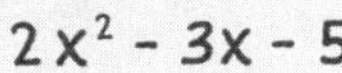

$2x^2 - 3x - 5$

•	x	1
2x	$2x^2$	2x
−5	−5x	−5

$2x^2 - 3x - 5 = (2x - 5)(x + 1)$

Elinor

$2x^2 + 3x - 5$

•	x	−1
2x	$2x^2$	−2x
5	5x	−5

$2x^2 + 3x - 5 = (2x + 5)(x - 1)$

ⓐ Compare the two given trinomials. What is the same and what is different about the values of a, b, and c?

REMEMBER . . .
The general form of a quadratic equation is a trinomial in the form $y = ax^2 + bx + c$.

ⓑ Compare the factored form of each trinomial. **What do you notice?**

© Carnegie Learning, Inc.

6 Choose from the list to write the correct factored form for each trinomial.

ⓐ $x^2 + 5x + 4 =$ ______________ • $(x + 1)(x - 4)$

$x^2 - 5x + 4 =$ ______________ • $(x + 1)(x + 4)$

$x^2 + 3x - 4 =$ ______________ • $(x - 1)(x + 4)$

$x^2 - 3x - 4 =$ ______________ • $(x - 1)(x - 4)$

ⓑ $2x^2 + 7x + 3 =$ ______________ • $(2x - 1)(x - 3)$

$2x^2 - 7x + 3 =$ ______________ • $(2x - 1)(x + 3)$

$2x^2 + 5x - 3 =$ ______________ • $(2x + 1)(x + 3)$

$2x^2 - 5x - 3 =$ ______________ • $(2x + 1)(x - 3)$

ⓒ $x^2 + 7x + 10 =$ ______________ • $(2x - 1)(x - 3)$

$x^2 - 7x + 10 =$ ______________ • $(2x - 1)(x + 3)$

$x^2 + 3x - 10 =$ ______________ • $(2x + 1)(x + 3)$

$x^2 - 3x - 10 =$ ______________ • $(2x + 1)(x - 3)$

7 Analyze the signs of each quadratic expression written in general form and the operations in the binomial factors in Question 6. Then, complete each sentence with a phrase from the word bank.

WORD BANK

the same

different

both positive

both negative

one positive and one negative

ⓐ If the constant term is positive, then the operations in the binomial factors are ______________.

ⓑ If the constant term is positive and the middle term is positive, then the operations in the binomial factors are ______________.

ⓒ If the constant term is positive and the middle term is negative, then the operations in the binomial factors are ______________.

ⓓ If the constant term is negative, then the operations in the binomial factors are______________.

ⓔ If the constant term is negative and the middle term is positive, then the operations in the binomial factors are ______________.

ⓕ If the constant term is negative and the middle term is negative, then the operations in the binomial factors are ______________.

© Carnegie Learning, Inc.

8 Factor each quadratic expression.

(a) $x^2 + 8x + 15 =$ ____________

$x^2 - 8x + 15 =$ ____________

$x^2 + 2x - 15 =$ ____________

$x^2 - 2x - 15 =$ ____________

(b) $x^2 + 10x + 24 =$ ____________

$x^2 - 10x + 24 =$ ____________

$x^2 + 2x - 24 =$ ____________

$x^2 - 2x - 24 =$ ____________

9 Grace, Elaine, and Maggie were asked to factor the trinomial $15 + 2x - x^2$. Who's correct? **Explain how the student(s) determined the factors. For the student(s) who is not correct, state why and make the correction.**

Grace

$15x + 2x - x^2$

$(5 - x)(3 + x)$

Elaine

$15 + 2x - x^2$

$(5 - x)(3 + x)$

$(x - 5)(x + 3)$

Maggie

$15 + 2x - x^2$

$-x^2 + 2x + 15$

$-(x^2 - 2x - 15)$

$-(x - 5)(x + 3)$

© Carnegie Learning, Inc.

Marilynn and Jake were working together to factor the trinomial $4x^2 + 22x + 24$. They first noticed that there was a greatest common factor and rewrote the trinomial as $2(2x^2 + 11x + 12)$.

Next, they considered the factor pairs for $2x^2$ and the factor pairs for 12.

$2x^2$: $(2x)(x)$
12: $(1)(12)$
$(2)(6)$
$(3)(4)$

Marilynn listed out all the possible combinations.

$2(2x + 1)(x + 12)$

$2(2x + 12)(x + 1)$

$2(2x + 2)(x + 6)$

$2(2x + 6)(x + 2)$

$2(2x + 3)(x + 4)$

$2(2x + 4)(x + 3)$

Jake immediately eliminated four out of the six possible combinations because the terms of one of the linear expressions contained common factors.

$2(2x + 1)(x + 12)$

~~$2(2x + 12)(x + 1)$~~

~~$2(2x + 2)(x + 6)$~~

~~$2(2x + 6)(x + 2)$~~

$2(2x + 3)(x + 4)$

~~$2(2x + 4)(x + 3)$~~

10 Explain Jake's reasoning. Then, circle the correct factored form of $4x^2 + 22x + 24$.

© Carnegie Learning, Inc.

MATHia CONNECTION

- Solving Quadratic Equations by Factoring
- Problem Solving Using Factoring

Solving Quadratic Equations by Factoring

HABIT OF MIND

- Attend to precision.

Consider the different forms of the equations you have solved using the Properties of Equality.

$$y = x^2 + d$$
$$y = (x - c)^2$$
$$y = a(x - c)^2$$
$$y = a(x - c)^2 + d$$

Let's consider strategies to solve quadratics in the form $y = ax^2 + bx + c$ using the factoring strategies you just learned.

WORKED EXAMPLE

You can calculate the roots for the quadratic equation $x^2 - 4x = -3$.

$$x^2 - 4x = -3$$
$$-4x + 3 = -3 + 3$$
$$x^2 - 4x + 3 = 0$$
$$(x - 3)(x - 1) = 0$$
$$(x - 3) = 0 \quad \text{and} \quad (x - 1) = 0$$
$$x - 3 + 3 = 0 + 3 \quad \text{and} \quad x - 1 + 1 = 0 + 1$$
$$x = 3 \quad \text{and} \quad x = 1$$

REMEMBER . . .

The Zero Product Property states that if the product of two or more factors is equal to zero, then at least one factor must be equal to zero.

1. Consider the Worked Example. Why is 3 added to both sides in the first step?

THINK ABOUT . . .

What is the connection between the Worked Example and determining the roots from factored form, $y = a(x - r_1)(x - r_2)$?

© Carnegie Learning, Inc.

2 Determine each student's error and then solve each equation correctly.

Jana

$x^2 + 6x = 7$

$x(x + 6) = 7$

$x = 7$ and $x + 6 = 7$

$x = 1$

Reese

$x^2 + 5x + 6 = 6$

$(x + 2)(x + 3) = 6$

$x + 2 = 6$ and $x + 3 = 6$

$x = 4$ and $x = 3$

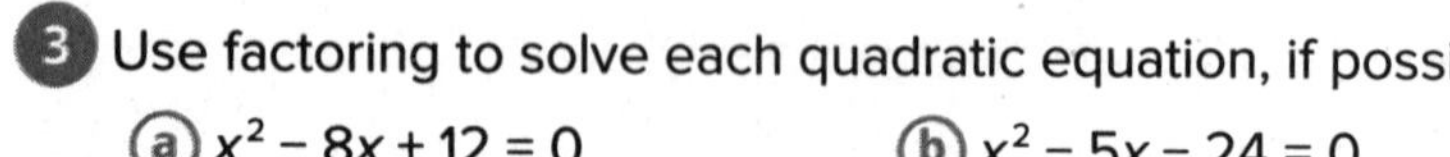

3 Use factoring to solve each quadratic equation, if possible.

ⓐ $x^2 - 8x + 12 = 0$

ⓑ $x^2 - 5x - 24 = 0$

ⓒ $x^2 + 10x - 75 = 0$

ⓓ $x^2 - 11x = 0$

THINK ABOUT . . .
What efficiency strategies did you use to solve linear equations with fractional coefficients?

© Carnegie Learning, Inc.

(e) $x^2 + 8x = -7$

(f) $x^2 - 5x = 13x - 81$

(g) $\frac{2}{3}x^2 - \frac{5}{6}x = 0$

(h) $f(x) = x^2 + 10x + 12$

TOPIC 2

4 Describe the different strategies and reasoning that Deon and Kayla used to solve $4x^2 - 25 = 0$.

Deon

$4x^2 - 25 = 0$

$4x^2 = 25$

$x^2 = \frac{25}{4}$

$x = \pm\sqrt{\frac{25}{4}}$

$x = \pm\frac{5}{2}$

Kayla

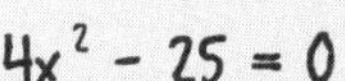

$4x^2 - 25 = 0$

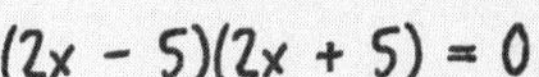

$(2x - 5)(2x + 5) = 0$

$2x - 5 = 0$ and $2x + 5 = 0$

$2x = 5$ $\quad$ $2x = -5$

$x = \frac{5}{2}$ and $\quad$ $x = -\frac{5}{2}$

© Carnegie Learning, Inc.

Completing the Square

HABITS OF MIND
- Model with mathematics.
- Use appropriate tools strategically.

If you cannot factor a quadratic function, does that mean it does not have zeros?

1. Consider the quadratic equation $y = x^2 + 10x + 12$. Use technology to graph the equation and then sketch it on the coordinate plane. Does this function have zeros? **Explain your reasoning.**

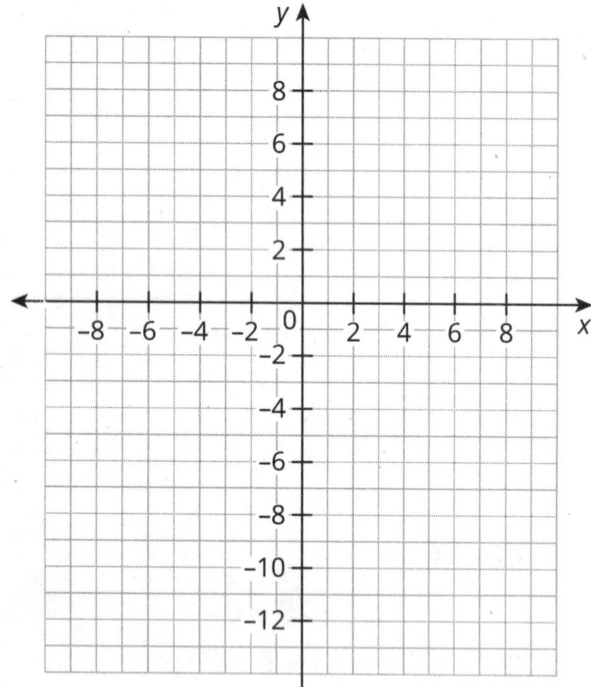

The quadratic function you graphed has zeros but you cannot factor it, so you must consider another method for calculating its zeros. You can use your understanding of the relationship among the coefficients of a perfect square trinomial to construct a procedure to solve any quadratic equation.

© Carnegie Learning, Inc.

Previously, you factored trinomials of the form $a^2 + 2ab + b^2$ as the perfect square $(a + b)^2$. This knowledge can help you develop a procedure to solve any quadratic equation.

2 You can represent the expression $x^2 + 10x$ geometrically, as shown. Write the area of each rectangle within the diagram.

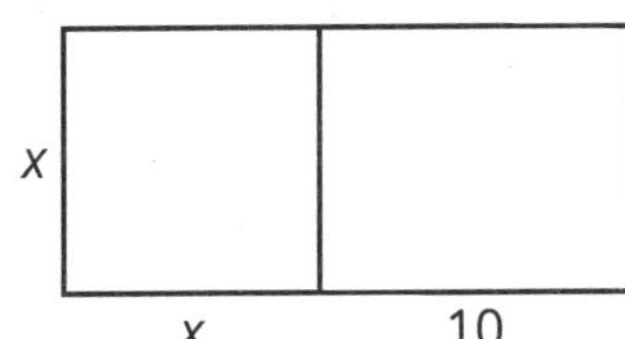

3 You can now modify this figure into the shape of a square by splitting the second rectangle in half and rearranging the pieces.

(a) Complete the side length labels for the split rectangle and write the area of each piece within the diagram.

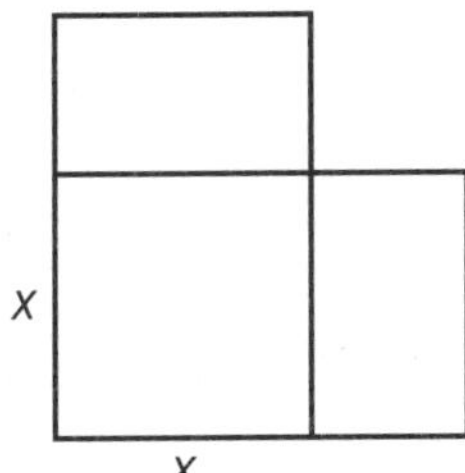

ASK YOURSELF . . .
Why do you divide the second rectangle in half?

(b) Do the two figures represent the same expression? **Explain your reasoning.**

(c) Complete the figure to form a square. Label the area of the piece you added.

(d) Add the term representing the additional area to the original expression. What is the new expression?

(e) Factor the new expression.

© Carnegie Learning, Inc.

The process you just worked through is a method known as *completing the square*. **Completing the square** is a process for writing a quadratic expression in vertex form which then allows you to solve for the zeros.

4 Draw a model to complete the square for each expression. Then, factor the resulting trinomial.

(a) $x^2 + 8x$

(b) $x^2 + 5x$

5 Analyze your work in Question 4.

(a) Explain how to complete the square on an expression of the form $x^2 + bx$, where b is an integer.

(b) Describe how the coefficient of the middle term, b, is related to the constant term, c, in each trinomial you wrote in Question 4.

© Carnegie Learning, Inc.

6 Use the descriptions you provided in Question 5 to determine the unknown second or third term to make each expression a perfect square trinomial. Then, write the expression as a binomial squared.

ⓐ $x^2 - 8x +$ __________ = __________

ⓑ $x^2 + 5x +$ __________ = __________

ⓒ $x^2 -$ __________ $+ 100$ = __________

ⓓ $x^2 +$ __________ $+ 144$ = __________

© Carnegie Learning, Inc.

MATHia CONNECTION
- Problem Solving Using Completing the Square

Completing the Square to Determine Roots

HABITS OF MIND
- Model with mathematics.
- Use appropriate tools strategically.

So far, you have considered quadratic equations that you can rewrite by completing the square or factoring a trinomial.

You can use the completing the square method to determine the roots of a quadratic equation that you cannot factor.

WORKED EXAMPLE

Determine the roots of the equation $x^2 + 10x + 12 = 0$.

Isolate $x^2 + 10x$. You can complete the square and rewrite this as a perfect square trinomial.

$$x^2 + 10x + 12 - 12 = 0 - 12$$
$$x^2 + 10x = -12$$

Determine the constant term that would complete the square. Add this term to both sides of the equation.

$$x^2 + 10x + \_\_\_\_ = -12 + \_\_\_\_$$
$$x^2 + 10x + \underline{\textbf{25}} = -12 + \underline{\textbf{25}}$$
$$x^2 + 10x + 25 = 13$$

Factor the left side of the equation.

$$(x + 5)^2 = 13$$

Take the square root of each side of the equation.

$$x + 5 = \pm\sqrt{13}$$

Set the factor of the perfect square trinomial equal to each square root of the constant.

$$x + 5 = \sqrt{13} \quad \text{and} \quad x + 5 = -\sqrt{13}$$
$$x = -5 + \sqrt{13} \quad \text{and} \quad x = -5 - \sqrt{13}$$

Solve for x.

$$x \approx -1.39 \quad \text{and} \quad x \approx -8.61$$

The roots are approximately (–1.39) and (–8.61).

ASK YOURSELF . . .
How was equality of the equation maintained through the completing the square process?

© Carnegie Learning, Inc.

1 Consider the equation $y = x^2 + 8x + 10$.

(a) Use this method to determine the roots of the equation. **Show your work.**

(b) Use your work to label the zeros on the graph of the function $f(x) = x^2 + 8x + 10$.

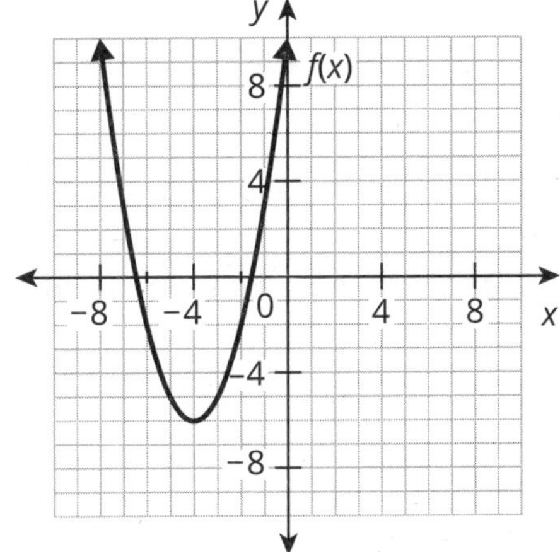

2 Determine the roots of each equation by completing the square.

(a) $x^2 - 6x + 4 = 0$

(b) $x^2 - 12x + 6 = 0$

© Carnegie Learning, Inc.

Rewriting a Quadratic in Vertex Form

You can identify the axis of symmetry and the vertex of any quadratic function written in general form by completing the square.

HABITS OF MIND
- Model with mathematics.
- Use appropriate tools strategically.

WORKED EXAMPLE

Consider the equation $y = ax^2 + bx + c$.

STEP 1 $y - c = ax^2 + bx$

STEP 2 $y - c = a\left(x^2 + \frac{b}{a}x\right)$

STEP 3 $y - c + a\left(\frac{b}{2a}\right)^2 = a\left(x^2 + \frac{b}{a}x + \left(\frac{b}{2a}\right)^2\right)$

STEP 4 $y - c + \frac{b^2}{4a} = a\left(x + \frac{b}{2a}\right)^2$

STEP 5 $y = a\left(x + \frac{b}{2a}\right)^2 + \left(c - \frac{b^2}{4a}\right)$

TAKE NOTE . . .

Notice that the a-value was factored out before completing the square!

1. Explain why the Worked Example adds $a\left(\frac{b}{2a}\right)^2$ to the left side of the equation in **STEP 3.**

2. Identify each characteristic given a quadratic function in the form $y = ax^2 + bx + c$.

   (a) Axis of symmetry

   (b) Location of the vertex

© Carnegie Learning, Inc.

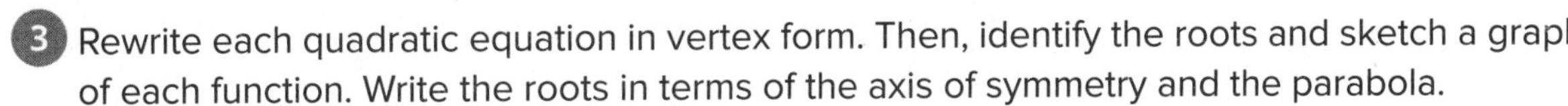

3 Rewrite each quadratic equation in vertex form. Then, identify the roots and sketch a graph of each function. Write the roots in terms of the axis of symmetry and the parabola.

(a) $y = x^2 + 8x - 9$

(b) $y = 3x^2 + 2x - 1$

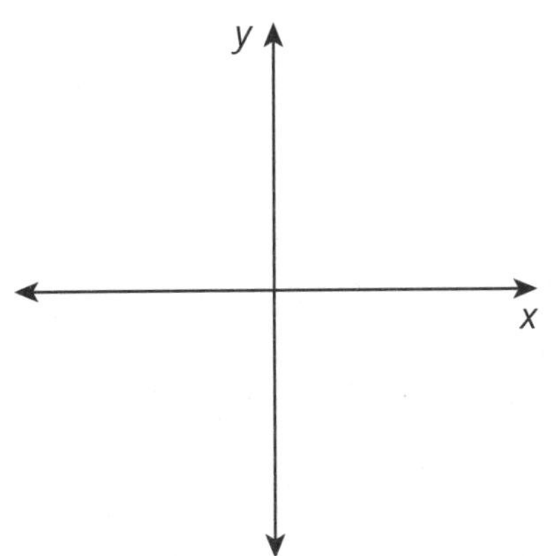

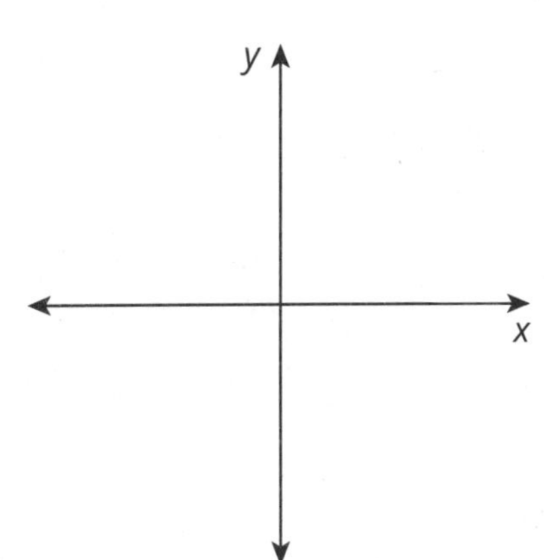

4 A ball is thrown straight up from 4 feet above the ground with a velocity of 32 feet per second. You can model the height of the ball over time using the function $h(t) = -16t^2 + 32t + 4$. What is the maximum height of the ball?

5 Jessie is fencing in a rectangular plot outside of her back door so that she can let her dogs out to play. She has 60 feet of fencing and only needs to place it on three sides of the rectangular plot because the fourth side will be bound by her house. What dimensions should Jesse use for the plot so that the maximum area is enclosed? What is the maximum area? **Draw a diagram to support your work.**

© Carnegie Learning, Inc.

Play It Again

In this activity, you learned how to complete the square to rewrite a quadratic function in a different form.

1. Consider the quadratic equation $y = x^2 - 4x - 5$.

   a. Rewrite the equation in factored form and vertex form.

   b. Graph the equation. Identify the vertex, x-and y-intercepts, and the axis of symmetry. Then, explain how these are evident in each form of the equation.

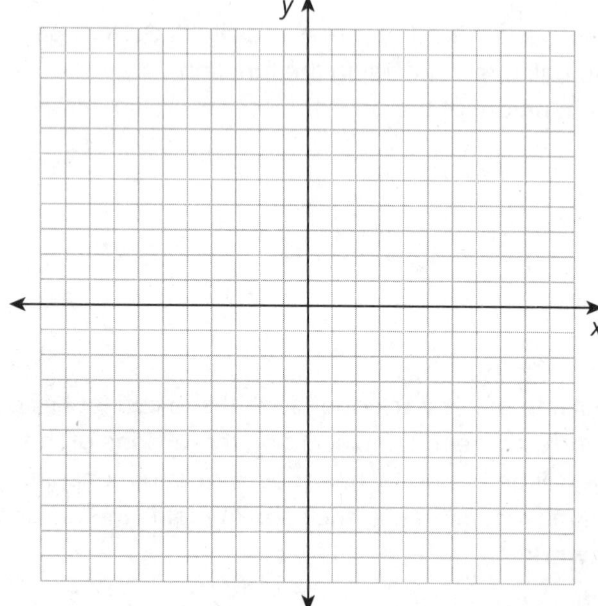

© Carnegie Learning, Inc.

LESSON 4 ASSIGNMENT

> Use a separate piece of paper for your Journal entry.

JOURNAL

Describe the process to solve a quadratic equation by factoring.

REMEMBER

- Completing the square is a process for writing a quadratic expression in vertex form, allowing you to solve for the zeros.
- Given a quadratic equation in the form $y = ax^2 + bx + c$, the location of the vertex of the function is at $x = \frac{-b}{2a}$ and $y = c - \frac{b^2}{4a}$.

PRACTICE

1 Solve each equation.

(a) $0 = x^2 - 7x - 18$

(b) $x^2 + 10x = 39$

(c) $3x^2 - 22x + 7 = 0$

(d) $2x^2 + 4x = 0$

(e) $0 = x^2 - 10x + 12$

2 Determine the roots of each equation. Check your solutions.

(a) $y = x^2 + 9x + 3$

(b) $y = 3x^2 + 24x - 6$

3 Consider the equation $y = 2x^2 + 10x - 8$.

(a) Graph the equation.

(b) Use the graph to estimate the solutions to the equation. Explain how you determined your answer.

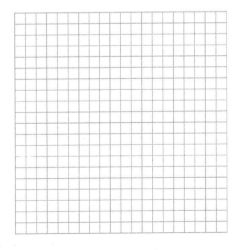

© Carnegie Learning, Inc.

Go to LiveHint.com for help on the PRACTICE questions.

ⓒ Two students completed the square to determine the solutions to this equation. Consider their work. Who is correct? Explain your reasoning.

Shreya

$$y = 2x^2 + 10x - 8$$
$$2x^2 + 10x - 8 = 0$$
$$2x^2 + 10x = 8$$
$$2x^2 + 10x + 25 = 8 + 25$$
$$(2x + 5)^2 = 33$$
$$\sqrt{(2x + 5)^2} = \pm\sqrt{33}$$
$$2x + 5 = \pm\sqrt{33}$$
$$x = \frac{-5 \pm \sqrt{33}}{2}$$
$$x \approx -5.372 \text{ and } x \approx 0.372$$

Shane

$$x^2 + 10x - 8 = y$$
$$2x^2 + 10x - 8 = 0$$
$$\frac{2x^2 + 10x - 8}{2} = 0$$
$$x^2 + 5x = 4$$
$$x^2 + 5x + \frac{25}{4} = 4 + \frac{25}{4}$$
$$\left(x + \frac{5}{2}\right)^2 = \frac{41}{4}$$
$$\sqrt{\left(x + \frac{5}{2}\right)^2} = \pm\sqrt{\frac{41}{4}}$$
$$x + \frac{5}{2} = \pm\frac{\sqrt{41}}{2}$$
$$x = \frac{-5 \pm \sqrt{41}}{2}$$
$$x \approx 5.702 \text{ and } x \approx 0.702$$

ⓓ Compare the different solutions. Identify what the student who got the correct answer did that allowed him or her to correctly complete the square.

ⓔ Write a statement about the value of the coefficient of the x^2-term before you can complete the square.

4 Determine the roots and the location of the vertex of $y = x^2 + 20x + 36$. Write the zeros in terms of the axis of symmetry and the parabola.

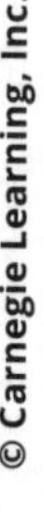

© Carnegie Learning, Inc.

STRETCH Optional

> Consider the function $g(x) = x^2 - 3x - 10$.

1 If $g(x + 3) = x^2 + bx - c$, what are the values of b and c? Show your work and justify your answer.

LESSON 5

Ladies and Gentlemen, Please Welcome the Quadratic Formula!

The Quadratic Formula

KEY TERMS

- **Quadratic Formula**
- **discriminant**
- **the number *i***
- **imaginary roots**
- **imaginary zeros**
- **complex numbers**
- **real part of a complex numbers**
- **imaginary part of a complex number**
- **imaginary numbers**
- **pure imaginary number**

Learning Goals

- Derive the Quadratic Formula and connect it to a graphical representation.
- Use the Quadratic Formula to determine roots and zeros.
- Determine whether a solution is rational or irrational when performing operations with rational and irrational numbers.
- Determine whether a function has complex solutions from a graph and from an equation in radical form.
- Understand that equations with no solutions in one number system may have solutions in a larger number system.

© Carnegie Learning, Inc.

REVIEW (1–2 minutes)

> Rewrite each radical by extracting all perfect squares.

1. $\sqrt{50}$

2. $\sqrt{80}$

3. $\sqrt{75}$

You know several strategies to solve quadratic equations, depending on the structure of the equation.

Is there a single strategy that will work to solve any quadratic equation?

Really, They Aren't the Same

> Consider each graph.

Graph A

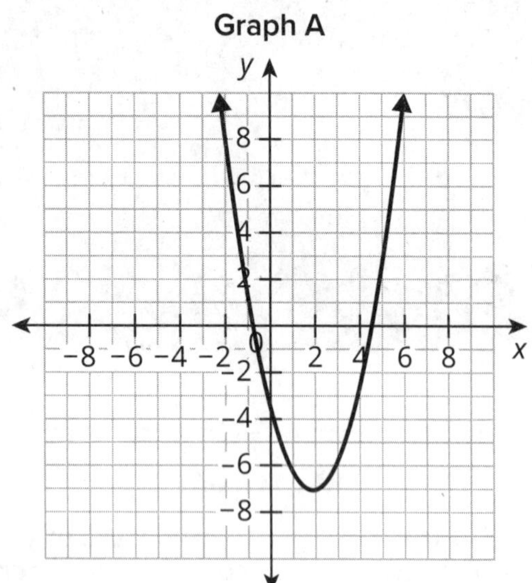

Graph B

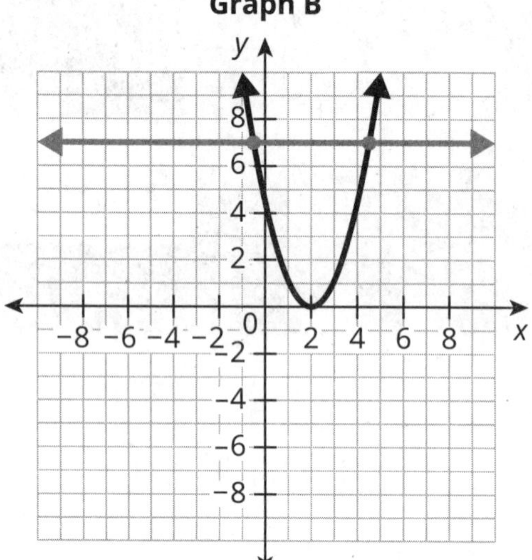

Graph C

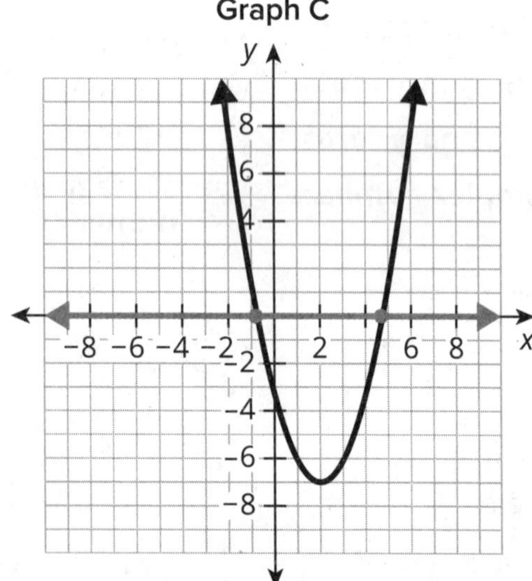

1. Match each equation to its corresponding graph.

   a) $(x - 2)^2 - 7 = 0$

   b) $y = (x - 2)^2 - 7$

   c) $(x - 2)^2 = 7$

2. How do each of the graphs show solutions? How are the solutions related to the axis of symmetry?

© Carnegie Learning, Inc.

Introducing the Quadratic Formula

HABITS OF MIND
- Reason abstractly and quantitatively.
- Construct viable arguments and critique the reasoning of others.

In the previous lesson, you took the general form of a quadratic equation, $y = ax^2 + bx + c$, and rewrote it in vertex form, $y = a\left(x + \frac{b}{2a}\right)^2 + \left(c - \frac{b^2}{4a}\right)$, by completing the square in order to determine the vertex and axis of symmetry for graphing purposes.

Now, let's take the general form of a quadratic equation, $y = ax^2 + bx + c$, and set $y = 0$ to determine the roots. You can complete the square in order to solve for the x-values when $y = 0$.

WORKED EXAMPLE

Write the equation in general form with $y = 0$.	$ax^2 + bx + c = 0$
Complete the square.	$ax^2 + bx = -c$ $x^2 + \frac{bx}{a} = -\frac{c}{a}$ $x^2 + \frac{bx}{a} + \left(\frac{b}{2a}\right)^2 = -\frac{c}{a} + \left(\frac{b}{2a}\right)^2$ $\left(x + \frac{b}{2a}\right)^2 = \left(\frac{b}{2a}\right)^2 - \frac{c}{a}$
Rewrite the right side of the equation.	$\left(x + \frac{b}{2a}\right)^2 = \frac{b^2}{4a^2} - \frac{c}{a}$ $\left(x + \frac{b}{2a}\right)^2 = \frac{b^2}{4a^2} - \frac{4ac}{4a^2}$ $\left(x + \frac{b}{2a}\right)^2 = \frac{b^2 - 4ac}{4a^2}$
Now that the equation is written in the form $(x - c)^2 = q$, you can take the square root on each side. Extract the square roots. Solve for x. These are the roots for the quadratic equation in the general form, $ax^2 + bx + c = 0$.	$x + \frac{b}{2a} = \pm\sqrt{\frac{b^2 - 4ac}{4a^2}}$ $= -\frac{b}{2a} \pm \frac{\sqrt{b^2 - 4ac}}{2a}$ $x = \frac{-b}{2a} + \frac{\sqrt{b^2 - 4ac}}{2a}$ $x = \frac{-b}{2a} - \frac{\sqrt{b^2 - 4ac}}{2a}$

You can take this approach one step further and rewrite the two roots as a single fraction.

$$x = \frac{-b \pm \sqrt{b^2 - 4ac}}{2a}$$

This equation is known as the *Quadratic Formula*. You can use the **Quadratic Formula**, $x = \frac{-b \pm \sqrt{b^2 - 4ac}}{2a}$, to calculate the solutions to any quadratic equation of the form $ax^2 + bx + c = 0$, where a, b, and c represent real numbers and $a \neq 0$.

© Carnegie Learning, Inc.

> Analyze the Worked Example.

WORKED EXAMPLE

You can use the Quadratic Formula to determine the zeros of the function $f(x) = -4x^2 - 40x - 99$.

Rewrite the function as an equation you can solve for x when $y = 0$.

$$-4x^2 - 40x - 99 = 0$$

Determine the values of a, b, and c.

$$a = -4, b = -40, c = -99$$

Substitute the values into the Quadratic Formula.

$$x = \frac{-(-40) \pm \sqrt{(-40)^2 - 4(-4)(-99)}}{2(-4)}$$

Perform operations to rewrite the expression.

$$x = \frac{40 \pm \sqrt{1600 - 1584}}{-8}$$

$$x = \frac{40 \pm \sqrt{16}}{-8}$$

$$x = \frac{40 \pm 4}{-8}$$

$$x = \frac{(40 + 4)}{-8} \text{ and } x = \frac{(40 - 4)}{-8}$$

$$x = \frac{44}{-8} \quad \text{and } x = \frac{36}{-8}$$

$$x = -5.5 \quad \text{and } x = -4.5$$

Interpret the solution.

The zeros of the function $f(x) = -4x^2 - 40x - 99$ are $x = -5.5$ and $x = -4.5$.

The Perris Pandas baseball team has a new promotional activity to encourage fans to attend games: launching free T-shirts! They can launch a T-shirt in the air with an initial velocity of 91 feet per second from $5\frac{1}{2}$ feet off the ground (the height of the team mascot). You can model a T-shirt's height using the quadratic function $h(t) = -16t^2 + 91t + 5.5$, where t is the time in seconds and $h(t)$ is the height of the launched T-shirt in feet. They want to know how long it will take for a T-shirt to land back on the ground after being launched (if no fans grab it before then!)

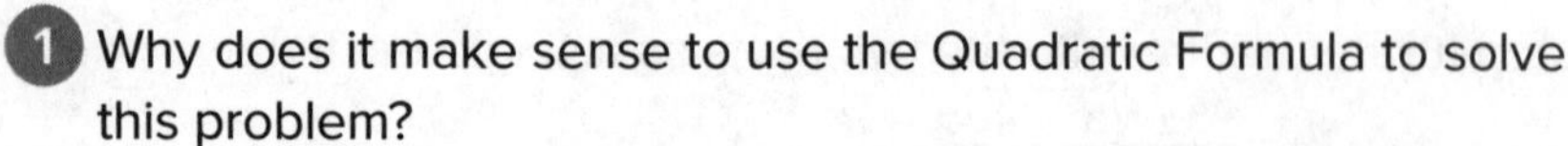

1 Why does it make sense to use the Quadratic Formula to solve this problem?

ASK YOURSELF . . .
What would a sketch showing the height of the T-shirt over time look like?

© Carnegie Learning, Inc.

2 Use the Quadratic Formula to determine how long it will take for a T-shirt to land back on the ground after the mascot launches it.

ASK YOURSELF . . .
Do you think an exact solution or approximate solution is more appropriate for this context?

3 Classify your solutions as rational or irrational.

Remember, you can write the Quadratic Formula to show two roots.

$$x = \frac{-b}{2a} \pm \frac{\sqrt{b^2 - 4ac}}{2a}$$

$$x = \frac{-b}{2a} + \frac{\sqrt{b^2 - 4ac}}{2a} \qquad x = \frac{-b}{2a} - \frac{\sqrt{b^2 - 4ac}}{2a}$$

THINK ABOUT . . .
How do the two roots relate to the graph?

4 Consider how the roots $x = \frac{-b}{2a} + \frac{\sqrt{b^2 - 4ac}}{2a}$ and $x = \frac{-b}{2a} - \frac{\sqrt{b^2 - 4ac}}{2a}$ relate to the graph.

(a) What does the first term of each root represent on the graph?

(b) The second term of each root represents the distance the root lies from the axis of symmetry. Why is the second term in each root the same except for the sign?

© Carnegie Learning, Inc.

Let's analyze how the structure of the Quadratic Formula is evident in the graphical representation of the zeros of a quadratic function.

WORKED EXAMPLE

Consider this graphical representation to determine the real roots of the quadratic equation $y = 2x^2 - x - 15$.

Steps

Set y equal to zero and identify the values of a, b, and c.

$0 = 2x^2 - x - 15$

$a = 2 \quad b = -1 \quad c = -15 \quad a > 0$

Identify the axis of symmetry and label the point where it intersects $y = 0$.

$x = \frac{-(-1)}{2(2)} = \frac{1}{4}$

Identify the distance from the axis of symmetry to the parabola along $y = 0$.

$+\frac{\sqrt{b^2 - 4ac}}{2a} =$

$\frac{\sqrt{(-1)^2 - 4(2)(-15)}}{2(2)} = \frac{\sqrt{121}}{4} = \frac{11}{4}$

$-\frac{\sqrt{b^2 - 4ac}}{2a} = -\frac{11}{4}$

Identify the roots and label them on the graph.

$\frac{1}{4} + \frac{11}{4} = \frac{12}{4} = 3$

$\frac{1}{4} - \frac{11}{4} = -\frac{10}{4} = -\frac{5}{2}$

Graph

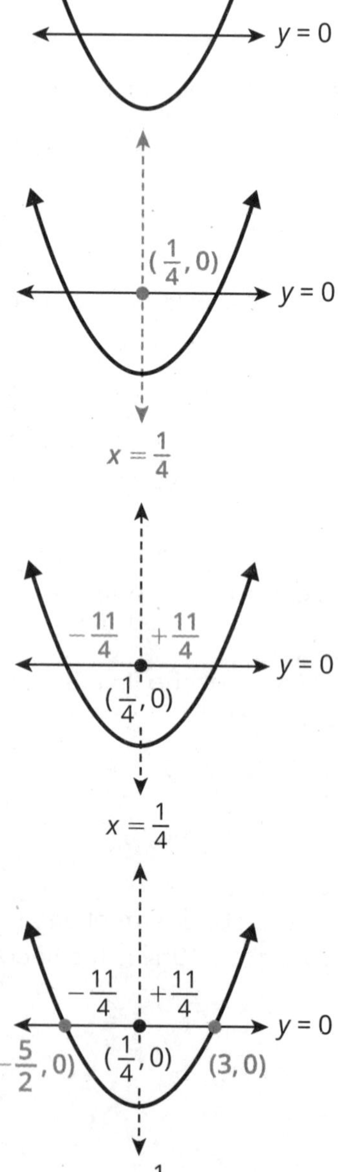

The real roots of $y = 2x^2 - x - 15$ are $x = 3$ and $x = -\frac{5}{2}$.

© Carnegie Learning, Inc.

5 Repeat the process to determine the real roots of the equation $y = 2x^2 - 9x + 4$.

Steps	Graph

ⓐ Let $y = 0$ and identify the values of a, b, and c.

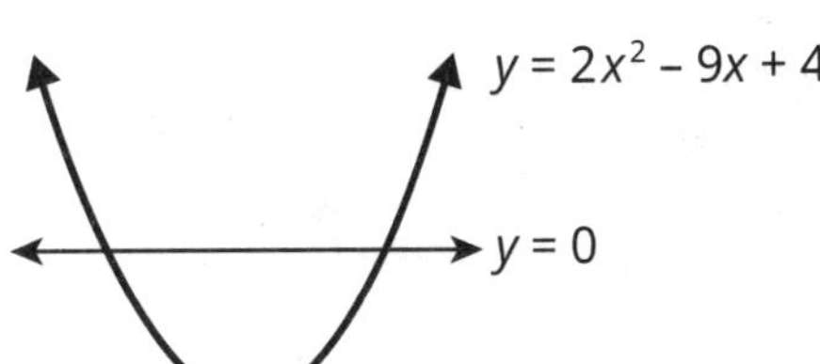

ⓑ Identify the axis of symmetry and label the point where it intersects the x-axis.

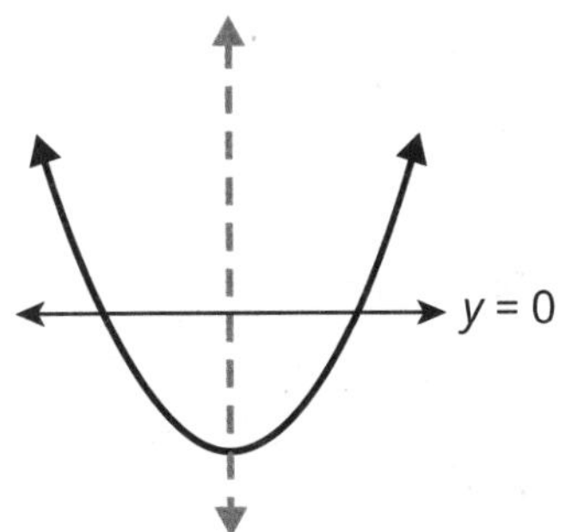

ⓒ Identify the distance from the axis of symmetry to the parabola along $y = 0$.

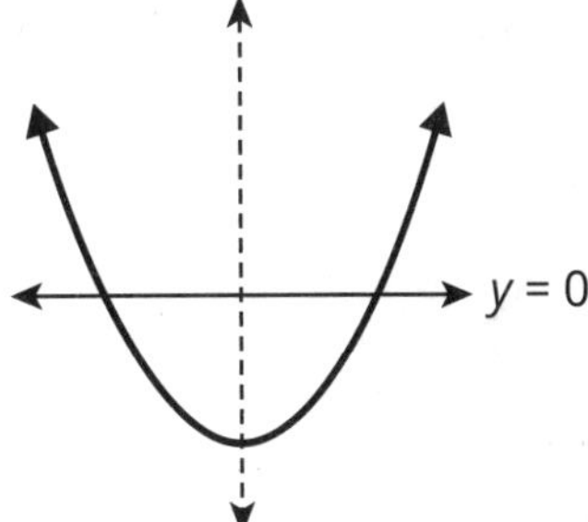

ⓓ Identify the roots and label them on the graph.

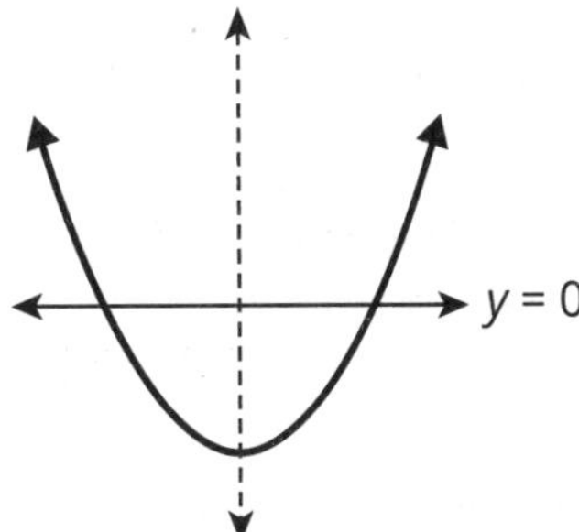

ⓔ Summarize.

The graphs of quadratic equations are parabolas that have either an absolute maximum or an absolute minimum.

© Carnegie Learning, Inc.

With Two Real Roots

A quadratic equation with two real roots crosses the x-axis in two places.

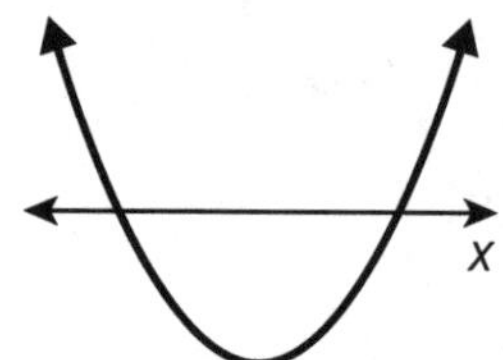

$y = ax^2 + bx + c$

$a > 0$

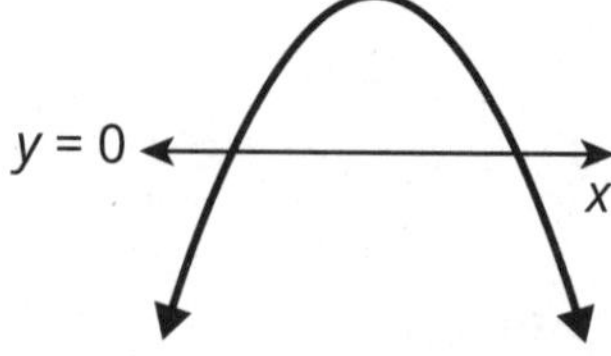

$y = ax^2 + bx + c$

$a < 0$

With Double Real Roots

A quadratic equation with a double real root, or one unique real root, touches the x-axis but does not cross it.

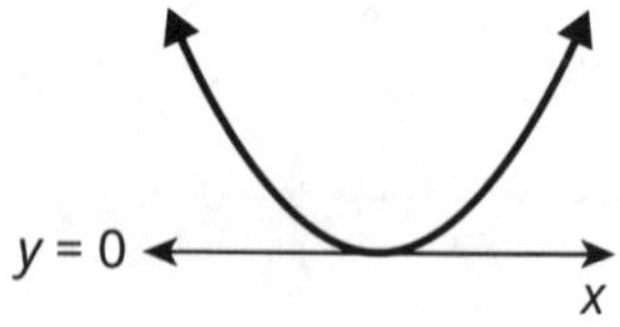

$y = ax^2 + bx + c$

$a > 0$

$y = 0$

x

$y = ax^2 + bx + c$

$a < 0$

6 Draw and label the following components on each graph in terms of the equation $y = ax^2 + bx + c$.

(a) Vertex

(b) Axis of symmetry

(c) Intersection of the x-axis and line of symmetry

(d) The distance represented by the expression $+\frac{\sqrt{b^2 - 4ac}}{2a}$

(e) The distance represented by the expression $-\frac{\sqrt{b^2 - 4ac}}{2a}$

(f) Each root

© Carnegie Learning, Inc.

Using the Quadratic Formula

HABITS OF MIND

- Model with mathematics.
- Use appropriate tools strategically.

Let's analyze the structure of the Quadratic Formula and examine common student mistakes.

1 Javier determines the exact zeros for $f(x) = x^2 - 14x + 19$. Consider his work.

(a) Identify the error Javier made when determining the zeros.

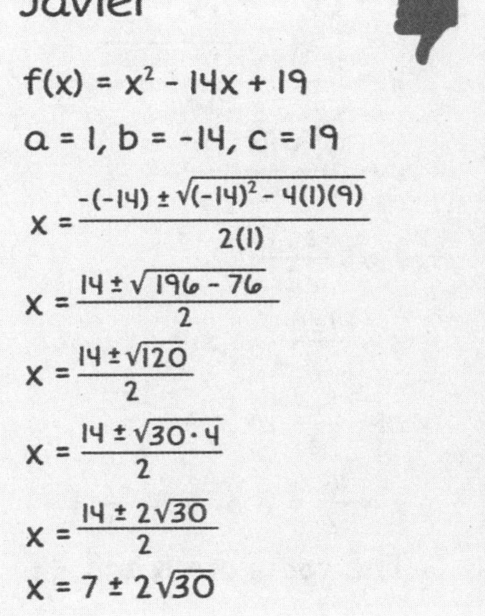

Javier
f(x) = x² - 14x + 19
a = 1, b = -14, c = 19
x = (-(-14) ± √((-14)² - 4(1)(9))) / 2(1)
x = (14 ± √(196 - 76)) / 2
x = (14 ± √120) / 2
x = (14 ± √(30·4)) / 2
x = (14 ± 2√30) / 2
x = 7 ± 2√30

(b) Determine the correct zeros of the function.

2 Use the Quadratic Formula to determine the zeros for each function given. Leave the solutions in exact form and classify them as rational or irrational.

(a) $f(x) = -2x^2 - 3x + 7$

(b) $r(x) = -3x^2 + 19x - 7$

TAKE NOTE . . .

"Leave the solutions in exact form" means not to estimate any radical values with rounded decimals.

TOPIC 2

© Carnegie Learning, Inc.

3 Lauren is solving the quadratic equation $x^2 - 7x - 8 = 3$. Consider her work.

ⓐ Identify Lauren's error.

Lauren

$x^2 - 7x - 8 = 3$

$a = 1, b = -7, c = -8$

$x = \dfrac{-(-7) \pm \sqrt{(-7)^2 - 4(1)(-8)}}{2(1)}$

$x = \dfrac{7 \pm \sqrt{49 + 32}}{2}$

$x = \dfrac{7 \pm \sqrt{81}}{2}$

$x = \dfrac{7 \pm 9}{2}$

$x = \dfrac{7+9}{2}$ or $x = \dfrac{7-9}{2}$

$x = \dfrac{16}{2} = 8$ or $x = \dfrac{-2}{2} = -1$

The roots are 8 and -1.

ⓑ Use the Quadratic Formula correctly to determine the solution to Lauren's quadratic equation. Classify the solutions as rational or irrational.

ⓒ Use technology to graph each side of the original quadratic equation $x^2 - 7x - 8 = 3$. Sketch your graph. **Then, interpret the meaning of the intersection points.**

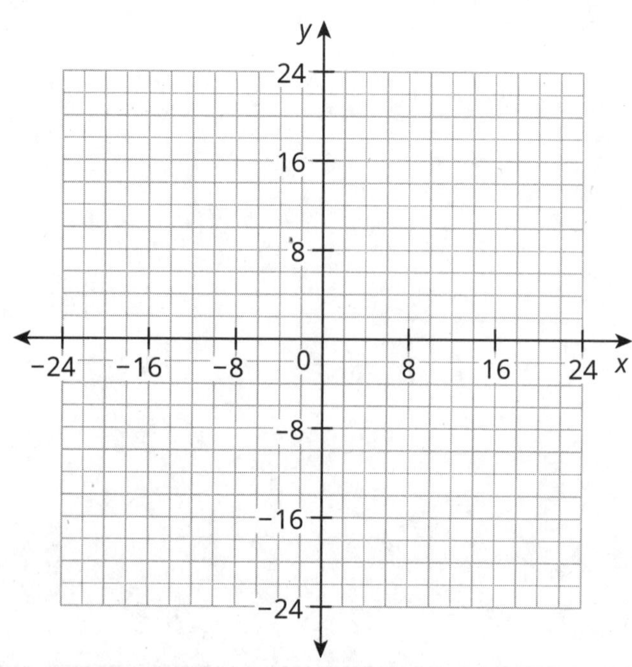

© Carnegie Learning, Inc.

(d) Next, rewrite the given quadratic equation so that one side of the equation is equal to zero. Use technology to graph each side of the quadratic equation. Sketch your graph. Interpret the meaning of the intersection points.

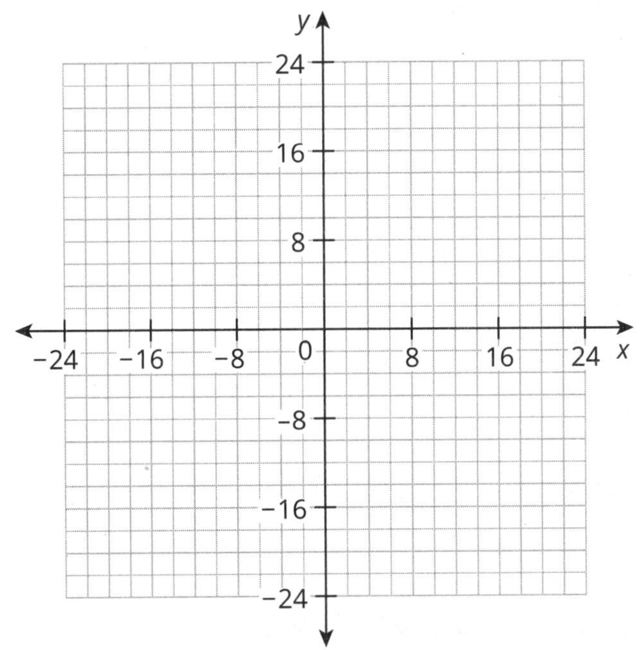

(e) Compare the x-values of the intersection points from part (c), the x-values of the intersection points in part (d), and the solutions using the Quadratic Formula. **What do you notice?**

THINK ABOUT . . .
What does it mean to determine the solutions to a quadratic equation? What does it mean to determine the roots of a quadratic equation?

TOPIC 2

© Carnegie Learning, Inc.

4 Use the Quadratic Formula to determine the zeros for each function. Round the solutions to the nearest hundredth and classify them as either rational or irrational.

(a) $f(x) = 2x^2 + 10x - 1.02$

(b) $h(x) = 3x^2 - 11x - 2$

5 Reflect on the different quadratic functions you have solved so far in this lesson.

(a) How many zeros does each quadratic function in this lesson have?

ASK YOURSELF . . .
How can you use graphs to support your reasoning?

(b) Do all quadratic functions have two zeros? **Explain why or why not.**

(c) Do you think that a quadratic function could have no zeros? **Explain why or why not.**

(d) Could a quadratic function have more than two zeros? **Explain why or why not.**

© Carnegie Learning, Inc.

Making Sense of the Discriminant

HABITS OF MIND
- Model with mathematics.
- Use appropriate tools strategically.

A quadratic function can have one unique real zero, two real zeros, or at times, no real zeros. Let's investigate how the Quadratic Formula can inform you about different types of zeros.

> Consider three quadratic equations and their graphs.

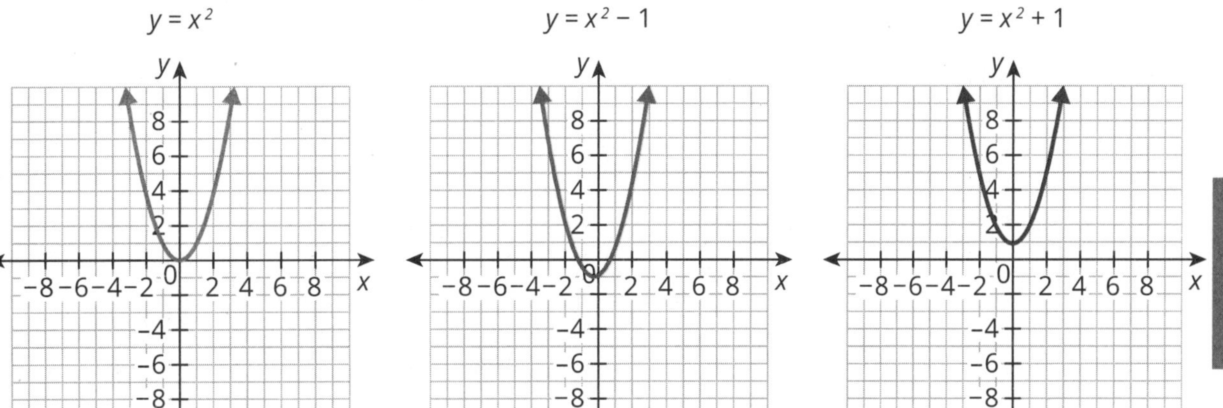

1 Use the Quadratic Formula to solve each quadratic equation. **Show your work.**

2 What do you notice about the relationship between the number of real roots, the graph, and the results of substituting the values a, b, and c into the Quadratic Formula?

THINK ABOUT . . .
You have analyzed many graphs of quadratic equations. What do you know about the roots of a quadratic equation that touches but does not intersect the x-axis or intersects the x-axis at two points?

© Carnegie Learning, Inc.

Because the $b^2 - 4ac$ portion of the Quadratic Formula "discriminates" the number of real zeros, or roots, it is the **discriminant**.

3 Using the discriminant, write an inequality to describe when a quadratic function has each solution.

(a) No real roots/zeros

(b) One unique real root/zero

(c) Two unique real roots/zeros

ASK YOURSELF . . .
How can you tell how many zeros a function will have by thinking about its graph before you use the Quadratic Formula?

This table summarizes the types of solutions for any quadratic equation or function.

Equation/ Function	Solutions	Interpretation of the Solutions: Number of Unique Real Zeros	Interpretation of the Solutions: Number of x-Intercepts	Sketch
$f(x) = x^2$	$x = \frac{-0 \pm \sqrt{0^2 - 4(1)(0)}}{2(1)}$ $= \frac{0 \pm \sqrt{0}}{2}$ $= 0 \pm \sqrt{0}$	1	1	y, x
$g(x) = x^2 - 1$	$x = \frac{-0 \pm \sqrt{0^2 - 4(1)(-1)}}{2\ (1)}$ $= \frac{0 \pm \sqrt{4}}{2}$ $= 0 \pm 1$	2	2	y, x
$h(x) = x^2 + 1$	$x = \frac{-0 \pm \sqrt{0^2 - 4(1)(1)}}{2(1)}$ $= \frac{0 \pm \sqrt{4}}{2}$	0	0	y, x

© Carnegie Learning, Inc.

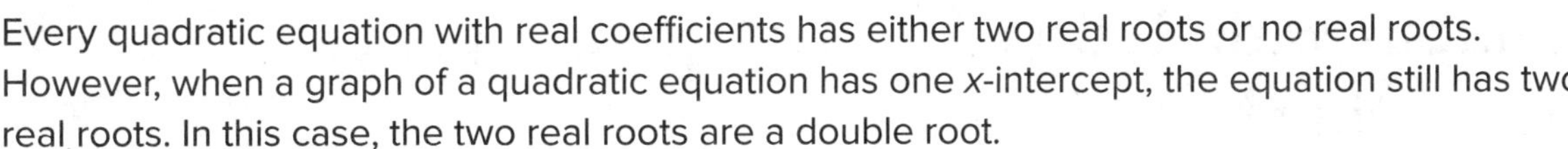

Every quadratic equation with real coefficients has either two real roots or no real roots. However, when a graph of a quadratic equation has one *x*-intercept, the equation still has two real roots. In this case, the two real roots are a double root.

4 Use the discriminant to determine the number of real roots for each equation. Then, solve for the roots/zeros.

ⓐ $y = 2x^2 + 12x - 2$

ⓑ $0 = 2x^2 + 12x + 20$

ⓒ $y = x^2 + 12x + 36$

ⓓ $y = 3x^2 + 7x - 20$

ⓔ $y = 4x^2 - 9$

ⓕ $0 = 9x^2 + 12x + 4$

© Carnegie Learning, Inc.

Operations with Rational and Irrational Numbers

HABITS OF MIND
- Reason abstractly and quantitatively.
- Construct viable arguments and critique the reasoning of others.

In the previous activity, you used the discriminant of the Quadratic Formula to determine whether there were two, one, or no real roots to a quadratic equation. Remember that the set of real numbers consists of the set of rational and the set of irrational numbers. Let's take a closer look at these two specific types of real numbers.

1 What characteristic of the discriminant determines whether the roots are rational or irrational?

2 Based on the number and nature of each of the roots, decide whether the discriminant is positive, negative, or zero and if the discriminant is or is not a perfect square.

(a) No real roots/zeros

(b) One rational root/zero

(c) Two rational roots/zeros

(d) Two irrational roots/zeros

© Carnegie Learning, Inc.

Throughout this lesson, you have solved quadratic equations with rational and irrational roots.

You have interpreted solutions as the sum or difference of a quantity from the axis of symmetry. In each case, the *c*-value that defines the axis of symmetry, $x = c$, is a rational number. In some cases, you added and subtracted a rational number. In other cases, you added and subtracted an irrational number.

ACTIVITY 4

Consider each equation and its corresponding roots.

$y = (x - 2)^2 - 9$

$x = 2 \pm 3$

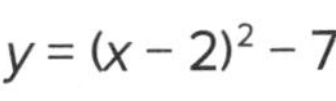

$y = (x - 2)^2 - 7$

$x = 2 \pm \sqrt{7}$

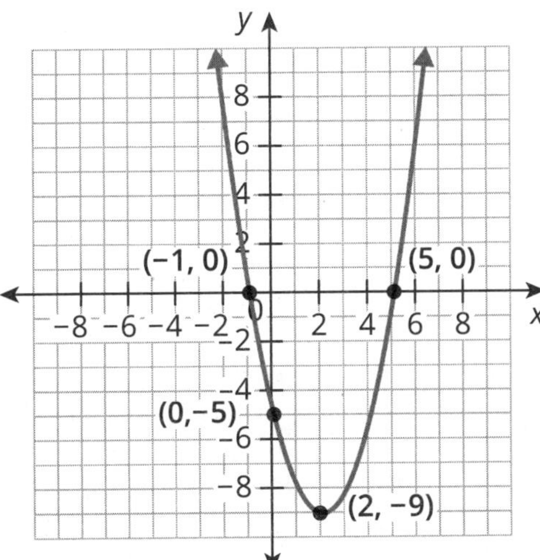

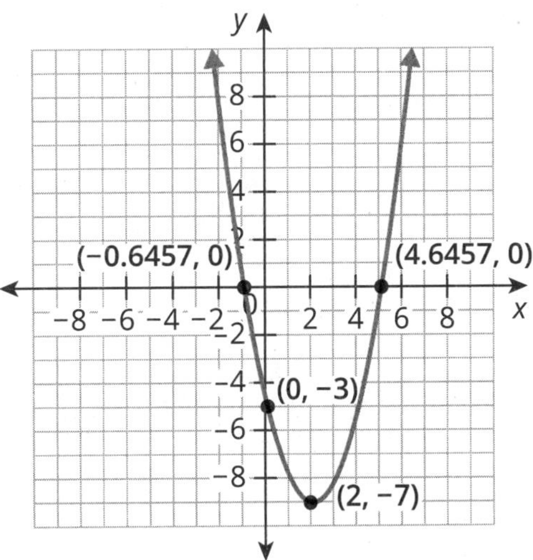

3 Describe the roots of each equation as rational or irrational.

4 Let m represent a nonzero rational number and let n represent an irrational number. Which expression could represent a rational number? **Explain your reasoning and provide an example.**

$m + n$ $\qquad$ mn $\qquad$ $-n$ $\qquad$ n^2

TOPIC 2

© Carnegie Learning, Inc.

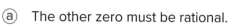

5 Consider a quadratic function with integer coefficients and two distinct zeros. If one zero is irrational, which statement is true about the other zero? **Explain your reasoning and provide an example.**

ⓐ The other zero must be rational.

ⓑ The other zero must be irrational.

ⓒ The other zero can be either rational or irrational.

ⓓ The other zero must be non-real.

6 Use the given values for *W*, *X*, *Y*, and *Z* to determine which expression results in a rational number. **Explain your reasoning.**

$W = \sqrt{4}$ $X = 2\sqrt{2}$ $Y = \sqrt{3}$ $Z = \sqrt{25}$

ⓐ $W + X$

ⓑ $X + Y$

ⓒ $Y + Z$

ⓓ $Z + W$

© Carnegie Learning, Inc.

The Number *i*

HABITS OF MIND
- Reason abstractly and quantitatively.
- Construct viable arguments and critique the reasoning of others.

> Consider the function $p(x) = x^2 + 1$ and its graph from the previous activity.

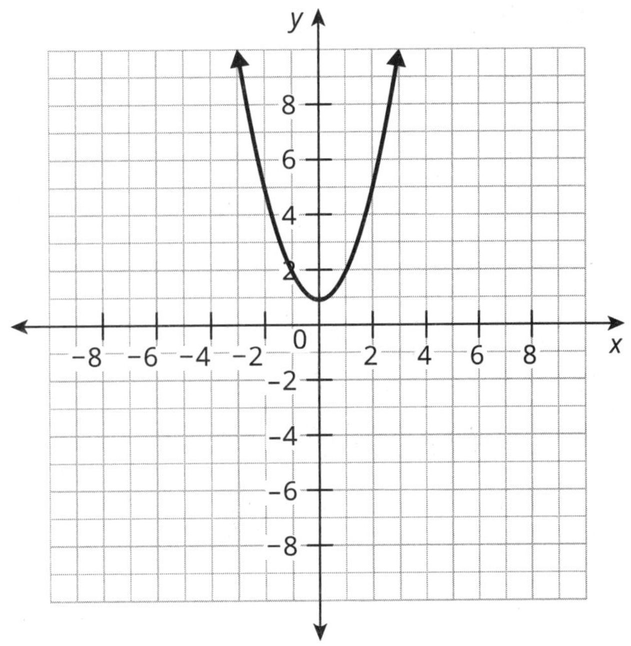

Elena and Mark determined the zeros of the function.

Elena

$x^2 + 1 = 0$

$x^2 = -1$

$x = \pm\sqrt{-1}$

Mark

$x^2 + 1 = 0$

$x^2 = 1$

$x = \pm 1$

1. What did Mark do wrong? **Use the graph to justify your answer.**

2. Consider Elena's solution. Does the solution fall within the real number system? **Explain your reasoning.**

© Carnegie Learning, Inc.

To calculate the square of any real number, you need a way to calculate the square root of a negative number. Therefore, there must be a number such that when you square it, it is equal to a negative number. For this reason, mathematicians defined *the number i*.

The number *i* is a number such that $i^2 = -1$. The number i is also the imaginary identity.

3 If $i^2 = -1$, then what is the value of i?

DID YOU KNOW?
The number i is similar to the number π. Even though they are both numbers, each is special enough that it gets its very own symbol.

4 Recall the function $p(x) = x + 1$. Write the roots of the function in terms of i.

Functions and equations that have solutions requiring i have **imaginary roots** or **imaginary zeros**.

5 How can you tell from the graph of a quadratic equation whether or not it has real solutions or imaginary solutions?

TAKE NOTE . . .
Equations with no solutions in one number system may have solutions in a larger number system.

6 Do you think you can determine the imaginary solutions by examining the graph? **Explain your reasoning.**

© Carnegie Learning, Inc.

The set of **complex numbers** is the set of all numbers in the form $a + bi$, where a and b are real numbers.

The term a is the **real part of a complex number**, and the term bi is the **imaginary part of a complex number**.

You represent the set of complex numbers using $\mathbb{C}$.

The set of **imaginary numbers** is the set of all numbers in the form $a + bi$, where a and b are real numbers and b is not equal to 0. You represent the set of imaginary numbers using the notation $\mathbb{I}$. A **pure imaginary number** is a number of the form $a + bi$, where a is equal to 0 and b is not equal to 0.

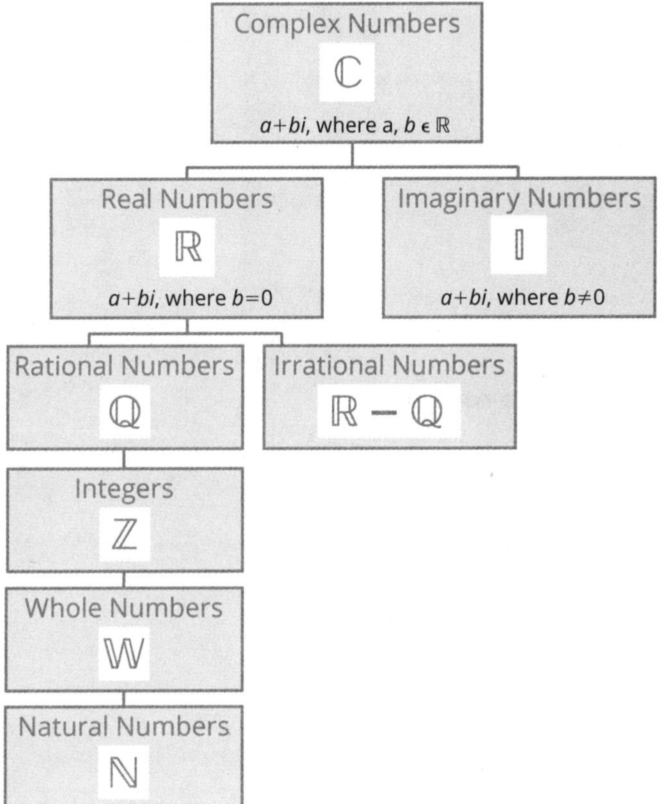

TAKE NOTE . . .

The ∈ symbol means "an element of." Therefore, "$a, b \in \mathbb{R}$" means that the values for a and b are elements of the set of real numbers.

7 Complete each statement with *always, sometimes, or never*.

(a) If a number is an imaginary number, then it is ________________ a complex number.

(b) If a number is a complex number, then it is ________________ an imaginary number.

(c) If a number is a real number, then it is ________________ a complex number.

(d) If a number is a real number, then it is ________________ an imaginary number.

(e) If a number is a complex number, then it is ________________ a real number.

DID YOU KNOW?

This is the entire universe of numbers. Seriously, like all of them!

© Carnegie Learning, Inc.

8 List all number sets that describe each given number.

(a) 3

(b) $\sqrt{7}$

(c) $3i$

(d) $5.\overline{45}$

(e) $\frac{7}{8}$

(f) $6 - i$

WORKED EXAMPLE

You can rewrite expressions involving negative roots using *i*.

Rewrite $\sqrt{-25}$ using i.

Factor out (−1).	$\sqrt{-25} = \sqrt{(-1)(25)}$
Rewrite the radical expression.	$= \sqrt{-1} \cdot \sqrt{25}$
Apply the square root on $\sqrt{25}$.	$= 5\sqrt{-1}$
Rewrite $\sqrt{-1}$ as i.	$= 5i$

So, you can rewrite $\sqrt{-25}$ as $5i$.

9 Rewrite each expression using i.

(a) $\sqrt{-4}$

(b) $\sqrt{-12}$

(c) $5 + \sqrt{-50}$

(d) $\frac{6 - \sqrt{-8}}{2}$

© Carnegie Learning, Inc.

Show Me the Ways

In this topic, you learned different methods for determining the real roots of a quadratic equation.

1 Determine the real roots of the quadratic equation $y = 2x^2 + 4x - 6$ using the four methods you learned in this topic.

$$y = 2x^2 + 4x - 6$$

Factoring

Using the Quadratic Formula

Completing the Square

Graphing

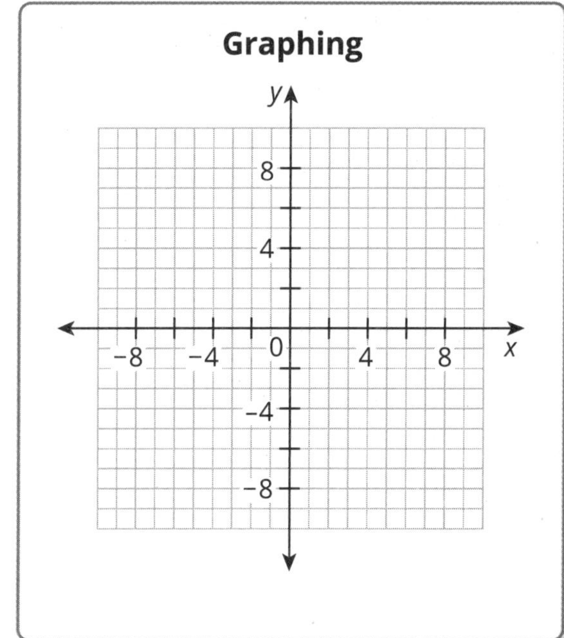

© Carnegie Learning, Inc.

2. Casey says that any quadratic equation has only one of these three types of solutions:
   - 2 unique real number solutions
   - 2 equal real number solutions (a double root)
   - 1 real and 1 imaginary solution

   Brandon says that any quadratic equation has only one of these three types of solutions:
   - 2 unique real number solutions
   - 2 equal real number solutions (a double root)
   - 2 imaginary solutions

   Karl says that any quadratic equation has only one of these four types of solutions:
   - 2 unique real number solutions
   - 2 equal real number solutions (a double root)
   - 2 imaginary solutions
   - 1 real and 1 imaginary solution

   Who's correct? **Explain your reasoning.**

© Carnegie Learning, Inc.

LESSON 5 ASSIGNMENT

> Use a separate piece of paper for your Journal entry.

JOURNAL

Describe how you can determine the types of solutions when using the Quadratic Formula.

REMEMBER

You can use the Quadratic Formula, $x = \frac{-b \pm \sqrt{b^2 - 4ac}}{2a}$, to calculate the solutions to any quadratic equation of the form $ax^2 + bx + c = 0$, where a, b, and c represent real numbers and $a \neq 0$.

On the graph of a quadratic function, $\pm \frac{\sqrt{b^2 - 4ac}}{2a}$ is the distance from $\left(-\frac{b}{2a}, 0\right)$ to each root.

PRACTICE

You can use this formula to calculate the distance, s, an object travels in t seconds. In this formula, u represents the initial velocity, and a represents a constant acceleration. Use this formula to answer each question.

$$s = ut + \frac{1}{2}at^2$$

1. Kian is driving 48 miles per hour and is starting to merge onto the highway; therefore, he must increase his speed. He gradually accelerates at a rate of 7 miles per hour for several seconds.

   a. Substitute the initial velocity and constant acceleration into the formula to write an equation to represent the distance Kian travels.

   b. Use the Quadratic Formula to determine the roots of the equation. What do the roots represent in the context of the problem situation? Explain your reasoning.

2. Sonja is driving her car 32 miles per hour when she passes Dominique's house. She then accelerates at a rate of 3 miles per hour for several minutes until she passes the movie theater. Sonja knows that the movie theater is 2.9 miles from Dominique's house.

   a. Substitute the initial velocity, constant acceleration, and distance into the formula to write an equation to represent the distance Sonja travels.

Go to LiveHint.com for help on the PRACTICE questions.

TOPIC 2

© Carnegie Learning, Inc.

(b) Use the Quadratic Formula to determine the roots of the equation you wrote in part (a). What do the roots represent in the context of the problem situation? Explain your reasoning.

3 Use the discriminant to determine the number of real roots for each equation. Then, solve the quadratic equations with real roots.

(a) $4x^2 + 8x - 12 = 0$

(b) $x^2 + 2x - 10 = 0$

(c) $9x^2 - 12x + 4 = 0$

(d) $3x^2 - 4 = 0$

(e) $3x^2 + 2x - 2 = 0$

(f) $x^2 - 3x + 5 = 0$

4 Classify each number according to its most specific number set.

(a) $\frac{-4}{9}$

(b) $\frac{\sqrt{-4}}{9}$

(c) $9 - \sqrt{-4}$

(d) $-4 - \sqrt{9}$

5 Rewrite each radical using *i*.

(a) $\sqrt{-16}$

(b) $\sqrt{-27}$

(c) $\sqrt{-200}$

(d) $5 + \sqrt{-20}$

© Carnegie Learning, Inc.

STRETCH Optional

> Consider the function $f(x) = -2x^2 + bx - 5$.

1 Determine the *b*-value(s) that would ensure the function has two real roots. Explain your reasoning.

MIXED PRACTICE

This Mixed Practice worksheet includes two sections: Spaced Review and End-of-Topic Review. **Use a separate piece of paper to show your work.**

Spaced Review

Practice concepts from previous topics.

1. Graph the function, $g(x)$, whose graph transforms the graph $f(x) = x^2$ by vertically compressing it by a factor of $\frac{1}{3}$ and translating it down 7 units.

2. Graph the function, $g(x)$, whose graph transforms the graph $f(x) = (x - 4)^2$ by vertically stretching it by a factor of 2, reflecting it across the x-axis, and moving it to the left 3 units.

3. Write the equation of the function, $g(x)$, whose graph transforms the graph $f(x) = x^2 + 1$ by reflecting it across the x-axis, shifting it up 6 units, and shifting it to the left 4 units.

4. Determine whether the table of values represents a linear function. If it does represent a linear function, write the function. If it does not represent a linear function, explain why.

x	$f(x)$
−2	4
−1	1
0	1
0	0
1	1

5. Write the piecewise function for this graph.

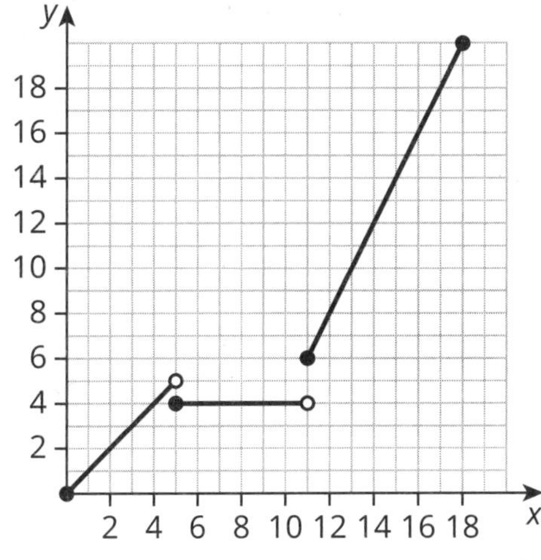

6. The Build-A-Dream construction company has plans for two models of the homes they build, Model A and Model B. The Model A home requires 18 single windows and 3 double windows. The Model B home requires 20 single windows and 5 double windows. A total of 1,800 single windows and 375 double windows have been ordered for the developments.

   a. Write and solve a system of equations to represent this situation. Define your variables.

   b. Interpret the solution of the linear system in terms of the problem situation.

© Carnegie Learning, Inc.

End-of-Topic Review

AVAILABLE ONLINE
1. A **Topic Summary** reviews the main concepts for the topic.
2. A video of the **Worked Example** is provided.

> Practice concepts you learned in **Solving Quadratic Equations**.

7. Complete the square to determine the roots of each equation. Show your work.

   (a) $y = 2x^2 + 5x - 14$

   (b) $y = -3x^2 - 6x + 10$

8. Consider the function $f(x) = \left(x + \frac{1}{2}\right)\left(x - \frac{3}{4}\right)$.

   (a) Identify the form of the function as factored, general, or vertex.

   (b) Identify the zeros and axis of symmetry of the function.

9. Determine each product.

   (a) $(3x - 9)^2$

   (b) $(6x^2 + 5x + 4)(-x - 3)$

10. Rewrite the quadratic function, $f(x) = 16x^2 - 3$, as the product of linear factors.

11. Solve each equation.

    (a) $x^2 = 5x - 4$

    (b) $x^2 + 9x - 23 = 0$

12. Estimate the value of the radical expression $\sqrt{54}$. Then, rewrite the radical by extracting all perfect squares, if possible.

13. Determine the roots of each function.

    (a) $f(x) = (x + 5)^2 + 9$

    (b) $g(x) = x^2 - 3x + 5$

14. Perform each operation.

    (a) $(7x^3 + 5x^2 - 8x) + (3x^3 - 4x^2 + 11)$

    (b) $(6x - 2y) - (3x - 5y)$

© Carnegie Learning, Inc.

LESSON 1

Ahead of the Curve

Solving Quadratic Inequalities

Learning Goals

- Solve a quadratic inequality by calculating the roots of the quadratic equation which corresponds to the inequality and testing values within intervals determined by the roots.
- Connect the graphical representation of a quadratic function and the solution to a corresponding quadratic inequality represented on a number line.
- Use interval notation to record the solutions to quadratic inequalities.

REVIEW (1–2 minutes)

> Determine the solution of each quadratic equation.

1. $x^2 - 100 = -64$

2. $x^2 + 3x + 5 = 15$

3. $4x^2 + 12x = 7$

4. $x^2 + 4x - 3 = 5$

© Carnegie Learning, Inc.

You have interpreted the solution sets to linear inequalities on a coordinate plane. You have also solved quadratic equations using a variety of methods.

How can you interpret the solutions sets to quadratic inequalities on a coordinate plane?

It Has Its Ups and Downs

A firework is shot straight up into the air with an initial velocity of 500 feet per second from 5 feet off the ground. Consider the graph of the function that represents this situation.

1. Use the graph to approximate when the firework will reach each given height off the ground.

   (a) 0 feet

   (b) 1000 feet

   (c) 2500 feet

   (d) 3900 feet

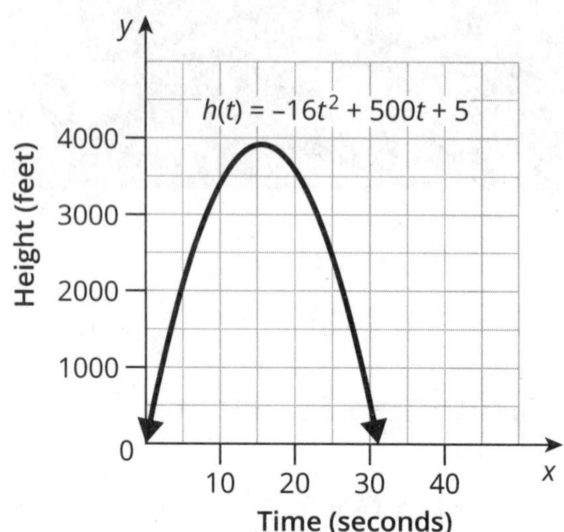

2. **Describe any patterns you notice for the number of times the firework reaches a given height.**

3. Draw a horizontal line on the graph to represent when the firework is 2000 feet off the ground.

   (a) When is the firework higher than 2000 feet? Circle this portion of the graph.

   (b) When is the firework below 2000 feet? Draw a box around this portion of the graph.

   (c) Write a quadratic inequality that represents the times when the firework is below 2000 feet.

© Carnegie Learning, Inc.

Solving Quadratic Inequalities

Just like with the other inequalities you have studied, the solution to a quadratic inequality is the set of values that satisfy the inequality.

HABITS OF MIND
- Reason abstractly and quantitatively.
- Construct viable arguments and critique the reasoning of others.

WORKED EXAMPLE

Let's determine the solution of the quadratic inequality $x^2 - 4x + 3 < 0$.

Write the corresponding quadratic equation. $x^2 - 4x + 3 = 0$

Calculate the roots of the quadratic equation using an appropriate method.

$(x - 3)(x - 1) = 0$

$(x - 3) = 0$ or $(x - 1) = 0$

$x = 3$ or $x = 1$

Plot the roots to divide the number line into three regions.

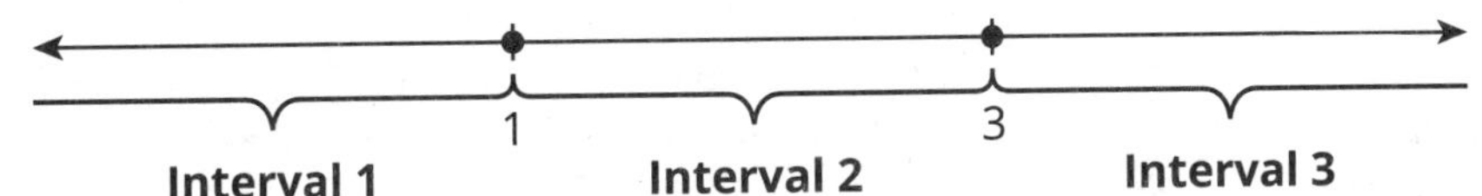

Choose a value from each interval to test in the original inequality.

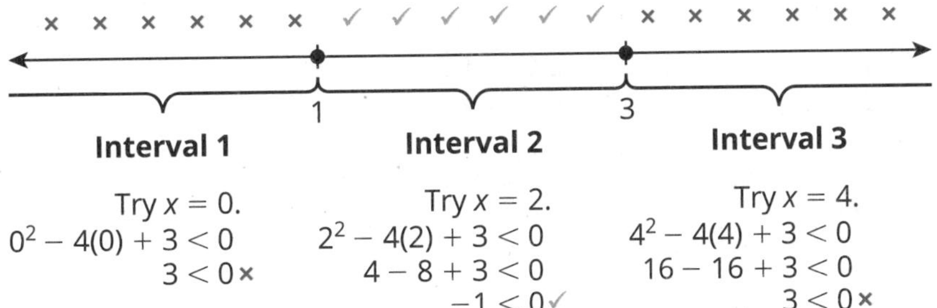

Interval 1	Interval 2	Interval 3
Try $x = 0$.	Try $x = 2$.	Try $x = 4$.
$0^2 - 4(0) + 3 < 0$	$2^2 - 4(2) + 3 < 0$	$4^2 - 4(4) + 3 < 0$
$3 < 0$ ×	$4 - 8 + 3 < 0$	$16 - 16 + 3 < 0$
	$-1 < 0$ ✓	$3 < 0$ ×

Identify the solution set as the interval(s) in which your test value satisfies the inequality.

- Interval 2 satisfies the original inequality, so the solution includes all numbers between 1 and 3.
- Solution: $x \in (1, 3)$

You read the symbol $\in$ as "is an element of," "is in," or "belongs to." The notation $x \in (1, 3)$ means the same as $1 < x < 3$.

© Carnegie Learning, Inc.

1 Analyze the Worked Example.

(a) How would the solution set change if the inequality was less than or equal to? **Explain your reasoning.**

(b) How would the solution set change if the inequality was greater than or equal to? **Explain your reasoning.**

REMEMBER . . .
The notation $x \in [1, 3]$ means the same as $1 \le x \le 3$.

2 Graph $y = x^2 - 4x + 3$ on this coordinate plane and label the roots of the equation and the vertex. Then, describe how the graph supports that the solution set for the associated quadratic inequality $x^2 - 4x + 3 < 0$ is $1 < x < 3$.

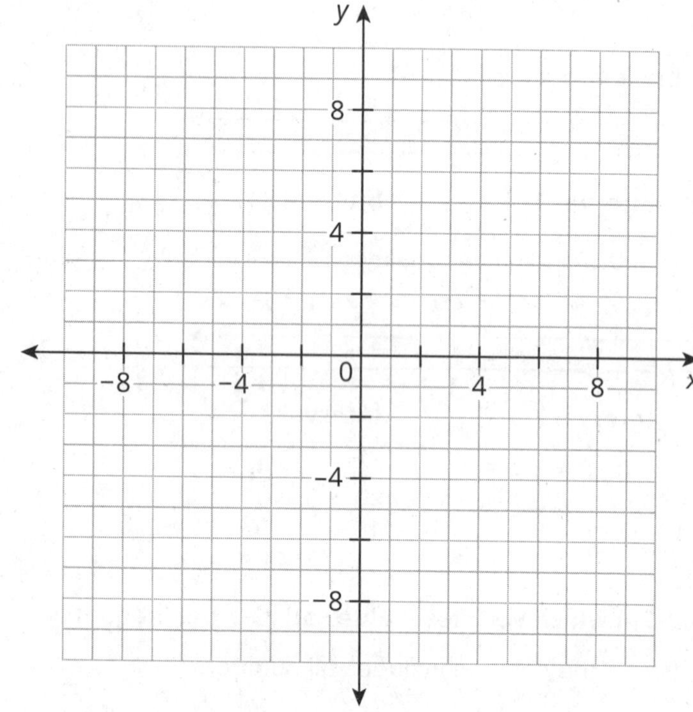

© Carnegie Learning, Inc.

Jeff correctly determined the roots of the quadratic inequality $2x^2 - 14x + 27 \geq 7$ to be $x = 5$ and $x = 2$. However, he incorrectly determined the solution set.

> Analyze Jeff's work.

Jeff

$2x^2 - 14x + 27 = 7$

$2x^2 - 14x + 20 = 0$

$2(x^2 - 7x + 10) = 0$

$2(x - 5)(x - 2) = 0$

$x = 5$ or $x = 2$

$x = 1$	$x = 3$	$x = 6$
$2(1)^2 - 14(1) + 27 \geq 7$	$2(3)^2 - 14(3) + 27 \geq 7$	$2(6)^2 - 14(6) + 27 \geq 7$
$2 - 14 + 27 \geq 7$	$18 - 42 + 27 \geq 7$	$72 - 84 + 27 \geq 7$
$15 \geq 7$ ✓	$3 \geq 7$ X	$15 \geq 7$ ✓

Solution: $x \in (-\infty, 1]$ or $x \in [6, \infty)$

3. Describe Jeff's error. Then, determine the correct solution set for the inequality.

ASK YOURSELF . . .
When testing values from each interval, could you use the factored form of the inequality rather than the original inequality?

© Carnegie Learning, Inc.

Modeling Quadratic Inequalities

You can use the graph of a quadratic function to model a quadratic inequality.

HABITS OF MIND
- Model with mathematics.
- Use appropriate tools strategically.

A water balloon is launched from a machine upward from a height of 10 feet with an initial velocity of 46 feet per second.

1. Identify the variables and write a quadratic function to represent this situation.

2. Use technology to sketch the graph of the function.

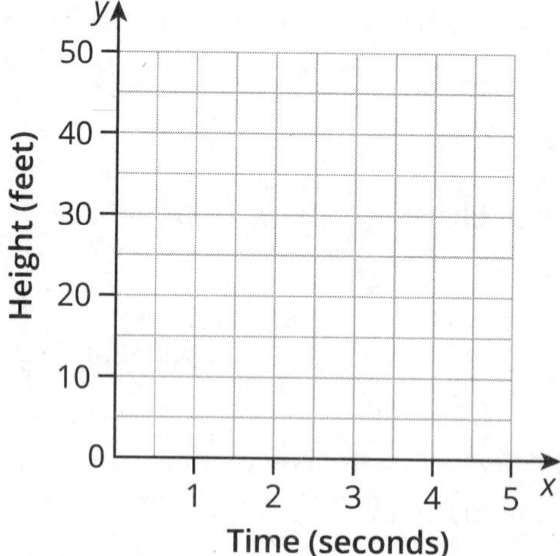

3. Draw a horizontal line on the graph to represent when the balloon is 30 feet off the ground.

   a. Circle the portion of the graph that represents when the balloon is above 30 feet.

   b. Write and solve an inequality to determine when the balloon is above 30 feet. **Use the graph to explain your solution.**

© Carnegie Learning, Inc.

4 Determine when the balloon is at or below 43 feet. **Interpret your solution in terms of the model you graphed**.

© Carnegie Learning, Inc.

Boom! Boom!

In the Getting Started activity, a firework was shot straight up into the air with an initial velocity of 500 feet per second from 5 feet off the ground. The function representing the situation was identified as $h(t) = -16t^2 + 500t + 5$. You determined the firework would be above 2000 feet between about 5 seconds and 27 seconds.

> Suppose a second firework was shot straight up into the air with an initial velocity of 500 feet per second from the ground.

1. Predict whether the second firework will be above 2000 feet for more time, less time, or the same amount of time as the first firework.

2. Write a quadratic inequality to represent when the second firework will be above 2000 feet.

3. Determine when the second firework will be above 2000 feet.

4. Was your prediction made in Question 1 correct?

5. Use technology to compare the graph of the first firework to the graph of the second firework. **What do you notice?**

© Carnegie Learning, Inc.

LESSON 1 ASSIGNMENT

> Use a separate piece of paper for your Journal entry.

JOURNAL

Describe the difference between the solutions of a quadratic equation and the solutions of a quadratic inequality.

REMEMBER

You determine the solution set of a quadratic inequality by first solving for the roots of the quadratic equation, then determining which intervals created by the roots satisfy the inequality.

PRACTICE

1. A nutrition company has determined that the fixed cost associated with producing cases of its special health bars is \$1000. The variable cost is $\frac{3}{4}x + 25$ dollars per case that they produce. The selling price of the cases of health bars is $135 - \frac{1}{4}x$ per case that they sell.

   a. Determine the cost function $C(x)$ for this product based on the number of cases, x, that they produce and sell. Rewrite if necessary.

   b. Determine the revenue function $R(x)$ for this product based on the number of cases, x, that they produce and sell. Rewrite if necessary.

   c. The profit that a company makes is the difference between the revenue and the cost. Determine the profit function $P(x)$ for this product.

   d. Determine when the company will break even.

   e. When they make and sell fewer than 10 cases of health bars, will they have a positive or negative profit? Explain your reasoning.

   f. When they make and sell more than 100 cases of health bars, will they have a positive or negative profit? Explain your reasoning.

   g. Determine how many units the company must produce and sell to make a profit of at least \$1800.

© Carnegie Learning, Inc.

Go to LiveHint.com for help on the PRACTICE questions.

2 Solve each inequality.

ⓐ $2y^2 + 2y - 12 > 0$

ⓑ $x^2 + 6x \leq 0$

ⓒ $4b^2 + 14b + 16 < 10$

ⓓ $a^2 \geq 4(2a - 3)$

ⓔ $2t^2 > 9t + 18$

ⓕ $k^2 + 3k + 2 < -3(k + 2)$

© Carnegie Learning, Inc.

STRETCH Optional

> Marelby and Merily both started their own companies with $3000. The inequality $g(x) \geq x^2 - 5x + 3$ represents Marelby's profits. The inequality $h(x) \leq -x^2 + 5x + 3$ represents Merily's profits.

1 Graph the solutions to the quadratic inequalities and state what the shaded region means in regards to Marelby and Merily's profits.

LESSON 2

All Systems Are Go!

Systems of Quadratic Equations

Learning Goals

- Solve systems of a linear equation and aquadratic equation.
- Solve systems of two quadratic equations.

REVIEW (1–2 minutes)

Solve each system of equations.

1. $\begin{cases} y = 2x - 5 \\ y = x - 1 \end{cases}$

2. $\begin{cases} y = -3x + 2 \\ y = 5x - 6 \end{cases}$

3. $\begin{cases} y = -2x + 7 \\ y = -4x + 3 \end{cases}$

4. $\begin{cases} y = 3x + 7 \\ y = x + 1 \end{cases}$

© Carnegie Learning, Inc.

You have solved systems of linear equations graphically by determining the point of intersection and algebraically using substitution.

What does a solution to a system involving quadratics look like?

Block That Kick!

A punter kicks a football. The function $h(t) = -4.9t^2 + 20t + 0.75$, where t represents time, in seconds, models the height of the football in meters. A blocker can only attempt to knock down the football as it travels upward from the punter's foot. You can model the height in meters of the approaching blocker's hands using the function $h(t) = -0.6t + 3$, where t represents the same time. Can the blocker knock down the football?

1. Describe the shape of the functions that model the football's height over time and the height of the blocker's hands over time.

2. Sketch a graph of the situation. Do you think it is possible for the blocker to knock down the football? **Explain your reasoning.**

© Carnegie Learning, Inc.

Modeling a System with a Linear and a Quadratic Equation

HABITS OF MIND
- Model with mathematics.
- Use appropriate tools strategically.

A system of equations can involve nonlinear equations, such as quadratic equations. The scenario described in the previous activity models the relationship between a quadratic and a linear equation.

1. Use technology to sketch the graph of the system described in the previous activity.

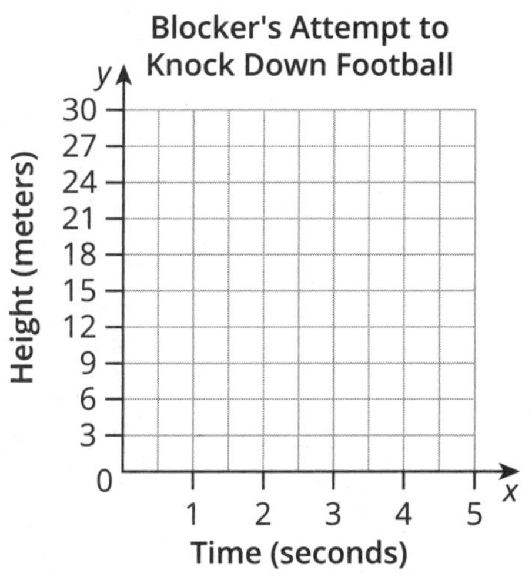

2. How many solutions does the system have? **Explain your reasoning.**

3. Does every solution make sense in the context of the problem situation? **Explain your reasoning.**

4. Use the graph to approximate at what point the blocker can block the football. Interpret your solution in the context of the problem.

© Carnegie Learning, Inc.

Solving a System With a Linear and a Quadratic Equation

HABITS OF MIND
- Reason abstractly and quantitatively.
- Construct viable arguments and critique the reasoning of others.

You can use similar methods for solving a system of nonlinear equations as the methods for solving a system of linear equations.

1. Consider the system of a linear equation and a quadratic equation.

$$\begin{cases} y = 2x + 7 \\ y = x^2 + 4 \end{cases}$$

(a) Write a new equation you can use to solve this system.

ASK YOURSELF . . .
Since y is equal to two different expressions, can you set the expressions equal to each other?

(b) Solve the resulting equation for x.

(c) Calculate the corresponding values for y.

(d) Identify the solution(s) to the system of equations.

© Carnegie Learning, Inc.

ⓔ Graph each equation of the system and identify the points of intersection.

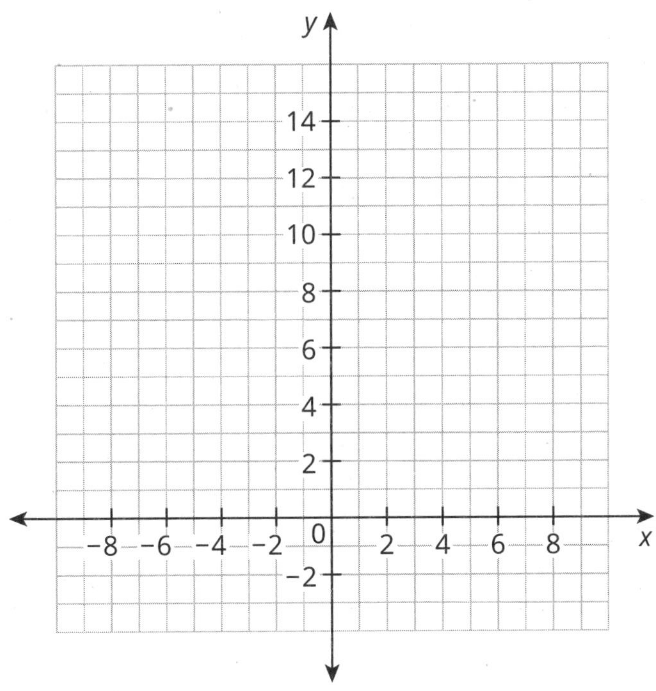

ⓕ What do you notice about the solutions you determined algebraically and graphically?

2 Think about the graphs of a linear equation and a quadratic equation. **Describe the different ways in which the two graphs can intersect and provide a sketch of each case.**

© Carnegie Learning, Inc.

3 Solve each system of equations algebraically over the set of real numbers. Then, verify the solution graphically.

ⓐ $\begin{cases} y = -2x + 4 \\ y = 4x^2 + 2x + 5 \end{cases}$

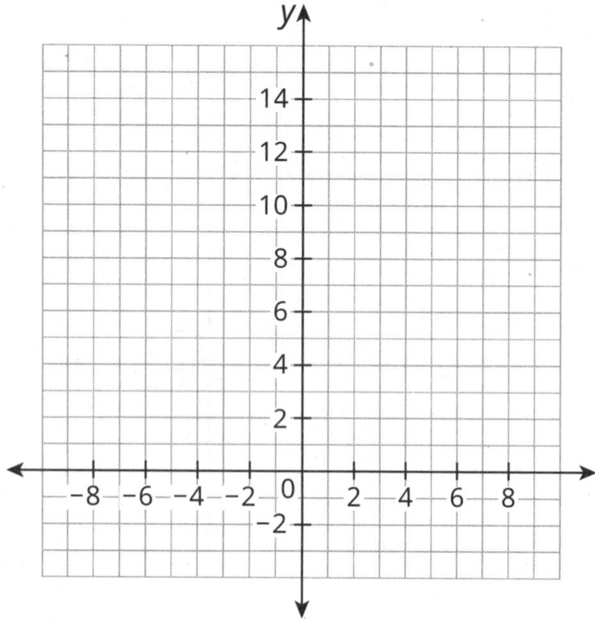

ⓑ $\begin{cases} y = -4x - 7 \\ y = 3x^2 + x - 3 \end{cases}$

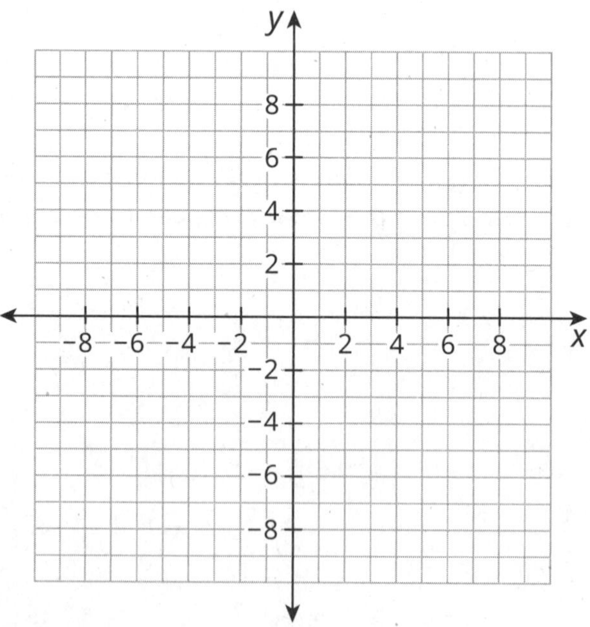

© Carnegie Learning, Inc.

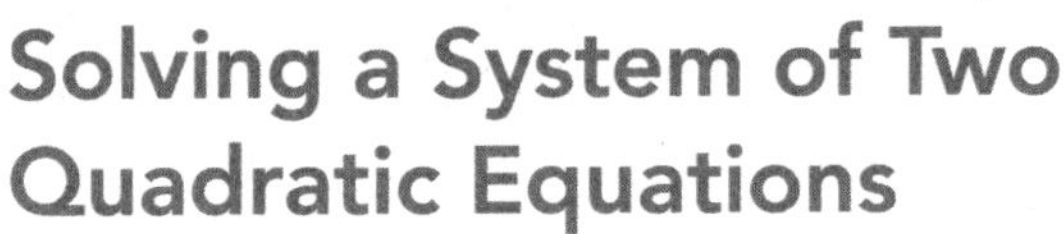

Solving a System of Two Quadratic Equations

HABITS OF MIND
- Reason abstractly and quantitatively.
- Construct viable arguments and critique the reasoning of others.

You have solved quadratic equations and systems of linear and quadratic equations. In this activity, you will apply your knowledge of these concepts to solve a system of two quadratic equations.

1 Consider the system of two quadratic equations.

$$\begin{cases} y = x^2 + 3x - 5 \\ y = -x^2 + 10x - 1 \end{cases}$$

(a) Use substitution to solve the system algebraically.

(b) Solve the system graphically. Graph each equation of the system and determine the points of intersection.

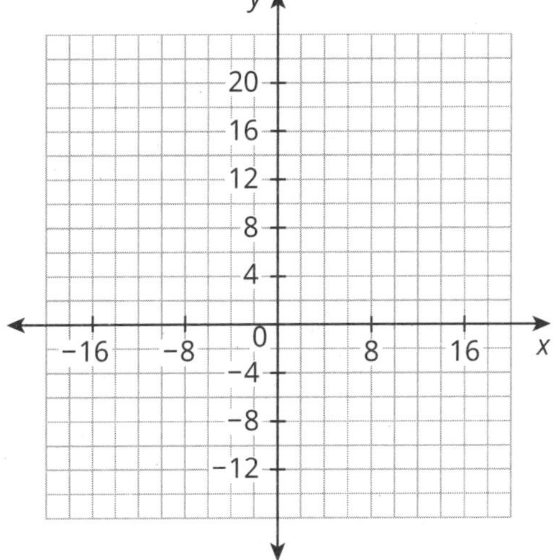

(c) What do you notice about the solutions you calculated algebraically and graphically?

2 Think about the graphs of two quadratic equations. **Describe the different ways in which the two graphs can intersect and provide a sketch of each case.**

© Carnegie Learning, Inc.

3 Solve each system of equations algebraically over the set of real numbers.
Then, verify the solution graphically.

ⓐ $\begin{cases} y = x^2 + 2x + 1 \\ y = 2x^2 - x - 3 \end{cases}$

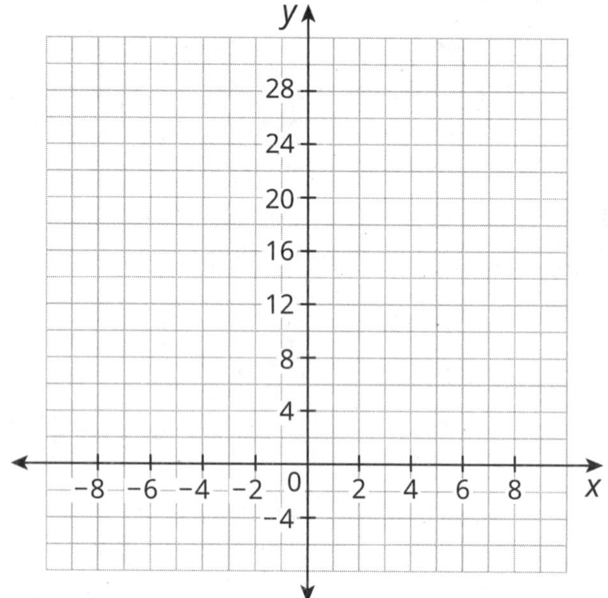

ⓑ $\begin{cases} y = 2x^2 - 7x + 6 \\ y = -2x^2 + 5x - 3 \end{cases}$

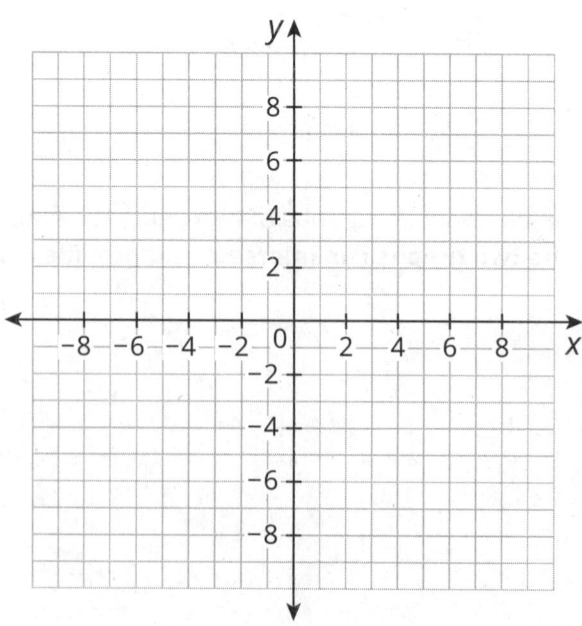

© Carnegie Learning, Inc.

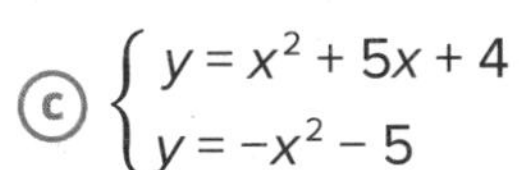

(c) $\begin{cases} y = x^2 + 5x + 4 \\ y = -x^2 - 5 \end{cases}$

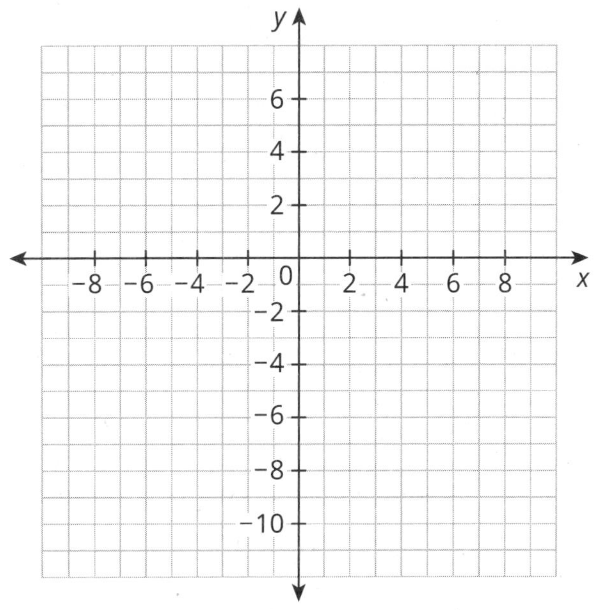

(d) $\begin{cases} y = x^2 + 4x + 4 \\ y = x^2 + 2x + 6 \end{cases}$

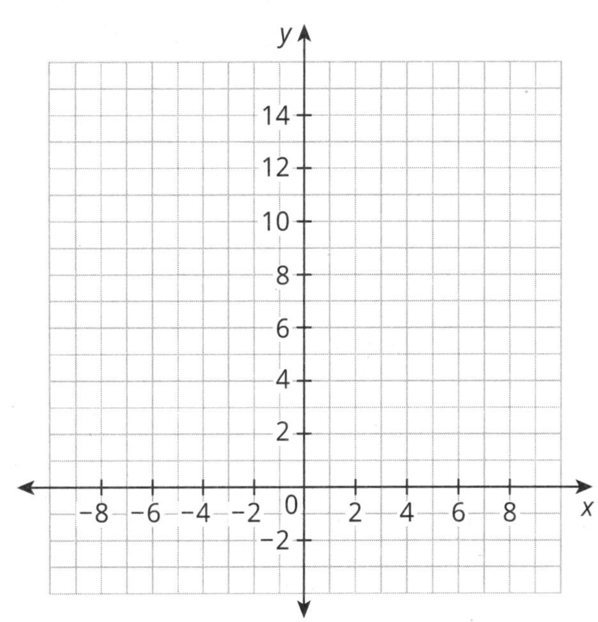

© Carnegie Learning, Inc.

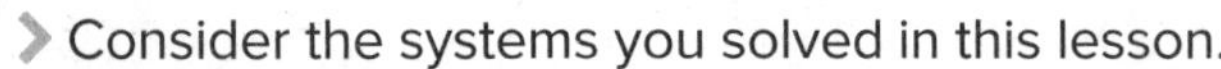

System Solutions

> Consider the systems you solved in this lesson.

1. A system of equations consisting of two linear equations has how many possible solutions?

2. A system of equations consisting of two quadratic equations has how many possible solutions?

3. A system of equations consisting of a linear equation and a quadratic equation has how many possible solutions?

4. Explain why a system of equations consisting of a linear equation and a quadratic equation cannot have an infinite number of solutions.

© Carnegie Learning, Inc.

LESSON 2 ASSIGNMENT

> Use a separate piece of paper for your Journal entry.

JOURNAL

Describe how you can use a graph to determine the solutions to a system of nonlinear equations in your own words.

REMEMBER

A system of equations consisting of a linear and a quadratic equation can have no solution, one solution, or two solutions. A system of equations consisting of two quadratic equations can have no solution, one solution, two solutions, or an infinite number of solutions.

PRACTICE

1. The Fandango Bike Company specializes in children's bikes. Each month, the company must keep track of their costs and revenue. Their costs consist of fixed costs that include rent, utilities, and workers' salaries, as well as the variable cost to make the bikes. You can represent the company's costs using the function $C(x) = 25x + 900$. You can represent the company's revenue for every bike sold using the function $R(x) = 100x - x^2$.

   (a) Determine the break-even point(s) for the month.

   (b) What is the solution to this system of equations? Explain what the solution means in terms of the problem.

   (c) Verify the solution by graphing both the cost and the revenue equations and interpreting the points of intersection.

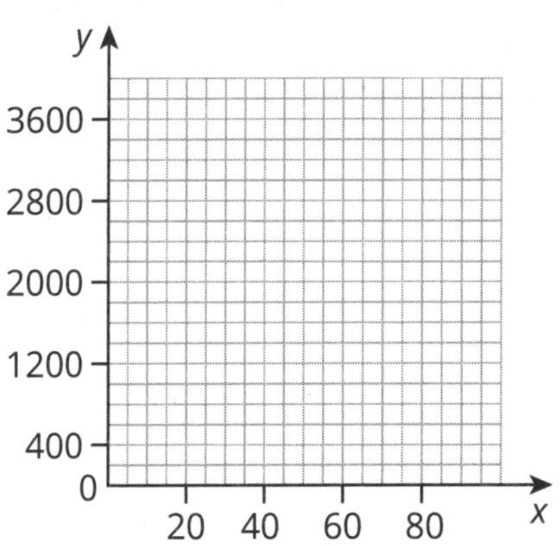

2. Due to the rising costs of running a business, the Fandango Bike Company anticipates fixed costs in the next year to be $1800 per month; whereas, the cost to make each bike will stay at $25 per bike.

   (a) Determine the number of bikes the company now needs to make for one month to break even when the revenue from selling bikes remains the same.

© Carnegie Learning, Inc.

Go to LiveHint.com for help on the PRACTICE questions.

ⓑ Verify the solution by graphing both the revenue and the cost equations.

ⓒ What does the company need to do to break even for the month?

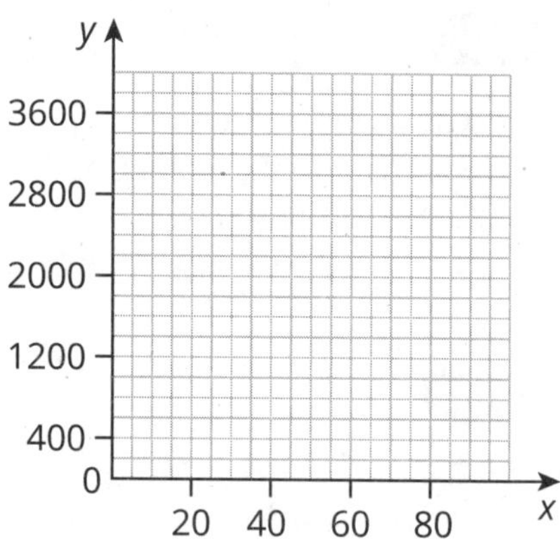

3 The company decides to change its location to a new building that is more energy efficient in order to help decrease fixed costs. It also invests in new machinery to reduce the number of employee hours needed to make a bike. The new monthly cost equation is $C = 0.4x^2 + 15x + 400$. The company then decides to sell the bikes strictly online. The new monthly revenue equation is $R = 100x + 0.6x^2$.

ⓐ Determine the break-even point(s) for the company for each month.

ⓑ Verify the solution by graphing both the revenue and the cost equations and interpreting the points of intersection.

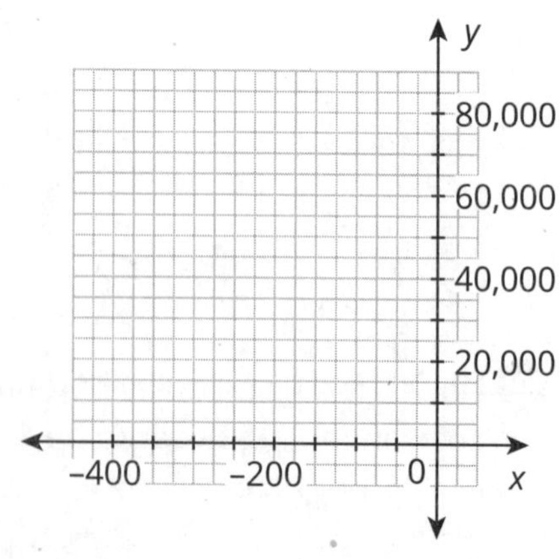

© Carnegie Learning, Inc.

STRETCH Optional

1 Graph the inequalities given and describe what the double-shaded region means in your own words.

$$\begin{cases} y > 2x + 5 \\ y \leq -3x^2 + 15x \end{cases}$$

LESSON 3

Model Behavior

Using Quadratic Functions to Model Data

KEY TERM

restrict the domain

Learning Goals

- Use a quadratic function to model data.
- Interpret characteristics of a quadratic function in terms of a problem situation.
- Use graphs of quadratic functions to make predictions.
- Interpret the inverse of a function in terms of a problem situation.
- Determine the inverse of a quadratic function using a graph.
- Determine the equation of the inverse of a quadratic function.
- Determine whether given functions are one-to-one functions.
- Identify function types that are always, sometimes, or never one-to-one functions.

REVIEW (1–2 minutes)

> Determine a linear regression equation that best models the data.

x	1	2	3	4	5	6	7	8	9
y	32	35	34	35	39	38	40	42	41

You know how to model data with regression equations and how to write inverses of linear functions.

How can you extend this understanding to quadratic relationships?

© Carnegie Learning, Inc.

That Might Be a Bad Idea . . .

A 12-ounce can of soda was put into a freezer. The table shows the volume of the soda in the can measured at different temperatures.

Temperature of Can (°F)	Soda Volume (cm^3)
68.0	355.51
50.0	354.98
42.8	354.89
39.2	354.88
35.6	354.89
32.0	354.93
23.0	355.13
14.0	355.54

TAKE NOTE . . .
The first step of the modeling process is to notice and wonder. What do you notice about the data? Is there a question it brings to mind that you wonder about?

1. Describe the data distribution.

2. Create a scatter plot of the data. Sketch the plot of points on this coordinate plane.

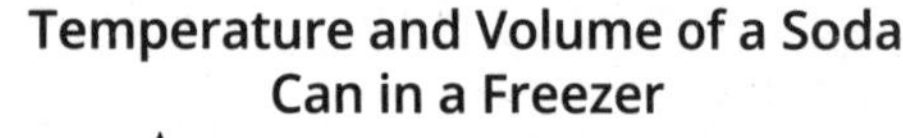

Temperature and Volume of a Soda Can in a Freezer

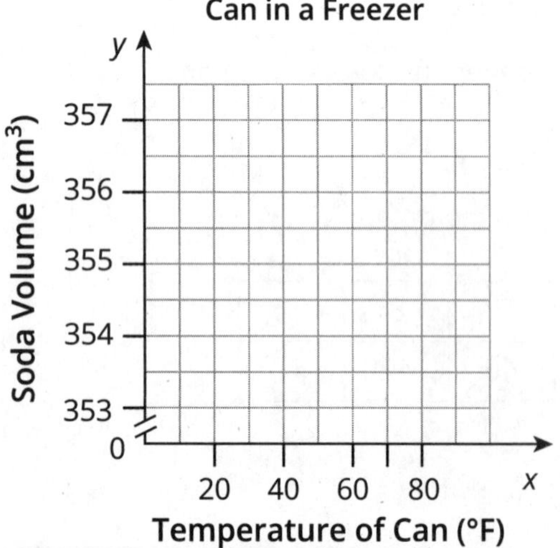

TAKE NOTE . . .
The second step of the modeling process is to organize and mathematize. The scatter plot is a way to organize the data.

© Carnegie Learning, Inc.

Using Quadratic Functions to Model Data

HABITS OF MIND
- Model with mathematics.
- Use appropriate tools strategically.

Let's continue to analyze the data and make some predictions about the volume of soda at different temperatures.

1. Use technology to calculate the regression equation that best models the data in the Getting Started. Sketch the graph of the regression equation on the coordinate plane on which you created your scatter plot. **Explain why the regression equation best models the data.**

TAKE NOTE . . .
You can mathematize the data by modeling it with an appropriate regression equation.

2. State the domain and range of your function. **How do they compare to the domain and range of this problem situation?**

3. Use the regression equation to answer each question.

   a. Determine the y-intercept and interpret its meaning in terms of this problem situation.

   b. Determine the x-intercepts and interpret the meaning of each in terms of this problem situation.

TAKE NOTE . . .
The third step of the modeling process is to predict and analyze, and the fourth step is to test and interpret. These questions focus on these two steps of the process.

© Carnegie Learning, Inc.

4 Predict the volume of the soda can at each temperature.

(a) 20°F

(b) 60°F

5 Write a summary of the problem situation, your model as the solution, and any limitations of your model.

© Carnegie Learning, Inc.

Analyzing a Quadratic Model and Its Inverse

HABITS OF MIND
- Model with mathematics.
- Use appropriate tools strategically.

In this activity, you will explore what happens when you interchange the independent and dependent quantities in a quadratic function.

Arlen City Police Department is offering special classes for interested high school students this summer. Elsa decides to enroll in an introductory forensic science class. On the first day, Dr. Suarez tells Elsa's class that crime scenes often involve speeding vehicles which leave skid marks on the road as evidence. Taking into account the road surface, weather conditions, the percent grade of the road, and vehicle type, they use the function

$$f(s) = 0.034s^2 + 0.96s - 26.6$$

to determine the length in feet of skid marks left by a vehicle based on its speed, s, in miles per hour.

1. Complete the table based on $f(s)$. Label the column titles with the independent and dependent quantities and their units.

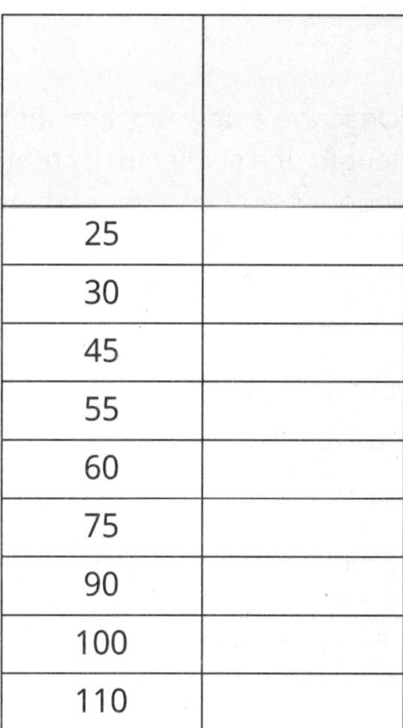

25	
30	
45	
55	
60	
75	
90	
100	
110	

2. According to the table, what are the domain and range for the problem situation?

3. Graph the table values and sketch the graph of $f(s)$ on the grid. **Label the axes.**

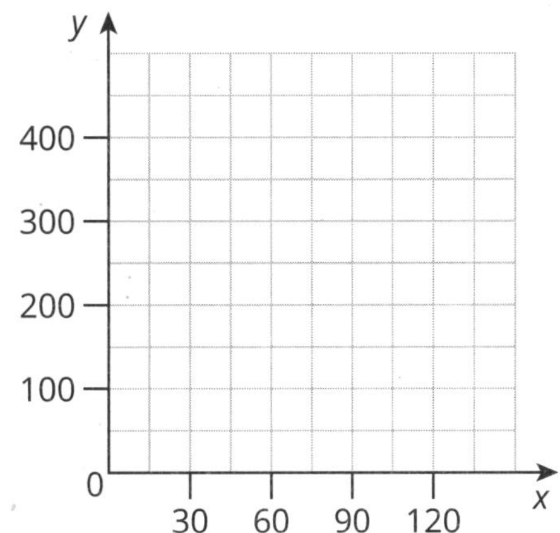

© Carnegie Learning, Inc.

During another class period, Dr. Suarez takes Elsa's class to a mock crime scene to collect evidence.

4 One piece of evidence is a skid mark that is 300 feet long.

(a) Use the graph to estimate the speed of the vehicle that created this skid mark. **Explain your process.**

(b) Determine the exact speed of the vehicle that created this skid mark. **Show your work.**

ASK YOURSELF . . .
How do these data differ from the data in the table?

5 Describe a new function that Elsa can use to determine the speed of a vehicle given the length of a skid mark it created. In your description, include information about the independent and dependent variables and the domain and range of this problem situation.

6 Predict what you think the graph of the new function will look like and sketch the graph on the grid. **Label the axes.**

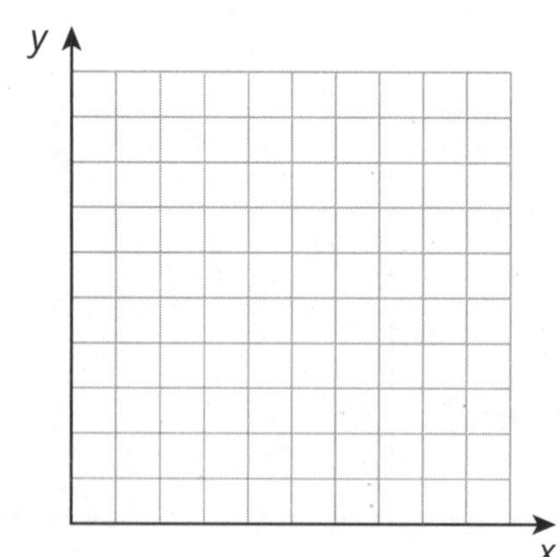

© Carnegie Learning, Inc.

7 Use your graph to estimate the car's speed before stopping for each given skid mark length.

(a) 50 feet

(b) 175 feet

(c) 350 feet

8 Write a report about the length of skid marks left by vehicles and vehicle speeds. Discuss possible factors that would affect the length of the skid marks left by a vehicle and what effect these factors would have on the graph of $f(s)$ and the graph of its inverse.

© Carnegie Learning, Inc.

MATHia CONNECTION
- Introduction to Inverses
- Recognizing Graphs of Inverses

Exploring Inverses of Quadratics

HABITS OF MIND
- Reason abstractly and quantitatively.
- Construct viable arguments and critique the reasoning of others.

You have determined inverses of linear functions by reflecting a function across the line $y = x$.

> Consider the basic quadratic function $f(x) = x^2$.

1. Use patty paper to reflect $f(x)$ across the line $y = x$ to graph its inverse.

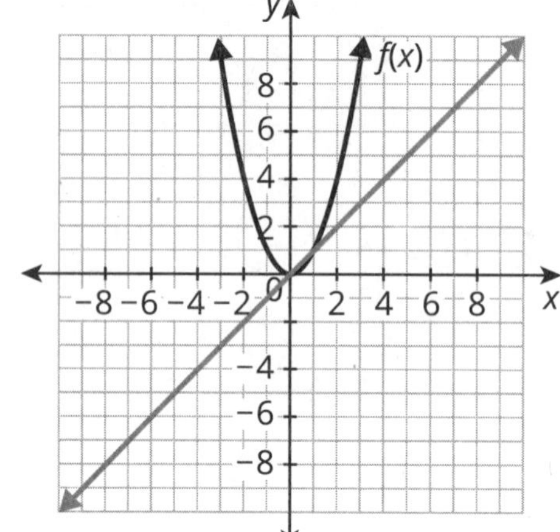

2. Explain why the inverse is not a function based on its graph.

3. What is the domain and range of the function?
What is the domain and range of the inverse of the function?

You can determine the equation of the inverse of the basic quadratic function $f(x) = x^2$ the same way you determined the equation of the inverse of a linear function.

WORKED EXAMPLE

Determine the inverse of $f(x) = x^2$.

STEP 1 Replace $f(x)$ with y. $y = x^2$

STEP 2 Switch the x and y variables. $x = y^2$

STEP 3 Solve for y. $\pm\sqrt{x} = y$

So, the equation of the inverse is $y = \pm\sqrt{x}$.

© Carnegie Learning, Inc.

4 Explain why the inverse is not a function based on its equation.

You know that the inverse of $f(x) = x^2$ is not a function. However, you can *restrict the domain* of this function so that the inverse is also a function. To **restrict the domain** of a function means to define a new domain for the function that is a subset of the original domain.

5 Consider the graph of $f(x) = x^2$ and the graphs of the two equations that represent its inverse.

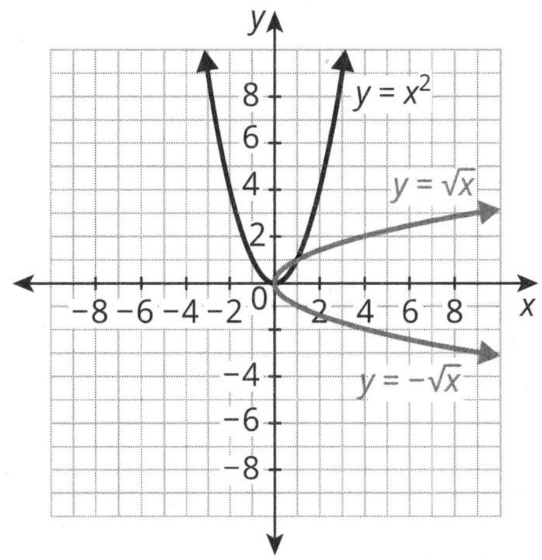

ⓐ Identify the restrictions of $f(x) = x^2$ to produce the inverse equations $y = \sqrt{x}$ and $y = -\sqrt{x}$. Then, state the domain and range of each inverse.

Restrictions for $y = x^2$

Domain: __________

Range: __________

$y = \sqrt{x}$

Domain: __________

Range: __________

Restrictions for $y = x^2$

Domain: __________

Range: __________

$y = -\sqrt{x}$

Domain: __________

Range: __________

ⓑ How does the domain and range of the inverse relate to the restricted domain and range of the original function?

ⓒ Do all the graphs represent functions? **Explain your reasoning.**

© Carnegie Learning, Inc.

TOPIC 3

More with Inverses of Quadratics

HABITS OF MIND
- Reason abstractly and quantitatively.
- Construct viable arguments and critique the reasoning of others.

Let's consider the inverse of another quadratic function that models a real-world situation.

Marissa is testing a container she built for an egg drop competition. She placed an egg in her container and dropped it from the roof of a building. You can model the height of the egg using the function $f(x) = -16x^2 + 64$, where x represents the time in seconds.

1. Define the independent and dependent quantities of $f(x)$.

2. What is the domain and range of $f(x)$ based on its equation?

3. Determine any restrictions on the domain of $f(x)$ based on this problem situation. **Explain your reasoning.**

4. Graph $f(x) = -16x^2 + 64$ with the restricted domain based on this problem situation. **Be sure to label your graph.**

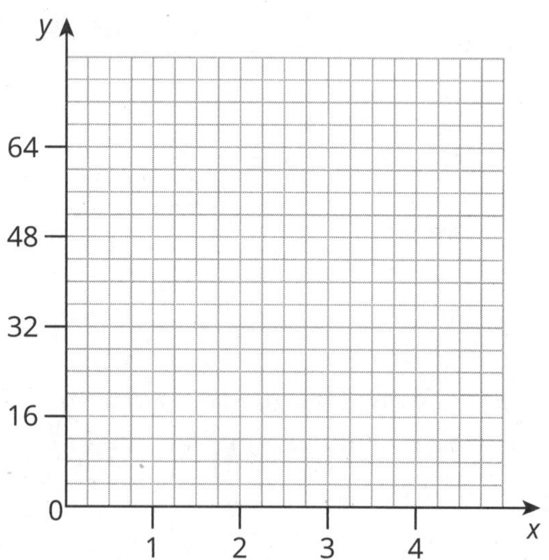

5. Define the independent and dependent quantities of the inverse of $f(x)$.

6. What is the domain and range of the inverse of $f(x)$ with the restricted domain?

© Carnegie Learning, Inc.

7 Graph the inverse of $f(x)$ with the restricted domain. You may use different bounds than used in Question 4.

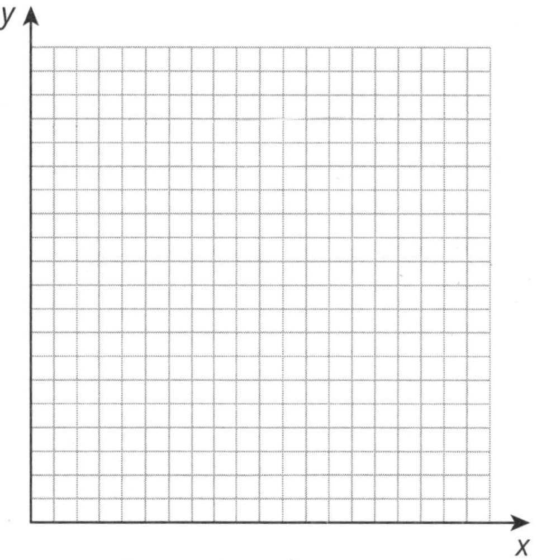

8 Explain why the inverse of $f(x)$ with the restricted domain is a function. Then, write an equation for the inverse.

9 **Explain what the inverse models in terms of this problem situation.**

10 After 1.5 seconds, what is the egg's height? **Explain which function you used and how you determined your answer.**

© Carnegie Learning, Inc.

11 After how many seconds is the egg at a height of 55 feet? **Explain which function you used and how you determined your answer.**

1-2-1

In a previous lesson, you determined the inverses of linear functions. You also determined whether the inverses were also functions.

Recall that a function is a one-to-one function when both the function and its inverse are functions.

1. Adam and Stacey are working on a homework assignment in which they must identify all functions that are one-to-one functions. Adam says that all linear functions are one-to-one functions, so they don't even need to look at the linear functions. Stacey disagrees and says that not all linear functions are one-to-one functions. Who is correct? **Explain how you determined which student is correct.**

2. Complete each sentence with *always*, *sometimes*, or *never*.

   a. A linear function is ________________ a one-to-one function.

   b. An exponential function is ________________ a one-to-one function.

   c. A quadratic function is ________________ a one-to-one function.

   d. A linear absolute value function is ________________ a one-to-one function.

© Carnegie Learning, Inc.

> Use a separate piece of paper for your Journal entry.

JOURNAL

Write a definition for each term in your own words.

1. restricted domain
2. one-to-one function

REMEMBER

You can use quadratic regression equations to model real-world situations.

Algebraically determining the inverse of a quadratic function is the same process as determining the inverse of a linear function.

PRACTICE

1. The number of catfish in Lake Paul is growing in a way that you can represent using the quadratic function $c(x) = 2x^2 + 50$, where x represents the number of months since the initial number of catfish was counted.

   a. Determine any restrictions on the domain of $c(x)$ based on the problem situation. Explain your reasoning.

   b. Graph $c(x)$ with the restricted domain based on the problem situation. Be sure to label your graph.

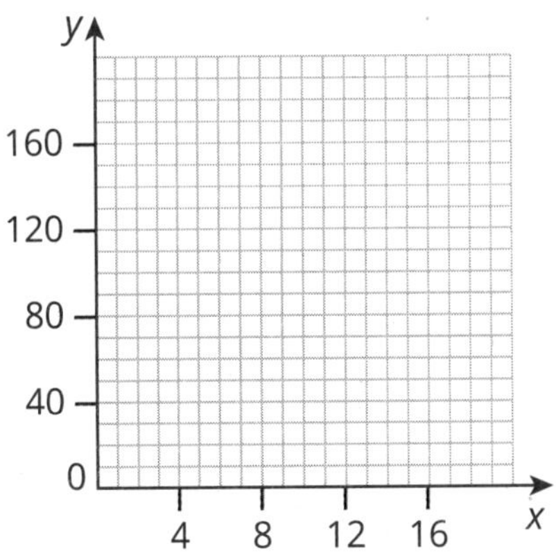

   c. What is the domain and range of the inverse of $c(x)$ with the restricted domain?

   d. Graph the inverse of $c(x)$ with the restricted domain. Be sure to label your graph.

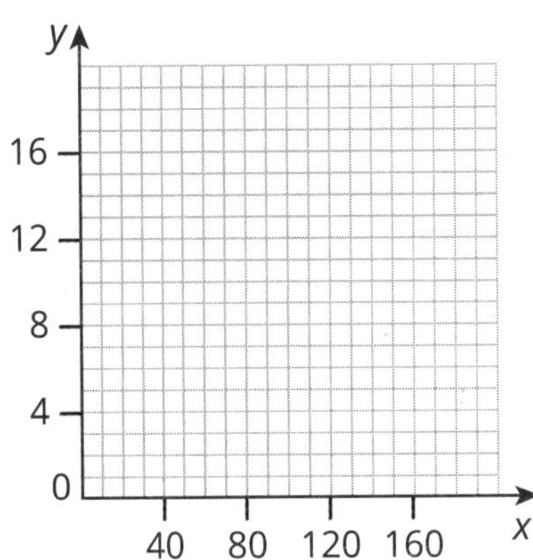

   e. Explain why the inverse of $c(x)$ with the restricted domain is a function. Then, write an equation for its inverse.

© Carnegie Learning, Inc.

Go to LiveHint.com for help on the PRACTICE questions.

2 Determine the inverse of each function.

(a) $y = x^2 - 9$

(b) $y = (x + 4)^2$

(c) $y = (x - 3)^2 + 7$

(d) $y = x^2 + 5$

© Carnegie Learning, Inc.

STRETCH Optional

Consider a triangle with a base represented as $6x$ and a height represented as $4x$.

1 What is the equation for the inverse of the area of the triangle? Explain your reasoning.

2 When the area of the triangle is 108 square meters, what is the value of the inverse of the function? Explain your reasoning.

MIXED PRACTICE

> This Mixed Practice worksheet includes two sections: Spaced Review and End-of-Topic Review. **Use a separate piece of paper to show your work.**

Spaced Review

> Practice concepts from previous topics.

1. Solve $x^2 - 12 = 5$.

2. Evaluate the function $f(x) = 0.4x^2 - 3x - 8$ for the value $x = -2$.

3. Solve each equation.
   - (a) $\frac{1}{3}x + 2 = 11$
   - (b) $-5p - 12 = 19$

4. The cost to install x number of central air conditioning units for a company is given by the function $C(x) = \frac{4000x + 1300}{3}$. Use the function to determine the cost to install 45 air conditioners.

5. Determine each product. Show your work.
   - (a) $(2x - 3)(4x + 7)$
   - (b) $(3x + 5)\left(-\frac{1}{2}x + 16\right)$

6. Identify the axis of symmetry of the graph of $f(x) = -5(x - 3)(x + 12)$.

7. Write a quadratic function in factored form to represent a parabola that opens downward and has zeros at (−6, 0) and (−2, 0).

8. Analyze each pair of representations. Then, answer each question and justify your reasoning.

   (a) Which function's axis of symmetry has a greater x-value?

   Function A

   $f(x) = x^2 - 4x + 9$

   Function B

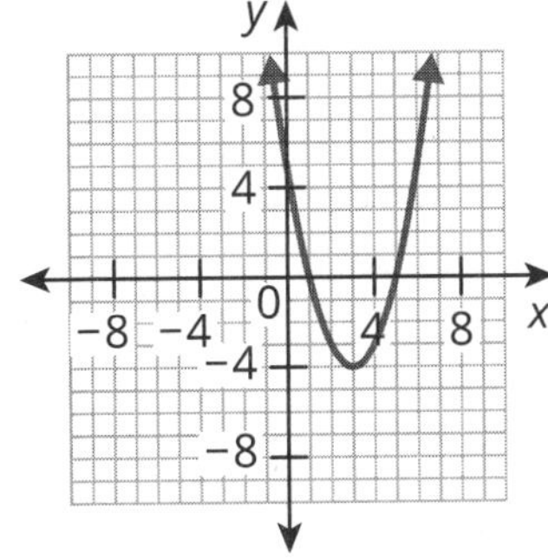

   (b) Which function has a greater rate of change over the interval (1, 5)?

   Function A

   $f(x) = 3(x - 2)^2 - 6$

   Function B

x	$f(x)$
1	2
3	5
5	18

© Carnegie Learning, Inc.

9 Consider the function $f(x) = x^2 - 2x - 2$.

(a) Graph the function.

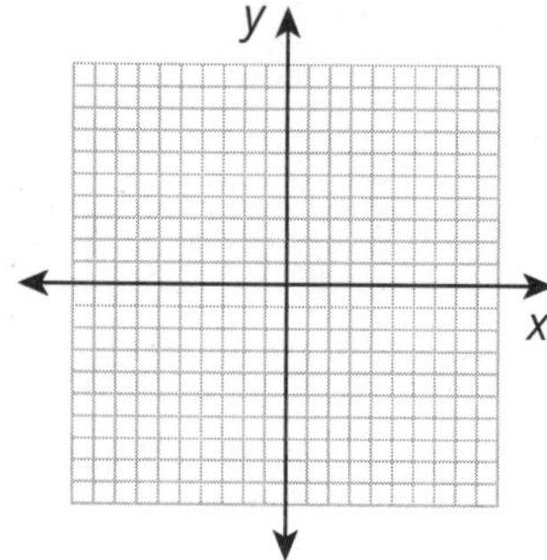

(b) Describe the key characteristics of the graph.

10 Consider the each function.

$t(x) = (x - 3)^2$

$w(x) = 3(x - 3)^2$

$z(x) = 3(x - 3)^2 + 1$

(a) Graph each function on the same coordinate plane.

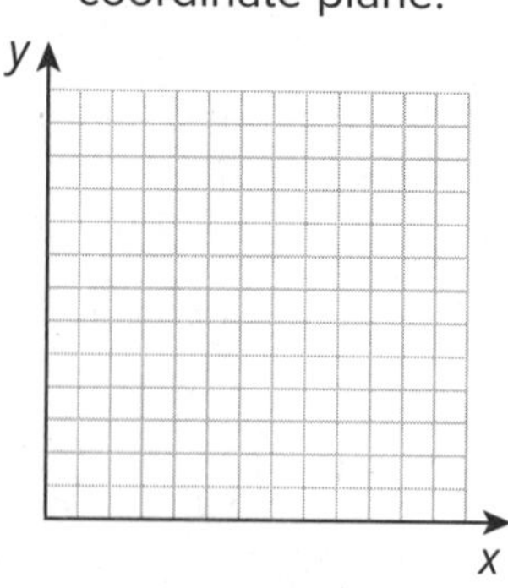

(b) Describe how functions w and z have been transformed from function t.

End-of-Topic Review

AVAILABLE ONLINE

1. A **Topic Summary** reviews the main concepts for the topic.
2. A video of the **Worked Example** is provided.

> Practice concepts you learned in **Applications of Quadratics**.

11 The cost of producing chapter books each month for a company is $C(x) = 6x + 81$. The company's revenue for every chapter book sold each month is $R(x) = 36x - x^2$.

(a) What are the company's break-even points for the production and sales of chapter books each month?

(b) What do the break-even points mean in context?

(c) Show the solution graphically.

12 Solve each inequality.

(a) $y^2 + y - 6 > 0$

(b) $a^2 \leq 4(2a - 3)$

13 Determine the inverse of each function.

(a) $y = x^2 - 16$

(b) $y = (x + 9)^2$

14 A soccer ball is kicked up off a 5-meter-high platform with an initial velocity of 27 meters per second.

(a) Write an inequality to represent when the soccer ball will be above 40 meters.

(b) Graph the inequality and state when the soccer ball will be above 40 meters.

© Carnegie Learning, Inc.

Appendix

Getting Ready for Module 1

Review Answers

Searching for Patterns

1. $7 - 15 = -8$
2. $2(7) + 3.1 = 14 + 3.1$
   $= 17.1$
3. $-3(7 - 5) = -3(2)$
   $= -6$
4. $\frac{2}{3}(7 + 2) - 2(7)$
   $\frac{2}{3}(9) - 14$
   $6 - 14 = -8$

Getting Ready for Module 2

Review Answers

Exploring Constant Change

1. $x = -17$
2. $x = -3$
3. $x = -14$
4. $x = \frac{15}{8} = 1\frac{7}{8}$

Getting Ready for Module 3

Review Answers

Investigating Growth and Decay

1. 7
2. 11
3. 3
4. 5

Getting Ready for Module 4

Review Answers

Describing Distributions

1. 57%
2. 7%
3. 72.1%
4. 25%

Getting Ready for Module 5

Review Answers

Maximizing and Minimizing

1. $x = \pm 9$
2. $x = \pm 5$
3. $x = \pm 11$
4. $x = \pm 7$
5. $x + 5 = 0$
   $x = -5$
6. $2x = -5$
   $x = -\frac{5}{2}$

© Carnegie Learning, Inc.

Glossary

A

absolute maximum

A function has an absolute maximum when there is a point that has a y-coordinate that is greater than the y-coordinates of every other point on the graph.

EXAMPLE

The absolute maximum of the graph of the function $f(x) = -\frac{1}{2}x^2 + 4x - 6$ is $y = 2$.

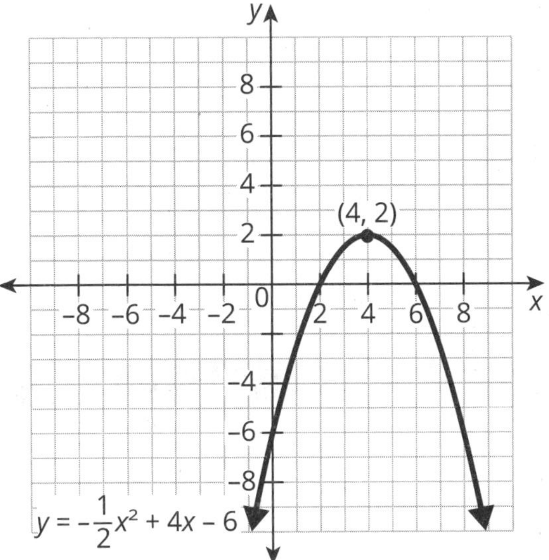

absolute minimum

A function has an absolute minimum when there is a point that has a y-coordinate that is less than the y-coordinates of every other point on the graph.

EXAMPLE

The absolute minimum of the graph of the function $y = \frac{2}{3}x^2 - \frac{4}{3}x - \frac{10}{3}$ is $y = -4$.

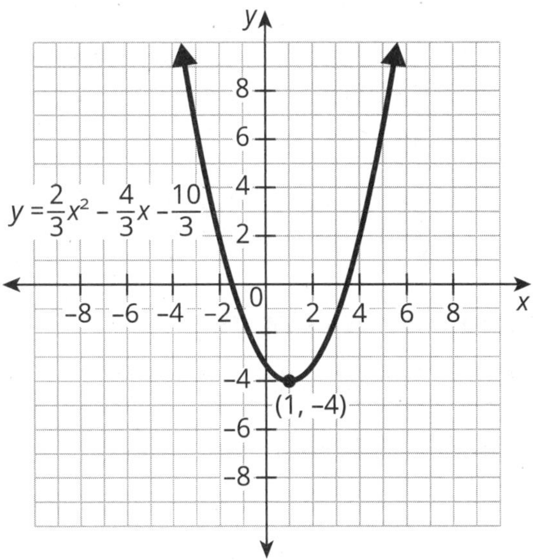

absolute value

The absolute value of a number is its distance from zero on the number line.

EXAMPLE

$|5| = 5$ because 5 is 5 units from 0 on the number line.
$|-3| = 3$ because -3 is 3 units from 0 on the number line.

additive inverses

You call two numbers with the sum of zero additive inverses.

EXAMPLE

$-19 + 19 = 0 \qquad a + -a = a$

© Carnegie Learning, Inc.

argument of a function

The argument of a function is the variable on which the function operates.

EXAMPLE

In the function $f(x + 5) = 32$, the argument is $x + 5$.

arithmetic sequence

An arithmetic sequence is a sequence of numbers in which the difference between any two consecutive terms is a constant.

EXAMPLE

The sequence 1, 3, 5, 7, ... is an arithmetic sequence with a common difference of 2.

average rate of change

Another name for the slope of a linear function is average rate of change. The formula for the average rate of change is $\frac{f(t) - f(s)}{t - s}$.

EXAMPLE

The average rate of change of the function shown is 3.

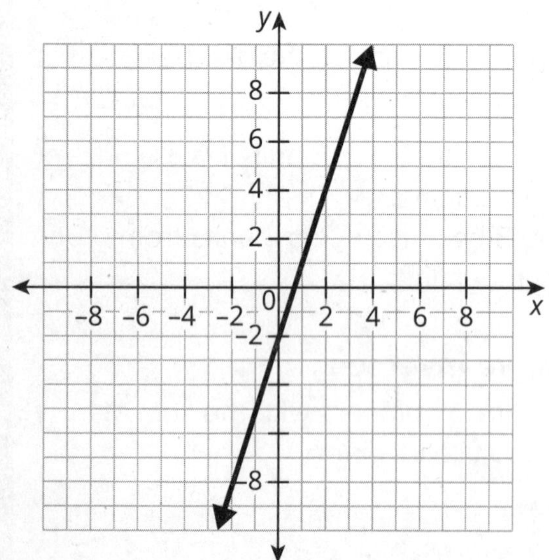

axis of symmetry

The axis of symmetry of a parabola is the vertical line that passes through the vertex and divides the parabola into two mirror images.

EXAMPLE

Line K is the axis of symmetry of this parabola.

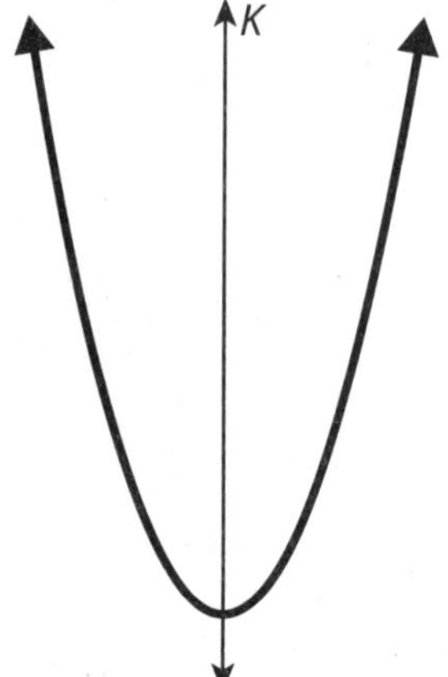

B

base

The base of a power is the expression that you use as a factor in the repeated multiplication.

EXAMPLES

$2^3 = 2 \times 2 \times 2 = 8$ — base: 2

$8^0 = 1$ — base: 8

basic function

A basic function is the simplest function of its type.

EXAMPLE

The basic linear function is $f(x) = x$.
The basic exponential function is $g(x) = 2^x$.
The basic quadratic function is $h(x) = x^2$.

© Carnegie Learning, Inc.

bin

The width of a bar in a histogram is a bin and it represents an interval of data.

binomial

Polynomials with exactly two terms are binomials.

EXAMPLE

The polynomial $3x + 5$ is a binomial.

boundary line

A boundary line, determined by the inequality in a linear inequality, divides the plane into two half-planes and the inequality symbol indicates which half-plane contains all the solutions.

EXAMPLE

For the linear inequality $y > -x + 8$, the boundary line is a dashed line because no point on that line is a solution.

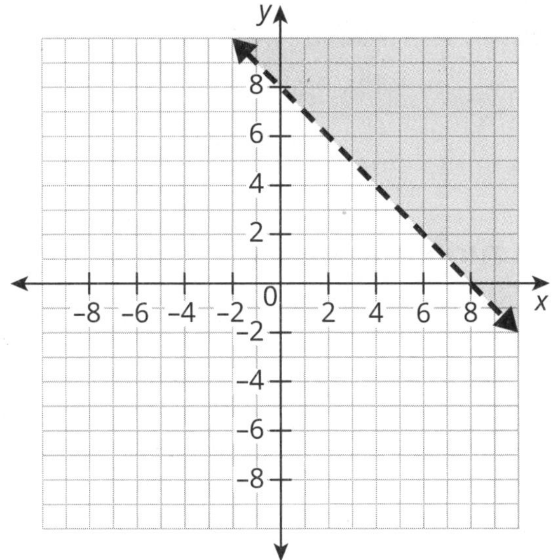

box-and-whisker plot

A box-and-whisker plot displays a data distribution based on a five-number summary.

EXAMPLE

The box-and-whisker plots compare the test scores from two algebra classes.

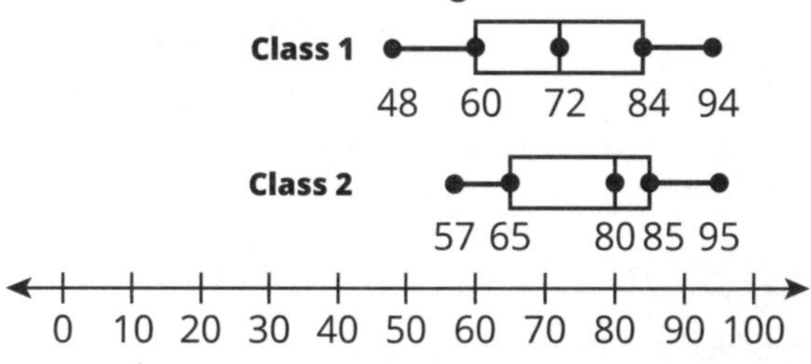

C

categorical data

Data that you can group into categories are categorical data.

causation

Causation is when one event affects the outcome of a second event.

centroid

The centroid is a point whose x-value is the mean of all the x-values of the points on the scatter plot and its y-value is the mean of all the y-values of the points on the scatter plot.

EXAMPLE

For the data points (1, 3), (1, 7), (2, 6), (3, 5), and (3, 4), the centroid is (2, 5).

© Carnegie Learning, Inc.

closed (closure)

When you perform an operation on any of the numbers in a set and the result is a number that is also in the same set, the set is closed (or has closure) under that operation.

EXAMPLE

The set of whole numbers is closed under addition. The sum of any two whole numbers is always another whole number.

coefficient of determination

The coefficient of determination measures how well the graph of a regression fits the data. It is calculated by squaring the correlation coefficient and represents the percentage of variation of the observed values of the data points from their predicted values.

EXAMPLE

The correlation coefficient for a data set is (-0.9935). The coefficient of determination for the same data set is approximately 0.987, which means 98.7% of the data values should fall within graph of the regression equation.

common difference

The difference between any two consecutive terms in an arithmetic sequence is the common difference. It is typically represented by the variable d.

EXAMPLE

The sequence 1, 3, 5, 7, ... is an arithmetic sequence with a common difference of 2.

common ratio

The ratio between any two consecutive terms in a geometric sequence is the common ratio. It is typically represented by the variable r.

EXAMPLE

The sequence 2, 4, 8, 16, ... is a geometric sequence with a common ratio of 2.

common response

A common response is when a variable other than the ones measured cause the same result as the one observed in the experiment.

completing the square

Completing the square is a process for writing a quadratic expression in vertex form which then allows you to solve for the zeros.

complex numbers

The set of complex numbers is the set of all numbers in the form $a + bi$, where a and b are real numbers.

compound inequality

A compound inequality is an inequality formed by the union, *or*, or the intersection, *and*, of two simple inequalities.

EXAMPLE

The statement $x > 5$ or $x < -5$ is a compound inequality.

© Carnegie Learning, Inc.

compound interest

In a compound interest account, the balance is multiplied by the same amount at each interval.

EXAMPLE

Sonya opens a savings account with \$100. She earns \$4 in compound interest the first year. You calculate the compound interest y using the equation $y = 100(1 + 0.04)^t$, where t is the time in years.

concave down

A graph that opens downward is concave down.

EXAMPLE

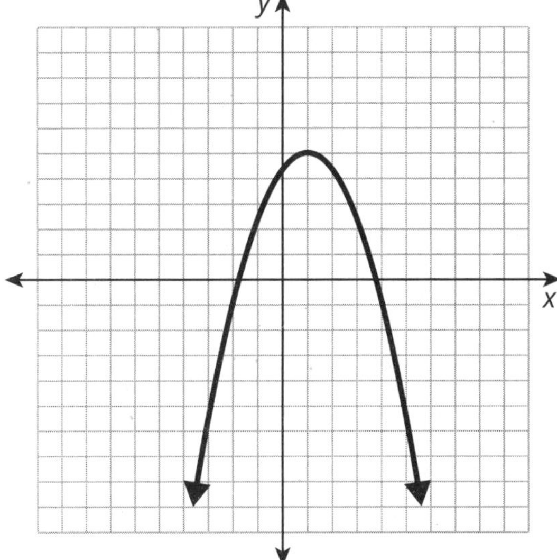

concave up

A graph that opens upward is concave up.

EXAMPLE

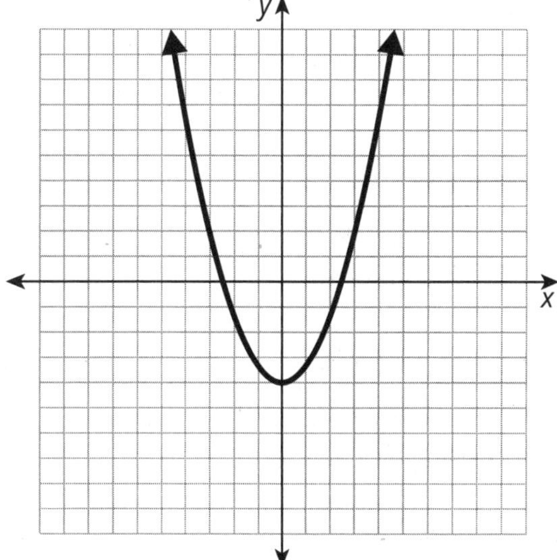

conditional relative frequency distribution

A conditional relative frequency distribution is the percent or proportion of occurrences of a category given the specific value of another category.

confounding variable

A confounding variable is when there are other variables in an experiment that are unknown or unobserved.

conjecture

A conjecture is a mathematical statement that appears to be true but you still need to prove.

© Carnegie Learning, Inc.

conjunction

A compound inequality in the form $a < x < b$, where a and b are any real numbers, is a conjunction.

EXAMPLE

The compound inequality $x \leq 1$ and $x > -3$ is a conjunction.

consistent systems

Systems that have one or many solutions are consistent systems.

constant function

If the dependent variable of a function does not change or remains constant over the entire domain, then the function is a constant function.

EXAMPLE

The function shown is a constant function.

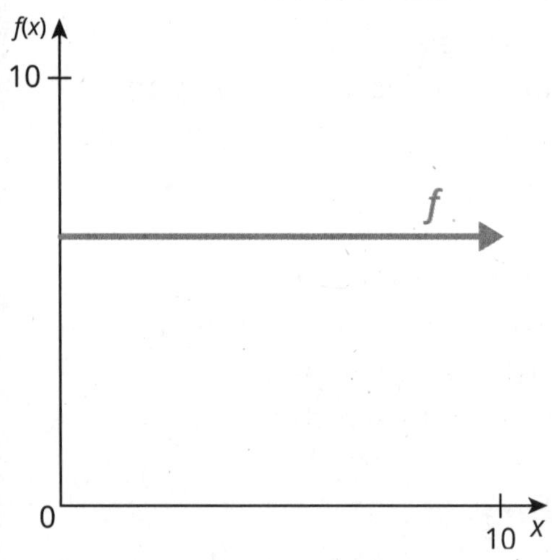

constraints

In a system of linear inequalities, the inequalities are known as constraints because the values of the expressions are "constrained" to lie within a certain region on the graph.

continuous graph

A continuous graph is a graph of points connected by a line or smooth curve. Continuous graphs have no breaks.

EXAMPLE

The graph shown is a continuous graph.

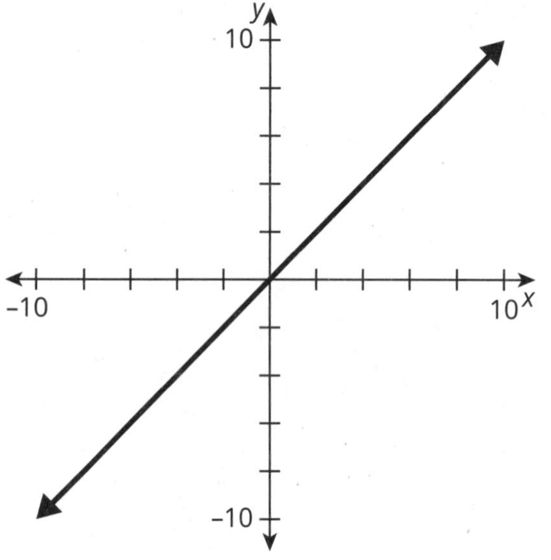

correlation

A measure of how well a regression fits a set of data is a correlation.

© Carnegie Learning, Inc.

discriminant

The discriminant is the radicand expression in the Quadratic Formula that "discriminates" the number of real roots of a quadratic equation.

EXAMPLE

The discriminant in the Quadratic Formula is the expression $b^2 - 4ac$.

disjunction

A compound inequality in the form $x < a$ or $x > b$, where a and b are any real numbers, is a disjunction.

EXAMPLE

The compound inequality $x < -2$ or $x > 1$ is a disjunction.

domain

The domain is the set of input values in a relation.

EXAMPLE

The domain of the function $y = 2x$ is the set of all real numbers.

dot plot

A dot plot is a graph that shows the distribution of discrete data on a number line.

EXAMPLE

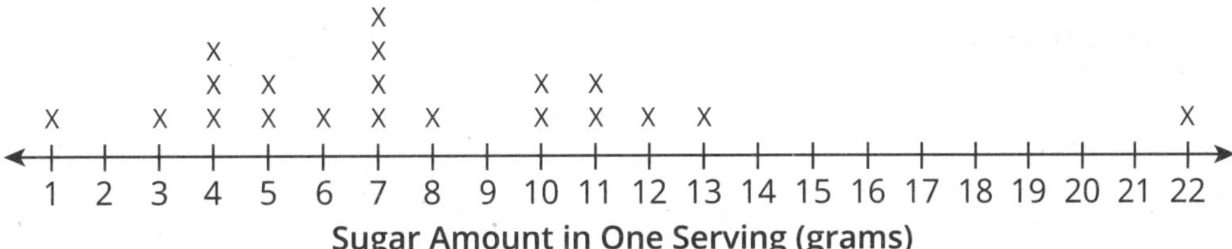

© Carnegie Learning, Inc.

double root

The root of an equation indicates where the graph of the equation crosses the x-axis.

A double root occurs when the graph just touches the x-axis but does not cross it.

EXAMPLE

The quadratic equation $y = (x - 2)^2$ has a double root at $x = 2$.

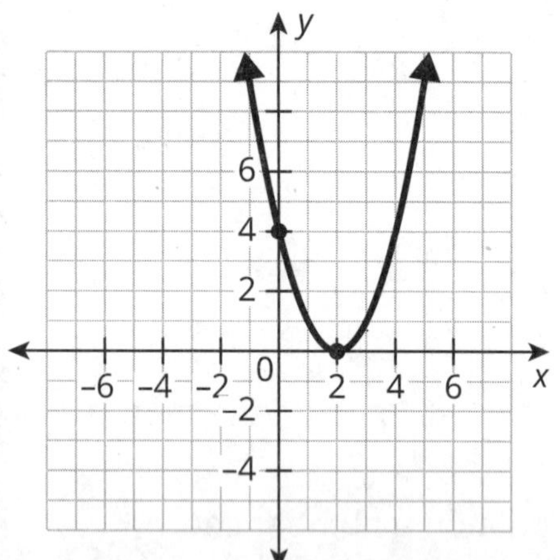

E

equivalent compound inequality

A compound inequality that is the equivalent of an absolute value inequality.

EXAMPLE

Absolute Value Inequality	Equivalent Compound Inequality
$\lvert ax + b \rvert < c$	$-c < ax + b < c$
$\lvert ax + b \rvert \le c$	$-c \le ax + b \le c$
$\lvert ax + b \rvert > c$	$ax + b < -c$ or $ax + b > c$
$\lvert ax + b \rvert \ge c$	$ax + b \le -c$ or $ax + b \ge c$

equivalent expressions

Equivalent expressions are two expressions that have the same value.

explicit formula

An explicit formula of a sequence is a formula for calculating the value of each term of a sequence using the term's position in the sequence. The explicit formula for an arithmetic sequence is $a_n = a_1 + d(n - 1)$. The explicit formula for a geometric sequence is $g_n = g_1 \cdot r^{n-1}$.

EXAMPLE

You can describe the sequence 1, 3, 5, 7, 9, ... by the rule $a_n = 2n - 1$, where n is the position of the term. The fourth term of the sequence a_4 is $2(4) - 1$, or 7.

exponent

The exponent of the power is the number of times you use the base as a factor.

EXAMPLES

exponent

$2^3 = 2 \times 2 \times 2 = 8$

exponential decay function

An exponential decay function is an exponential function with a b-value greater than 0 and less than 1 and is of the form $y = a \cdot (1 - r)^x$, where r is the rate of decay.

EXAMPLE

Greenville has a population of 7000. Its population is decreasing at a rate of 1.75%. The exponential decay function that models this situation is $f(x) = 7000 \cdot 0.9825^x$.

© Carnegie Learning, Inc.

exponential functions

The family of exponential functions includes functions of the form $f(x) = a \cdot b^x + c$, where a, b, and c are real numbers, and b is greater than 0 but is not equal to 1.

EXAMPLE

The function $f(x) = 2^x$ is an exponential function.

exponential growth function

An exponential growth function is an exponential function with a b-value greater than 1 and is of the form $y = a \cdot (1 + r)^x$, where r is the rate of growth.

EXAMPLE

Blueville has a population of 7000. Its population is increasing at a rate of 1.4%. The exponential growth function that models this situation is $f(x) = 7000 \cdot 1.014^x$.

extract the square root

To extract a square root, solve an equation of the form $a^2 = b$ for a.

extrapolation

To make predictions for values of x that are outside of the data set is extrapolation.

F

factored form

A quadratic function in the form $f(x) = a(x - r_1)(x - r_2)$, where $a \neq 0$, is in factored form.

EXAMPLE

The function $h(x) = x^2 - 8x + 12$ in factored form is $h(x) = (x - 6)(x - 2)$.

finite sequence

If a sequence terminates, it is a finite sequence.

EXAMPLE

The sequence 22, 26, 30 is a finite sequence.

first differences

First differences are the values determined by subtracting consecutive output values in a table when the input values have an interval of 1.

EXAMPLE

	Time (minutes)	Height (feet)	First Differences
	0	0	
$1 - 0 = 1$	1	1800	$1800 - 0 = 1800$
$2 - 1 = 1$	2	3600	$3600 - 1800 = 1800$
$3 - 2 = 1$	3	5400	$5400 - 3600 = 1800$

© Carnegie Learning, Inc.

five-number summary

The five-number summary consists of the minimum value, the first quartile (Q1), the median, the third quartile (Q3), and the maximum value.

EXAMPLE

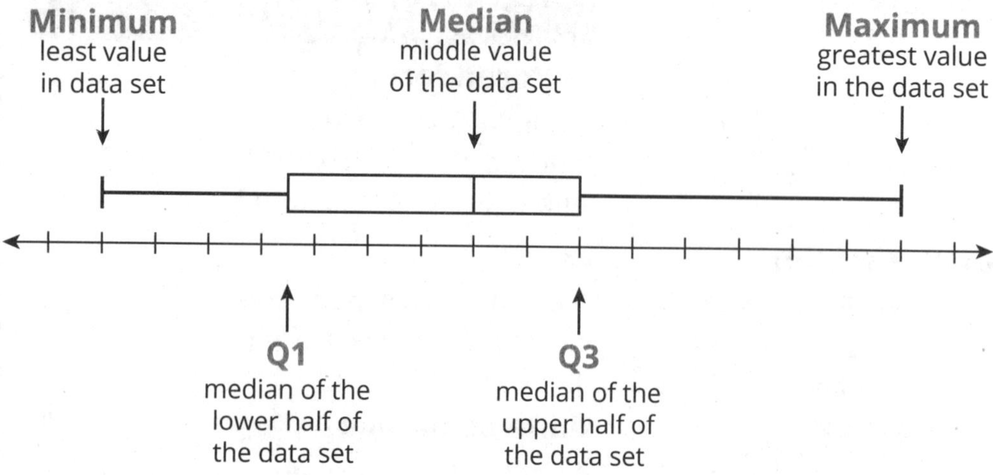

frequency

The height of each bar in a histogram indicates the frequency, which is the number of data values included in any given bin.

frequency distribution

A frequency distribution displays the frequencies for categorical data in a two-way table.

EXAMPLE

Favorite Meals of Students

Grade Level	Burgers	Chicken Nuggets	Pizza	Salad Bar	Total
9th Grade	4	1	3	5	13
10th Grade	3	7	3	4	17
Total	7	8	6	9	30

© Carnegie Learning, Inc.

function

A function is a relation that assigns to each element of the domain exactly one element of the range.

EXAMPLE

The equation $y = 2x$ is a function. Every value of x has exactly one corresponding y-value.

function family

A function family is a group of functions that share certain characteristics.

EXAMPLE

Linear functions and exponential functions are examples of function families.

function notation

Function notation is a way of representing functions algebraically.

EXAMPLE

In the function $f(x) = 0.75x$, f is the name of the function, x represents the domain, and $f(x)$ represents the range.

G

general form (standard form) of a quadratic function

A quadratic function in the form $f(x) = ax^2 + bx + c$, where $a \neq 0$, is in general form, or standard form.

EXAMPLE

The function $f(x) = -5x^2 - 10x + 1$ is in general form.

geometric sequence

A geometric sequence is a sequence of numbers in which the ratio between any two consecutive terms is a constant.

EXAMPLE

The sequence 2, 4, 8, 16, ... is a geometric sequence with a common ratio of 2.

greatest common factor (GCF)

The greatest common factor, or GCF, is the largest factor two or more numbers have in common.

EXAMPLE

Factors of 16: **1**, **2**, **4**, 8, 16

Factors of 12: **1**, **2**, 3, **4**, 6, 12

Common factors: 1, 2, 4

Greatest common factor: 4

greatest integer function (floor function)

The greatest integer function, also known as a floor function, is the greatest integer less than or equal to x.

EXAMPLE

For $f(x) = \lfloor x \rfloor$, if $x = 3.16$, $f(x) = 3$.

H

half-plane

The graph of a linear inequality is a half-plane, or half of a coordinate plane.

EXAMPLE

The shaded portion of the graph is a half-plane.

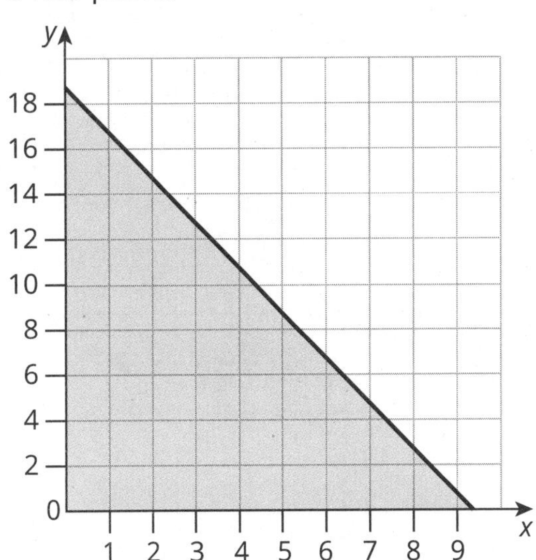

© Carnegie Learning, Inc.

histogram

A histogram is a graphical way to display quantitative data using vertical bars.

EXAMPLE

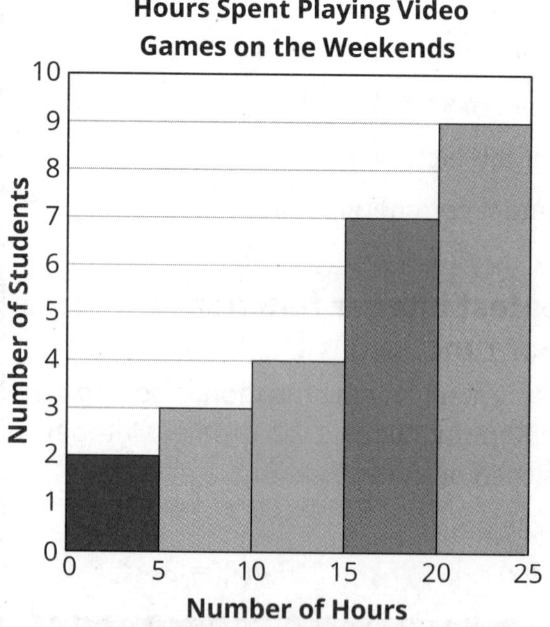

horizontal asymptote

A horizontal asymptote is a horizontal line that a function gets closer and closer to.

EXAMPLE

The graph shows a horizontal asymptote at $y = -1$.

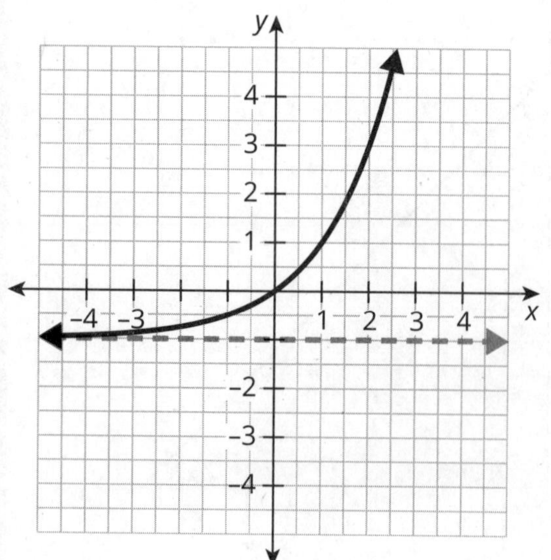

I

imaginary numbers

The set of imaginary numbers is the set of all numbers in the form $a + bi$, where a and b are real numbers and b is not equal to 0.

imaginary part of a complex number

In a complex number of the form $a + bi$, the term bi is the imaginary part of a complex number.

imaginary roots/imaginary zeros

Imaginary roots are imaginary solutions to equations. Quadratic functions that do not cross the x-axis have imaginary zeros.

inconsistent systems

Systems with no solution are inconsistent systems.

increasing function

If a function increases across the entire domain, then the function is an increasing function.

EXAMPLE

The function shown is an increasing function.

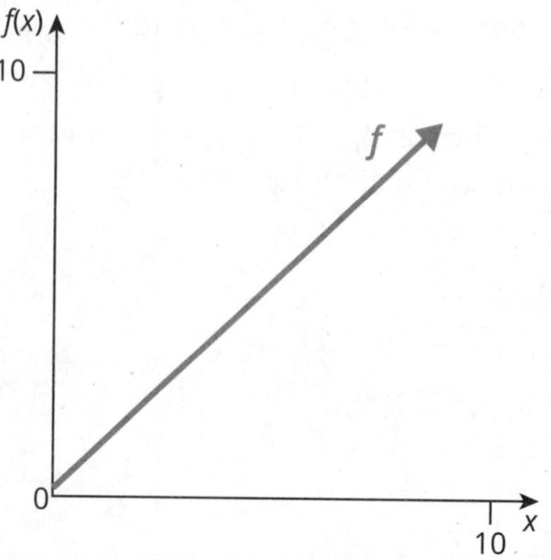

© Carnegie Learning, Inc.

inequality

An inequality is a comparison of two values that shows that one value is greater than (>), less than (<), or not equal to ($\neq$) the second value.

EXAMPLES

$0.3 > 0.28$	0.3 is greater than 0.28.
$\frac{3}{8} < \frac{3}{4}$	$\frac{3}{8}$ is less than $\frac{3}{4}$.
$7 \neq 11$	7 is not equal to 11.

independent quantity

The quantity that the dependent quantity depends upon is the independent quantity.

EXAMPLE

In the relationship between driving time and distance traveled, driving time is the independent quantity, because it does not depend on any other quantity.

infinite sequence

If a sequence continues on forever, it is an infinite sequence.

EXAMPLE

The sequence 22, 26, 30, 34, ... is an infinite sequence.

infinite solutions

An equation with infinite solutions means that any value for the variable makes the equation true.

EXAMPLE

The equation $2x + 1 = 2x + 1$ has infinite solutions.

interpolation

Using a linear regression to make predictions within the data set is interpolation.

interquartile range (IQR)

The interquartile range, IQR, measures how far the data are spread out from the median.

EXAMPLE

In the data set 13, 17, 23, 24, 25, 29, 31, 45, 46, 53, 60, the median, 29, divides the data into two halves. The first quartile, 23, is the median of the lower half of the data. The third quartile, 46, is the median of the upper half of the data. The interquartile range is $46 - 23$, or 23.

inverse of a function

An inverse of a function takes the output value, performs some operation(s) on this value, and arrives back at the original function's input value.

EXAMPLE

The inverse of the function $y = 2x$ is the function $x = 2y$, or $y = \frac{x}{2}$.

J

joint frequency

Any frequency recorded within the body of a two-way frequency table is a joint frequency.

L

leading coefficient

The leading coefficient of a polynomial is the numeric coefficient of the term with the greatest power.

EXAMPLE

In the polynomial $-7x^2 + x + 25$, the value -7 is the leading coefficient.

© Carnegie Learning, Inc.

least integer function (ceiling function)

The least integer function, also known as the ceiling function, is the least integer greater than or equal to x.

EXAMPLE

For $f(x) = \lceil x \rceil$, if $x = 3.16$, $f(x) = 4$.

Least Squares Method

The Least Squares Method is a method that creates a regression line for a scatter plot that has two basic requirements: 1) the line must contain the centroid of the data set, and 2) the sum of the squares of the vertical distances from each given data point is at a minimum with the line.

EXAMPLE

The regression line shown was created using the Least Squares Method.

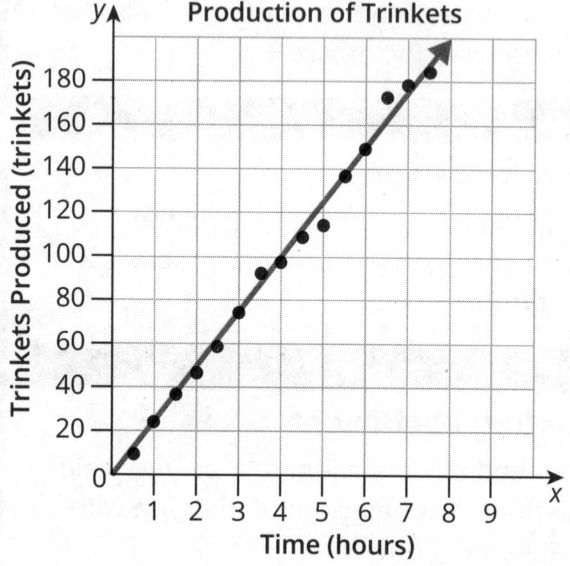

line of best fit

A line of best fit is a line that is as close to as many points as possible but doesn't have to go through all of the points.

EXAMPLE

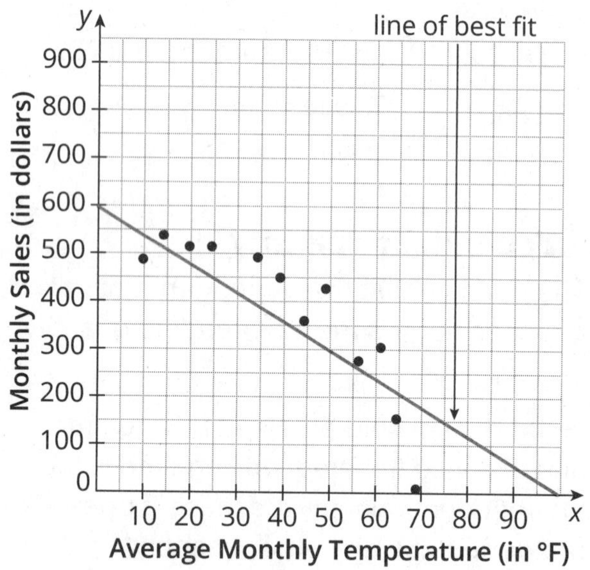

line of reflection

A line of reflection is the line that the graph is reflected across.

EXAMPLE

The graph of $y = |x| + 2$ is a reflection across the line of reflection, $y = 0$.

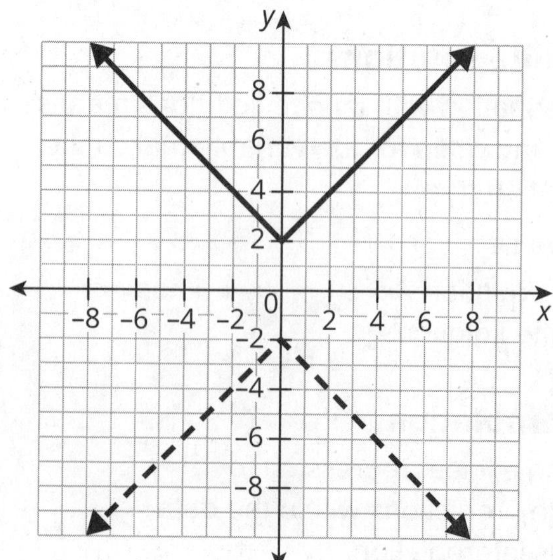

© Carnegie Learning, Inc.

line of symmetry

A line of symmetry is an imaginary line that passes through a shape or object and divides it into two identical halves.

EXAMPLE

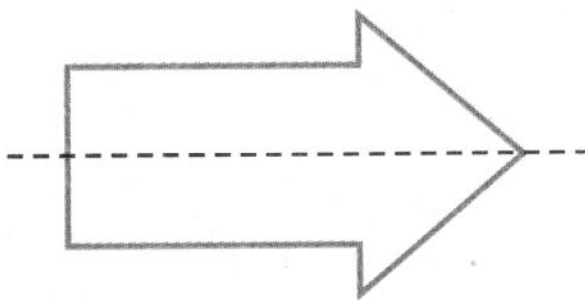

linear absolute value equation

An equation in the form $|x + a| = c$ is a linear absolute value equation.

EXAMPLE

The equation $|x - 1| = 6$ is a linear absolute value equation.

linear absolute value functions

The family of linear absolute value functions includes functions of the form $f(x) = a|x + b| + c$, where a, b, and c are real numbers, and a is not equal to 0.

EXAMPLE

The function $f(x) = |x - 3| - 2$ is a linear absolute value function.

linear absolute value inequality

An inequality in the form $|x + a| < c$ is a linear absolute value inequality.

EXAMPLE

The inequality $|w - 145.045| \leq 3.295$ is a linear absolute value inequality.

linear combinations method

The linear combinations method is a process used to solve a system of equations by adding two equations together, resulting in an equation with one variable.

EXAMPLE

Solve the following system of equations by using the linear combinations method:

$$\begin{cases} 6x - 5y = 3 \\ 2x + 2y = 12 \end{cases}$$

First, multiply the second equation by (−3). Then, add the equations and solve for the remaining variable. Finally, substitute $y = 3$ into the first equation and solve for x. The solution of the system is (3, 3).

linear functions

The family of linear functions includes functions of the form $f(x) = ax + b$, where a and b are real numbers.

EXAMPLE

The function $f(x) = 3x + 2$ is a linear function.

linear piecewise functions

Linear piecewise functions include linear functions that have equation changes for different parts, or pieces, of the domain.

EXAMPLE

The function $f(x)$ is a linear piecewise function.

$$f(x) = \begin{cases} x + 5, & x \leq -2 \\ -2x + 1, & -2 < x \leq 2 \\ 2x - 9, & x > 2 \end{cases}$$

© Carnegie Learning, Inc.

linear programming

Linear programming is a branch of mathematics that determines the maximum and minimum value of linear expressions on a region produced by a system of linear inequalities.

literal equation

Literal equations are equations in which the variables represent specific measures.

EXAMPLE

The equations $\ell = Prt$ and $A = \ell w$ are literal equations.

lower fence

The value of Q1 − (IQR · 1.5) is the lower fence.

M

marginal frequency distribution

A marginal frequency distribution displays the total of the frequencies of the rows or columns of a frequency distribution.

marginal relative frequency distribution

Displaying the relative frequencies for the rows or columns in a two-way table is a marginal relative frequency distribution. The marginal relative frequency distribution provides the ratio of total occurrences for each category to the total number of occurrences.

mathematical modeling

Mathematical modeling is explaining patterns in the real world based on mathematical ideas.

mean

The mean is the arithmetic average of the numbers in a data set.

EXAMPLE

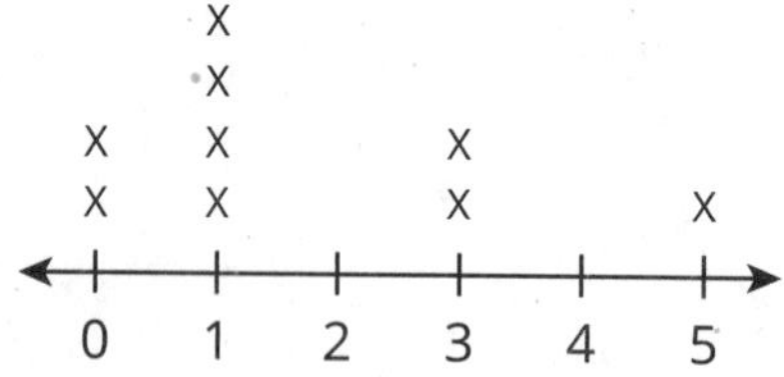

$$\text{Mean} = \frac{0+0+1+1+1+1+3+3+5}{9}$$
$$= \frac{15}{9} = 1\frac{2}{3} \text{ pets}$$

measure of center

A measure of center tells you how data values cluster, or the location of the center of the data.

EXAMPLES

Mean, median, and mode are each a measure of center for data.

measure of variation

A measure of variation describes the spread of data values.

EXAMPLE

Range is a measure of variation for data.

measure of central tendency

A measure of central tendency is a numeric value used to describe the overall clustering of data in a set.

EXAMPLE

The mean, median, and mode are the most common measures of central tendency.

© Carnegie Learning, Inc.

monomial

Polynomials with only one term are monomials.

EXAMPLE

The expressions $5x$, 7, $-2xy$, and $13x^3$ are monomials.

N

no solution

An equation with no solution means that there is no value for the variable that makes the equation true.

EXAMPLE

The equation $2x + 1 = 2x + 3$ has no solution.

the number *i*

The number i is a number such that $i^2 = -1$.

numeric pattern

A numeric pattern is a sequence, or ordered set, of numbers that is created by following a given rule.

EXAMPLE

Rule: Multiply by 2.

Input	1	2	3	4
Output	2	4	6	8

O

one-to-one function

A function is a one-to-one function when both the function and its inverse are functions.

EXAMPLE

The equation $y = x^3$ is a one-to-one function because its inverse, $\sqrt[3]{x} = y$, is a function. The equation $y = x^2$ is not a one-to-one function because its inverse, $\pm\sqrt{x} = y$, is not a function.

outlier

An outlier is a data value that is significantly greater or lesser than other data values in a data set.

EXAMPLE

In the data set 1, 1, 3, 3, 4, 4, 5, 1000, the outlier is 1000.

P

parabola

The shape that a quadratic function forms when graphed is a parabola. A parabola is a smooth curve with reflectional symmetry.

EXAMPLE

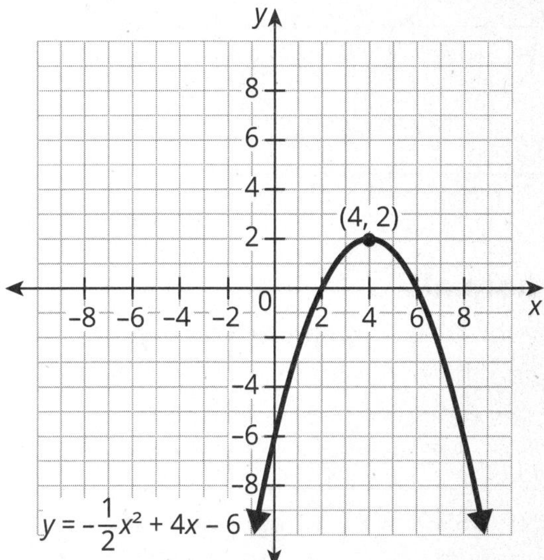

© Carnegie Learning, Inc.

perfect square

A perfect square is the product of two equal integers.

EXAMPLES

9 is a perfect square: $3 \cdot 3 = 9$

25 is a perfect square: $5 \cdot 5 = 25$

perfect square trinomial

A perfect square trinomial is an expression in the form $a^2 + 2ab + b^2$ or in the form $a^2 - 2ab + b^2$.

piecewise function

A piecewise function is a function that you can represent using more than one function, each which corresponds to a part of the domain.

EXAMPLE

The graph represents a piecewise function.

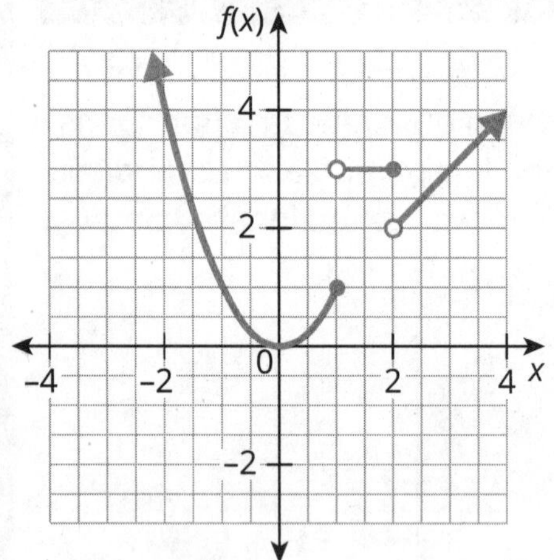

polynomial

A polynomial is a mathematical expression involving the sum of powers in one or more variables multiplied by coefficients.

EXAMPLE

The expression $3x^3 + 5x - 6x + 1$ is a polynomial.

prime factorization

Prime factorization is the process of writing numbers as the product of prime factors. You can use a factor tree to determine prime factors.

EXAMPLES

The factor tree shows the prime factorization of 30.

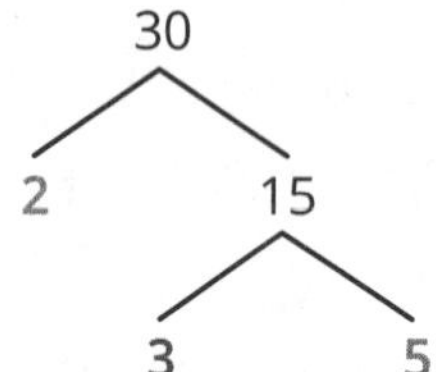

principal square root

The positive square root of a number is the principal square root.

pure imaginary number

A pure imaginary number is a number of the form bi, where b is not equal to 0.

Q

Quadratic Formula

The Quadratic Formula is $x = \frac{-b \pm \sqrt{b^2 - 4ac}}{2a}$, and you can use it to calculate the solutions to any quadratic equation of the form $ax^2 + bx + c$, where a, b, and c represent real numbers and $a \neq 0$.

quadratic functions

The family of quadratic functions includes functions of the form $f(x) = ax^2 + bx + c$, where a, b, and c are real numbers, and a is not equal to 0.

EXAMPLES

The equations $y = x^2 + 2x + 5$ and $y = -4x^2 - 7x + 1$ are quadratic functions.

© Carnegie Learning, Inc.

R

range

The range is the set of output values in a relation.

EXAMPLE

The range of the function $y = x^2$ is the set of all numbers greater than or equal to zero.

rate of change

The rate of change for a situation describes the amount that the dependent variable changes compared to the amount the independent variable changes.

real part of a complex number

In a complex number of the form $a + bi$, the term a is the real part of a complex number.

recursive formula

A recursive formula expresses each new term of a sequence based on the preceding term in the sequence. The recursive formula for an arithmetic sequence is $a_n = a_{n-1} + d$. The recursive formula for a geometric sequence is $g_n = g_{n-1} \cdot r$.

EXAMPLE

The formula $a_n = a_{n-1} + 2$ is a recursive formula. Each successive term is calculated by adding 2 to the previous term. If $a_1 = 1$, then $a_2 = 1 + 2 = 3$.

© Carnegie Learning, Inc.

reflection

A reflection of a graph is a mirror image of the graph about a line of reflection.

EXAMPLE

The triangle on the right is a reflection of the triangle on the left.

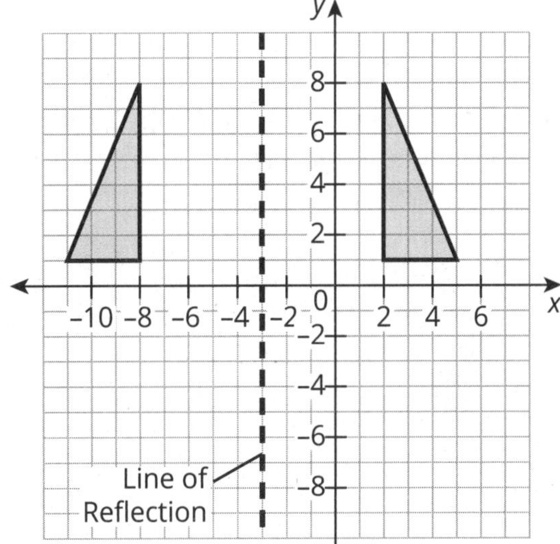

regression line

On a scatter plot, a regression line is a mathematical model you can use to predict the values of a dependent variable based upon the values of an independent variable.

relation

A relation is the mapping between a set of input values called the domain and a set of output values called the range.

EXAMPLE

The set of points {(0, 1), (1, 8), (2, 5), (3, 7)} is a relation.

relative frequency distribution

Representing the relative frequencies for joint data displayed in a two-way table is a relative frequency distribution. The relative frequency distribution provides the ratio of occurrences in each category to the total number of occurrences.

residual

A residual is the vertical distance between an observed data value and its predicted value using a regression equation.

residual plot

A residual plot is a scatter plot of the independent variable on the x-axis and the residuals on the y-axis.

EXAMPLE

The graph on the right shows a residual plot of the braking distance data.

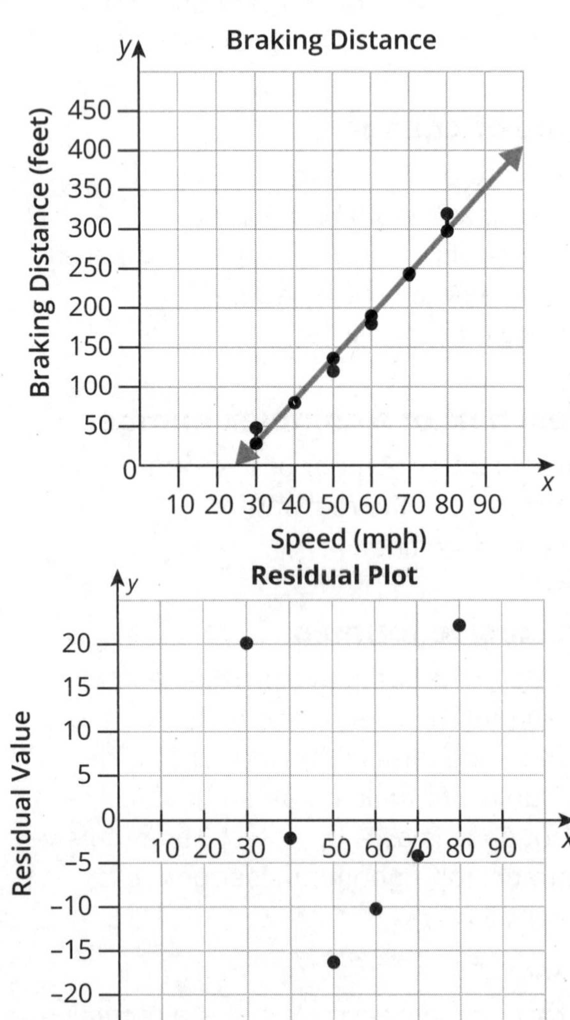

restrict the domain

To restrict the domain of a function means to define a new domain for the function that is a subset of the original domain.

© Carnegie Learning, Inc.

root (roots)

The root or roots of an equation indicate where the graph of the equation crosses the *x*-axis.

EXAMPLE

The roots of the quadratic equation $x^2 - 4x + 3 = 0$ are $x = 3$ and $x = 1$.

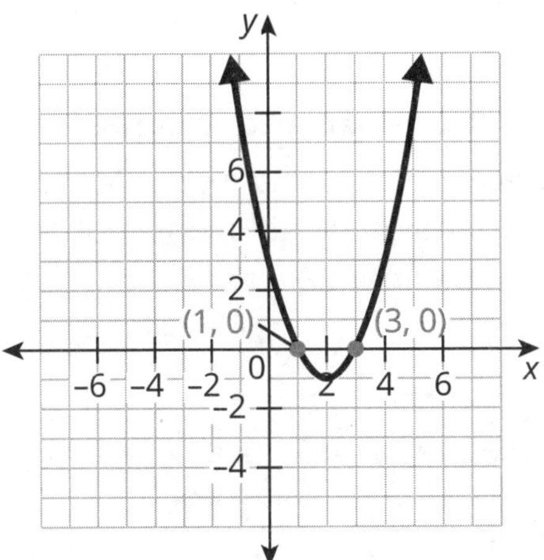

S

second differences

Second differences are the differences between consecutive values of the first differences.

EXAMPLE

x	y	First Differences	Second Differences
−3	−5		
−2	0	5	
−1	3	3	−2
0	4	1	−2
1	3	−1	−2
2	0	−3	−2
3	−5	−5	−2

sequence

A sequence is a pattern involving an ordered arrangement of numbers, geometric figures, letters, or other objects.

EXAMPLE

The numbers 1, 1, 2, 3, 5, 8, 13, ... form a sequence.

simple interest

In a simple interest account, the interest earned at the end of each interval is a percent of the starting balance (also known as the principal).

EXAMPLE

Tonya deposits $200 in a 3-year certificate of deposit that earns 4% simple interest. You calculate the amount of interest that Tonya earns using the simple interest formula.

$$I = (200)(0.04)(3)$$

$$I = 24$$

Tonya earns $24 in interest.

© Carnegie Learning, Inc.

skewed distribution

In a skewed distribution, the peak of the data is to the left or the right side of the graph.

EXAMPLE

The data in the dot plot have a skewed distribution.

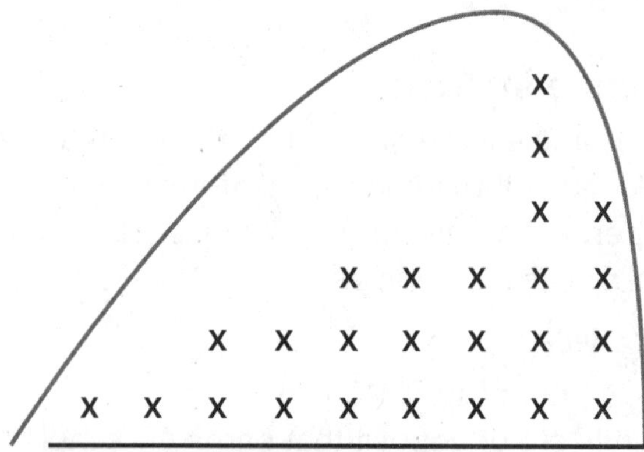

slope

In any linear relationship, slope describes the direction and steepness of a line and you usually represent it with the variable *m*. Slope is another name for rate of change. (See *rate of change*.)

EXAMPLE

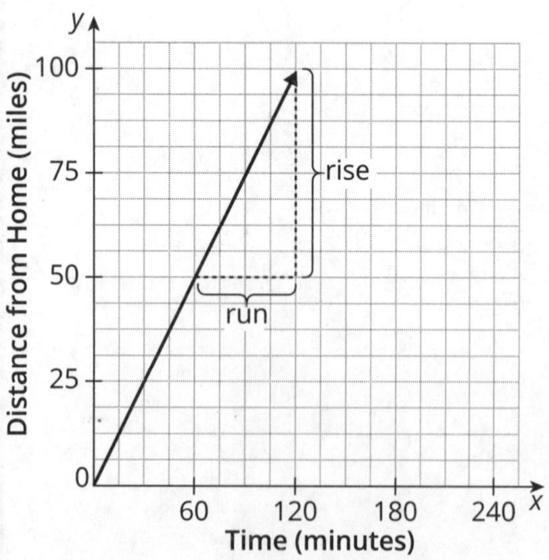

The slope of the line is $\frac{50}{60}$, or $\frac{5}{6}$.

solution

The solution to an equation is any value for the variable that makes the equation a true statement.

EXAMPLE

The solution of the equation $3x + 4 = 25$ is 7 because 7 makes the equation true: $3(7) + 4 = 25$, or $25 = 25$.

solution of a compound inequality

The solution of a compound inequality is the part or parts of the solutions that satisfy both of the inequalities.

EXAMPLE

The number line shows the solution of the compound inequality $x < -2$ or $x > 1$.

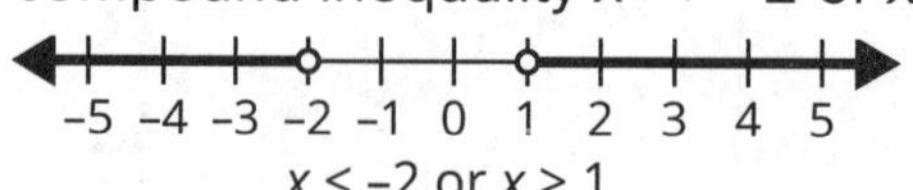

© Carnegie Learning, Inc.

solution of a system of linear inequalities

The solution of a system of linear inequalities is the intersection of the solutions to each inequality. Every point in the intersection region satisfies all inequalities in the system.

EXAMPLE

$$\begin{cases} 200a + 100c \leq 800 \\ 75(a - 1) + 50c \geq 150 \end{cases}$$

The solution of this system of linear inequalities is shown by the shaded region, which represents the intersection of the solutions to each inequality.

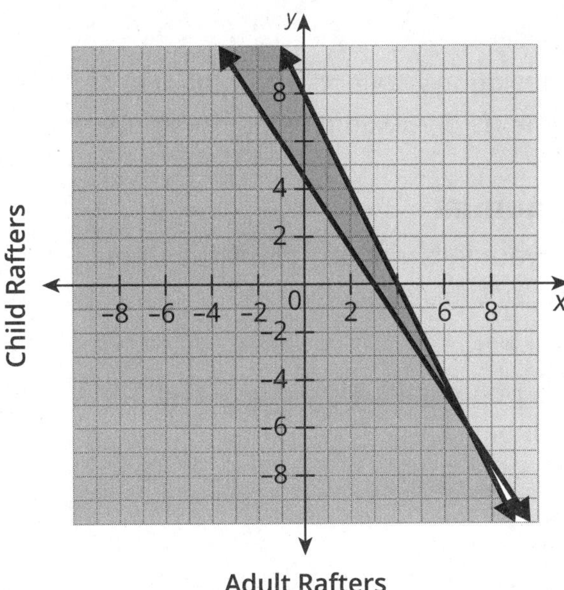

solve an inequality

To solve an inequality means to determine the values of the variable that make the inequality true.

EXAMPLE

You can solve the inequality $x + 5 > 6$ by subtracting 5 from each side of the inequality. The solution is $x > 1$. Any number greater than 1 will make the inequality $x + 5 > 6$ true.

square root

A square root is one of two equal factors of a number.

EXAMPLE

The square root of 36, $\sqrt{36}$, is 6, because $6 \cdot 6 = 36$.

standard deviation

Standard deviation is a measure of how spread out the data are from the mean.

statistics

Statistics are numeric characteristics of data.

step function

A step function is a piecewise function on a given interval whose pieces are discontinuous constant functions.

EXAMPLE

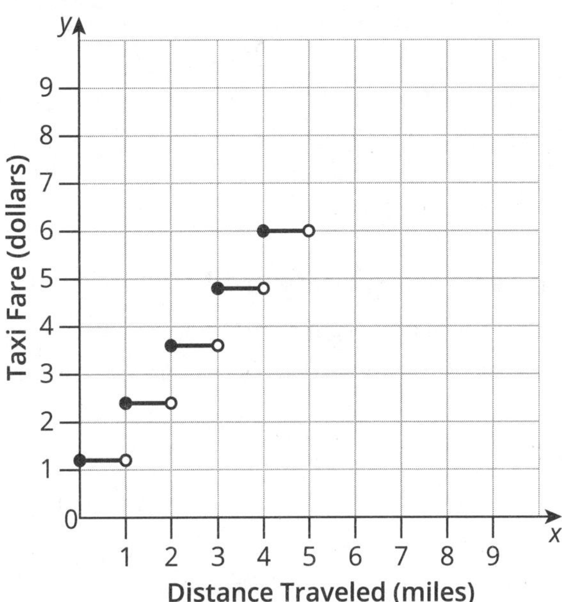

© Carnegie Learning, Inc.

system of linear equations

When two or more linear equations define a relationship between quantities, they form a system of linear equations.

EXAMPLE

The equations $y = 3x + 7$ and $y = -4x$ are a system of linear equations.

$$\begin{cases} y = 3x + 7 \\ y = -4x \end{cases}$$

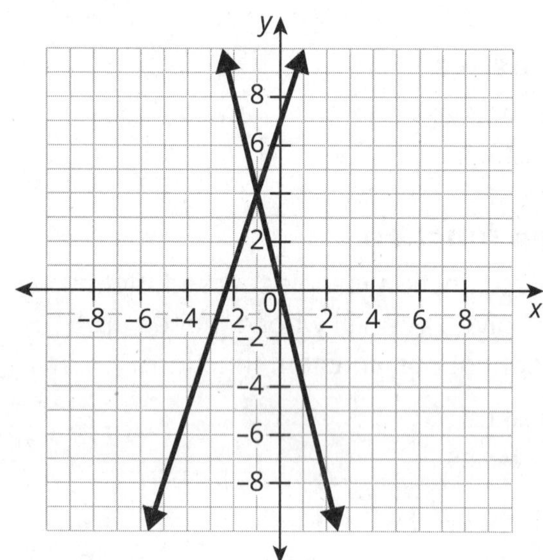

T

term of a sequence

A term of a sequence is an individual number, figure, or letter in the sequence.

EXAMPLE

In the sequence 2, 4, 6, 8, 10, ... the first term is 2, the second term is 4, and the third term is 6.

transformation

A transformation is the mapping, or movement, of a plane and all the points of a figure on a plane according to a common action or operation.

EXAMPLES

Translations, reflections, rotations, and dilations are examples of transformations.

trinomial

Polynomials with exactly three terms are trinomials.

EXAMPLE

The polynomial $5x^2 - 6x + 9$ is a trinomial.

two-way frequency table

A two-way frequency table displays categorical data by representing the number of occurrences that fall into each group for two variables.

EXAMPLE

Favorite Meals of Students

Grade Level	Burgers	Chicken Nuggets	Pizza	Salad Bar
9th Grade	//// 4	/ 1	/// 3	~~////~~ 5
10th Grade	/// 3	~~////~~ // 7	/// 3	//// 4

© Carnegie Learning, Inc.

U

upper fence

The value of Q3 + (IQR • 1.5) is the upper fence.

V

vertex form

A quadratic function in the form $f(x) = a(x - h)^2 + k$, where $a \neq 0$, is in vertex form.

EXAMPLE

The equation $y = 2(x - 5)^2 + 10$ is in vertex form. The vertex of the graph is the point (5, 10).

vertex of a parabola

The vertex of a parabola is the lowest or highest point on the graph of the quadratic function.

EXAMPLE

The vertex of the graph of $f(x)$ is the point (1, −4).

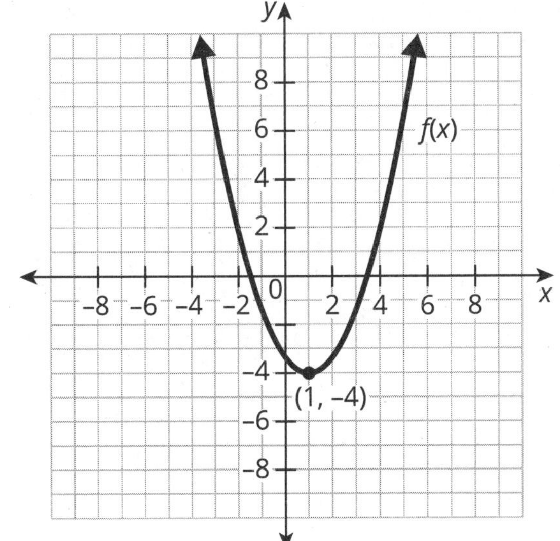

vertical line test

The vertical line test is a visual method used to determine whether a relation represented as a graph is a function.

EXAMPLE

The equation $y = 3x^2$ is a function. The graph passes the vertical line test because there are no vertical lines you can draw that would intersect the graph at more than one point.

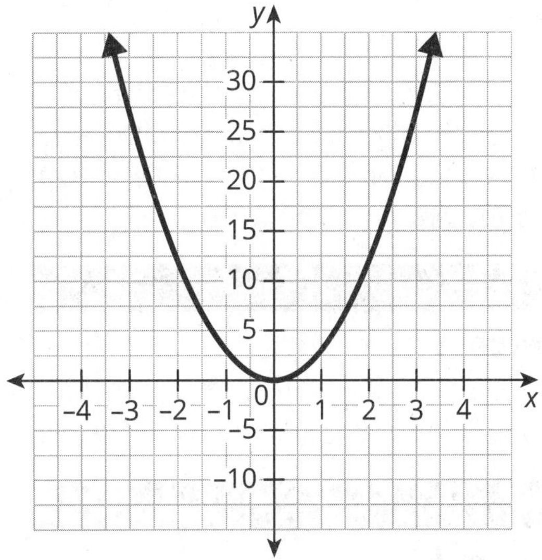

The equation $x^2 + y^2 = 9$ is not a function. The graph fails the vertical line test because you can draw a vertical line that intersects the graph at more than one point.

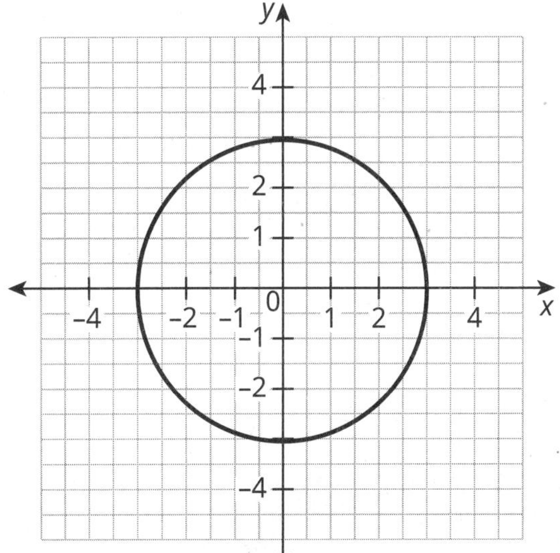

© Carnegie Learning, Inc.

vertical motion model

A vertical motion model is a quadratic equation that models the height of an object at a given time. The equation is of the form $g(t) = -16t^2 + v_0t + h_0$, where $g(t)$ represents the height of the object in feet, t represents the time in seconds that the object has been moving, v_0 represents the initial velocity (speed) of the object in feet per second, and h_0 represents the initial height of the object in feet.

EXAMPLE

A rock is thrown in the air at a velocity of 10 feet per second from a cliff that is 100 feet high. The equation $y = -16t^2 + 10t + 100$ models the height of the rock.

X

x-intercept

The point where a graph crosses the x-axis is an x-intercept.

Y

y-intercept

The point where a graph crosses the y-axis is a y-intercept.

Z

zero of a function

A zero of a function is a real number that makes the value of the function equal to zero, or $f(x) = 0$.

EXAMPLE

The zero of the linear function $f(x) = 2(x - 4)$ is (4, 0).

The zeros of the quadratic function $f(x) = -2x^2 + 4x$ are (0, 0) and (2, 0).

Zero Product Property

The Zero Product Property states that if the product of two or more factors is equal to zero, then at least one factor must be equal to zero.

© Carnegie Learning, Inc.

Index

INDEX

© Carnegie Learning, Inc.

D

E

© Carnegie Learning, Inc.

© Carnegie Learning, Inc.

H

I

L

© Carnegie Learning, Inc.

M

N

O

P

© Carnegie Learning, Inc.

Q

R

© Carnegie Learning, Inc.

S

© Carnegie Learning, Inc.

© Carnegie Learning, Inc.

Photo Credits

All images obtained via Getty Images: 3 sukanya sitthikongsak/Moment; 17 Marc Romanelli/Royalty-free; 31 drnadig/E+; 53 View Pictures/Contributor/Universal Images Group; 65 MirageC/Moment; 79 feellife/Plant; 109 cmannphoto/E+; 121 Kameleon007/E+; 135 Eugene4873/Garment; 147 Shanna Baker/Moment; 161 mikkelwilliam/Composition; 173 artisteer/Arts Culture and Entertainment; 189 simarik/Concepts; 203 Inna Giliarova/Symbol; 221 harpazo_hope/Moment; 237 Irina274/Small Group Of Objects; 247 Barcin/E+; 259 SimpleImages/Moment; 271 Yevgen Romanenko/Moment; 285 Photography Aubrey Stoll/Moment; 301 retales botijero/Moment; 317 cmannphoto/Household Fixture; 331 eugenesergeev/Building Feature; 347 Alaska Photography/Moment; 359 Travis Wolfe/ EyeEm/EyeEm; 369 gregepperson/Climbing; 381 Fraser McAlister/Moment Open; 399 cmannphoto/E+; 413 undefined undefined/ Geographical Locations; 429 Mint Images/Mint Images RF; 441 Pachai-Leknettip/Concepts; 461 Maren Winter/Food Staple; 477 GK Hart/Vikki Hart/Stone; 497 jayk7/Moment; 523 Richard T. Nowitz/The Image Bank; 535 zhaojiankang/Topics; 545 cmannphoto/Hot Drink; 557 Kameleon007/Key; 571 xphiyya sx hnxngbaw/EyeEm/EyeEm; 581 Ignacio Palacios/Stone; 599 PLAINVIEW/Fish Tank; 609 Viktoryia Vinnikava/EyeEm/EyeEm; 625 Kevin Trimmer/Moment; 635 krisanapong detraphiphat/Moment; 643 trekandshoot/ Residential Building; 657 Rudy Malmquist/Moment; 673 omersukrugox/Commercial Activity; 697 Hans Strand/Corbis Documentary; 723 Toshiro Shimada/Moment; 741 Peter Dazeley/The Image Bank; 765 Bill Ross/The Image Bank; 779 coldsnowstorm/Lepidoptera; 791 marekuliasz/Leisure Games; 813 sturti/Entertainment Event; 841 peepo/Domestic Car; 851 3DSculptor/Spaceship; 863 kunst-mp/ Container.

© Carnegie Learning, Inc.